THE NETWORK TROUBLESHOOT

INTERNETWORKING

A Guide to Network Communications LAN to LAN; LAN to WAN

Second Edition

Mark A. Miller, P.E.

M&T BOOKS

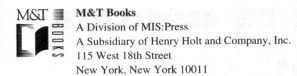

M&T Books
A Division of MIS:Press
A Subsidiary of Henry Holt and Company, Inc.
115 West 18th Street
New York, New York 10011

Limits of Liability and Disclaimer of Warranty
The Author and Publisher of this book have used their best efforts in preparing the book and the programs contained in it. These efforts include the development, research, and testing of the theories and programs to determine their effectiveness.

The Author and Publisher make no warranty of any kind, expressed or implied, with regard to these programs or the documentation contained in this book. The Author and Publisher shall not be liable in any event for incidental or consequential damages in connection with, or arising out of, the furnishing, performance, or use of these programs.

Trademarks: All products, names, and services are trademarks, registered trademarks of their respective companies. See "Trademarks" section.

Several figures in Chapter 1 reprinted from IEEE Std 802.1D-1990 Local and Metropolitan Area Networks: Media Access Control (MAC) Bridges, Copyright © 1991 by the Institute of Electrical and Electronics Engineers, Inc. The IEEE disclaims any responsibility or liability resulting from the placement and use in this publication. Information is reprinted with the permission of the IEEE.

Library of Congress Cataloging-in-Publication Data

Miller, Mark
    Internetworking: a guide to network communications LAN to LAN, LAN to WAN/
    Mark A. Miller. — 2nd ed.
      p. cm. —
    ISBN 1-55851-436-8
    1. Computer networks.   2. Local area networks (Computer networks)   3. Computer network
    protocols.   4. Internetworking (Telecommunications) I. Title.
TK5105.5.M55   1995   95-15035
004.6--dc20   CIP

98   95   96   4

Editor-in-Chief: Paul Farrell   **Technical Editor:** John Thompson
Managing Editor: Cary Sullivan   **Copy Edit Manager:** Shari Chappell
Development Editor: Debra Williams Cauley   **Copy Editor:** Annette Sroka Devlin
Production Editor: Eileen Mullin

To Holly

Contents

Chapter 3: Analog and Digital Data Transmission Facilities
for Internetworks. 95

X

BRIEF

BRIEF

X

Table of Illustrations

Preface to the Second Edition

Think back to where you were in 1991. Among other things, I was researching the first edition of *Internetworking*. And while 1991 does not seem like ages ago, many LAN and WAN techologies that we take for granted today, such as Fast Ethernet and Frame Relay, were not available at that time. My, how time flies!

These technological advances, plus suggestions from many readers and seminar attendees, prompted this second look at internetworking technologies—circa 1995. As in the first edition, this book is organized along the lines of the Open Systems Interconnection (OSI) Reference Model, beginning with a discussion of internetworking principles and standards in Chapter 1.

Chapter 2 is devoted to LAN to LAN internetworking, including repeaters, bridges, switches and routers. Chapters 3 through 5 are devoted to WAN transmission facilities and systems, including analog and digital leased lines, X.25-based networks, and broadband networks including Frame Relay, Switched Multimegabit Data Service (SMDS) and Asynchronous Transfer Mode, or ATM. Chapter 6 discusses the design of the LAN-to-WAN connection, and provides examples of internetworks that used these broadband systems.

Chapters 7 and 8 are devoted to a discussion of two popular protocol suites for internetworking, the Transmission Control Protocol/Internet Protocol (TCP/IP) and the Xerox Network Systems (XNS) protocols, respectively. These protocols are used extensively in many Network Operating Systems (NOSs). The internetworking and interoperability capabilities of five popular NOSs are studied in Chapter 9. These include: Apple Computer's AppleTalk, Banyan Systems' VINES, Novell's NetWare, Microsoft's Windows NT and IBM's LAN Server.

Chapter 10 rounds out the tour of the OSI Model by looking at application gateways, and Chapter 11 discusses internetwork implementation. The balance of the text is devoted to appendices that provide reference information for the reader.

As was the case with the first edition, a number of a number of companies and individuals supported this project by providing information on their internetworking solutions. In alphabetical order, they are: Karin Bakis, several individuals from Banyan Systems, Inc., Steve Bauer, Vivian Beaulieu, Rich Black, Rich Borden, Andy Boyer, Scott Braddock, Patricia Brett, Dave Brooks, Elizabeth Buckalew, Christy

Chapman, Bryan Clark, Chris Connor, Steve Crow, Tom Dambly, Jay Duncanson, Trudy Edelson, Lynn Epstein, Maggie Faber, Anne Ferris, Greg Goodman, Joe Grillo, Cheryl Hall, Diane Hamilton, several individuals from Hill Associates, Inc., Garry Hornbuckle, April Jacobs, Laura Knapp, Peter Lau, Ed Liebing, Donna Loughlin, John Majonen, Marianne McCarthy, David Michelson, Eileen Miller, Nan Miller, Mark Monday, Ike Mustafa, Harry Noborikawa, Marc Norwood, Amy Novakoff, Dan Price, Cynthia Provin, Don Reckles, David Rodewald, Gerald Ryan, Dick Shimizu, Eitan Schwartz, Tami Schwerin, Beverly Stevens, Fred Stevens, Farzad Tari, Harvey Walseth, Wayne Wilkinson, Tom Woolf, Victoria Wright, and Bob Yori.

Carol Goodwin did much of the research on the appendices, and David Hertzke of Integrated Graphics Communication took numerous sketches and data sheets drawings and turned them into figures that illustrate the capabilities of these solutions.

I have a superb team of editors. These include: Paul Farrell, Jono Hardjowirogo, Debra Williams Cauley, Eileen Mullin, John Thompson, and Annette Sroka Devlin.

Most importantly, Holly, Nathan and Nicholas, assisted by the faithful efforts of Boomer and Brutus, provided the support such an undertaking requires.

I am thankful to be part of such a complete internetwork!

mark@diginet.com

May 1995

Why This Book is for You

This, the third volume in the Network Troubleshooting Library, is written for network designers, managers, and administrators who need to connect their LANs to any other type of network. Examples would be links to another, dissimilar LAN (such as a Token Ring connecting to an Ethernet) or to a remote host system across the country.

Individual sections of this handbook discuss:

- Internetworking standards-detailing the differences between Transparent Routing, Source Routing, and Source Routing Transparent bridging methods.

- Selecting hardware-when to use a repeater, bridge, switch, router, or gateway in the internetwork.

- Selecting the optimum LAN-to-WAN transmission facility, such as an analog or digital leased line, ISDN, T1 or T3 circuits, or Packet Switched Public Data Network connections using the X.25 protocol.

- Broadband technologies, including Frame Relay, Switched Multimegabit Data Service (SMDS) and Asynchronous Transfer Mode (ATM).

- Implementing internetworking protocols, including TCP/IP and XNS.

- Designing the internetwork, with over 40 examples of internetworking hardware and software solutions.

- Interoperability functions for popular LAN operating systems, including Apple Computer's AppleTalk, Banyan Systems' VINES, Novell's NetWare, Microsoft's Windows NT and IBM's LAN Server.

- Providing gateways to connect your LAN to minicomputers mainframes or application servers.

If your LAN requires local or remote connectivity to any other system, this handbook belongs in your technical library.

# Internetworking Principles and Standards

The term internetworking has many different meanings for many different people. The *IBM Dictionary of Computing* defines internetworking as "communication between two or more networks." The term network has several definitions, one of which is "a configuration of data processing devices and software connected for information interchange." A new definition for internetworking might be "communication between data processing devices on one network and other, possibly dissimilar, devices on another network."

A simple definition of the term internetworking doesn't describe the dissimilar problems that network designers and administrators experience, however. One network manager may need to have a DEC minicomputer communicate with an IBM mainframe. Another may wish to set up an Ethernet Local Area Network (LAN) that has remote access capabilities. Maybe an administrator is dealing with dissimilar hardware or software platforms, and needs to integrate Macintosh, PC, or UNIX workstations. Perhaps an internetwork is outgrowing its digital leased lines, and the system designer is considering an upgrade to a broadband transmission technology such as Frame Relay, Switched Multimegabit Data Service (SMDS), or Asynchronous Transfer Mode (ATM). All of these are specific, and very different, examples of internetworking possibilities.

This book focuses on the internetworking of LANs, minicomputers, and mainframes. Our discussions will be about linking dissimilar systems—such as

Ethernet and token ring networks—together, over a wide variety of Wide Area Network (WAN) transmission facilities, ranging from analog dial-up lines to Integrated Services Digital Network (ISDN) and ATM services. We'll explore the many techniques, employing either hardware and/or software products, for making the necessary connections.

The book is organized according to the OSI Reference Model, starting with the Physical Layer issues and ending with Application Layer challenges. This first chapter lays the foundation by discussing internetworking standards. Chapter 2 discusses LAN-to-LAN connections, and the integration of repeaters, bridges, switches, and routers into the LAN. Chapter 3 discusses Wide Area Network (WAN) transmission facilities, including analog and digital leased lines, T1 and T3 circuits, and ISDN. Chapter 4 discusses a widely-used WAN interface standard, X.25, and Chapter 5 looks at broadband transmission technologies, including frame relay, SMDS, and ATM. LAN-to-WAN design issues and solutions are explored in Chapter 6. Chapters 7 and 8 deal primarily with the OSI Network and Transport Layers, discussing TCP/IP and the XNS protocols, respectively, in detail. Chapter 9 explores how popular networking software architectures, such as those of Banyan, Microsoft, and Novell, handle internetworking. In Chapter 10, we'll look at the OSI Application Layer, considering gateways to link dissimilar applications. Chapter 11 concludes with a plan to facilitate the implementation of these previously discussed ideas. Let's begin our study by looking at a brief history of the concept of computer internetworking.

1.1 Internetworking History

In the late 1960s and early 1970s, computer networks were defined by the mainframe used. After careful consideration, a company would select the minicomputer or mainframe environment of a proprietary vendor such as IBM or DEC. The customer was committed to their architecture of choice until obsolescence necessitated a complete redesign. If the system required minor additions or alterations, the company called the manufacturer's rep, who supplied the required upgrade. The company rarely considered adding on third-party equipment because of the proprietary nature of the network architectures in use.

The mid-1970s brought a change to the concept of proprietary computer architecture. The idea of an "open" system—an architecture adhering to published standards with defined interfaces—became popular. A crack thus appeared in the foundation of proprietary architectures. The possibility of a DEC minicomputer accessing an IBM mainframe became more than a wild idea. (DEC, in its DECnet Phase IV [released in 1982], did in fact implement connections into IBM's System Network Architecture [SNA].) Two groups became the driving forces behind the movement to develop open-system standards: users, who wanted vendor-independent solutions; and vendors, who wished to develop marketable products. The collaboration of these two groups resulted in jointly-developed standards. A number of standards organizations emerged, including the International Telecommunications Union—Telecommunications Standardization Sector [ITU-T, formerly known as the International Telegraph and Telephone Consultative Committee (CCITT)]; the International Organization for Standardization (ISO); and the American National Standards Institute (ANSI). (Appendix A lists addresses of these and other standards organizations.)

The growing need for network-to-network communication (or internetworking) inspired the research that led to what we now know as the Open Systems Interconnection (OSI) Reference Model. First published in 1978 by the ISO, the familiar OSI model defined the computer communication function in terms of seven distinct layers. In the next section, we'll briefly examine the functions of the seven layers, and then see how they are used to solve internetworking requirements.

Excellent texts on the subject of the OSI reference model include references [1-1] through [1-5]. We'll reference specifics of these works throughout this chapter.

1.2 Open Systems Interconnection Principles

The Open Systems Interconnection (OSI) Reference Model is designed as a standard to allow various "open" systems to communicate. A system that complies with standards (specifically OSI standards)—also referred to as protocols—for communication with other systems is defined as being open. An open system is standards-based instead of proprietary-based; my system can thus communicate and cooperate with your system using interfaces and protocols that both systems understand.

In creating the OSI model, the International Organization for Standardization (ISO) divided the network communication functions into seven layers (Figure 1-1). We'll summarize the seven functions here; for a more in-depth discussion, refer to the complete standard [1-6], Tanenbaum [1-1], or Black [1-3].

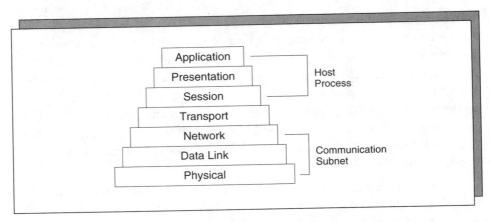

Figure 1-1. The Open System Interconnection (OSI) reference model

The *Physical Layer* handles bit-transmission between one node (e.g., host, workstation) and the next. The Physical Layer functions include interfacing with the transmission media; encoding the data signal; defining the range of the voltage or current magnitudes; defining the connector sizes, shapes, and pinouts; and anything generally associated with the physical transmission of the bit stream.

The *Data Link Layer* maintains a reliable communication link between adjacent nodes. As such, it assumes that the Physical Layer is noisy or prone to errors. Data Link provides a reliable delivery mechanism to transmit a frame (or package) of data bits to the next node. The Data Link Layer inserts addresses in the data frame (including source and destination) and provides error control for the data—usually implemented with a Cyclic Redundancy Check (CRC).

The *Network Layer* establishes a path for the traveling data packet along the communication subnet from the source node to the destination node. The Network Layer switches, routes, and controls the congestion of these information packets within the subnet.

The *Transport Layer* provides reliable delivery of host messages originating at Layer 7, the Application Layer, in the same way that the Data Link Layer assures reliable delivery of frames between adjacent nodes. The major difference between the Data Link and Transport Layers is that the Data Link domain lies between adjacent nodes, whereas the Transport Layer's domain extends from the source to the destination (or end-to-end) within the communication subnet. Issues concerning source-to-destination messages are important in the Transport Layer. For example, the Transport Layer segments a long message into smaller units (packets) prior to transmission, and assures the reassembly of those packets into the original message at the receiver's end.

The *Session Layer* establishes and terminates process-to-process communication sessions between hosts. Translation between name and address databases, as well as synchronization between the two hosts, may be required to manage the sessions.

The *Presentation Layer* establishes the syntax (or form) in which data is exchanged between the two hosts. As such, the Presentation Layer provides a data manipulation function, not a communication function. Data compression and data encryption are two examples of Presentation Layer services.

The *Application Layer* provides end-user services, such as Application Layer file transfers, electronic messages, virtual terminal emulation, remote database access, and network management. The end user interacts with the Application Layer.

The seven layers divide into two important subsets. The first is comprised of the lower three layers (the Physical, Data Link, and Network Layers) and is termed the communications subnetwork, subnet, or the carrier portion of the system. The upper three layers (the Session, Presentation, and Application Layers) are collectively known as the host process, sometimes called the customer portion of the system. The middle layer (Transport) is the first end-to-end layer, and acts as a buffer between the two subsets. As such, the Transport Layer is often grouped with the upper layers as part of the host process.

A specific internetwork architecture results when two open systems are linked directly—with a single cable, for example (Figure 1-2). In this configuration, protocols operate on a peer-to-peer basis between each of the layers and are shown as dashed lines to indicate their logical (or virtual) communication paths. The interface between the layers within the same system is a vertical relationship, whereas the protocol is a horizontal relationship between peer layers of the adjacent systems. The actual communication path originates in Open System A as an input to its Application Layer. The message then proceeds down through the seven layers (7 through 1) of System A, across the physical media (cable), and up the seven layers (1 through 7) of System B. Details of this process are shown in Figure 1-3, taken from reference [1-7]. Data from Application process X is passed to the Application Layer protocol, which adds its Application Header (AH). The header contains protocol control information (PCI) necessary for the peer process (Y) to interpret the data. The AH plus Application Data (AD) is then passed down to the Presentation Layer. The Presentation Layer treats the AH and AD as its own data, appends the Presentation Header (PH), and passes the data unit down to the Session, Transport, and Network Layers in turn.

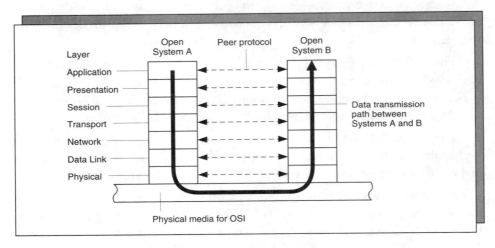

Figure 1-2. Seven layer reference model and peer protocols

When the encapsulated message reaches the Data Link Layer, Framing (F), Address (A), and Control (C) information is added as the Data Link Layer header. The Frame Check Sequence (FCS) and possibly additional Framing (F) characters are appended as the Data Link Layer trailer. The assembled frame is then passed to the Physical Layer. The Physical Layer encodes the data for transmission, accesses the transmission medium, and monitors the serial bit transmission. At the destination node, the reverse of this process occurs. The Physical Layer hands its bits to the Data Link Layer, which decodes and then strips off the Data Link Layer header and trailer. The Data Link Layer data unit is then passed to the Network, Transport, Session, and higher layers in turn. The process is completed when the electronic message (shown again as Application data) is delivered to Application Y.

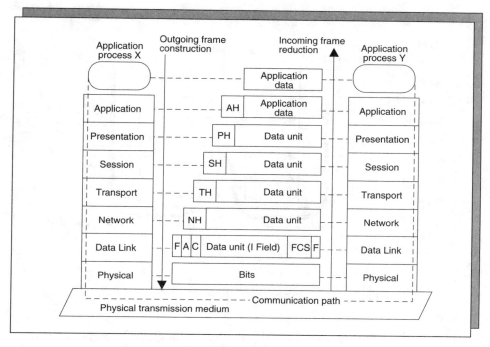

Figure 1-3. Building a frame for transmission *(© 1987 IEEE)*

When the systems are not connected by the same physical cable, a relay open system must be used (Figure 1-4). The relay is also known as a switching node, and implements the lower three (communication subnet) layers of the OSI model. More than one relay may (and most likely will) exist. A good example of the relay open system is the Public Switched Telephone Network (PSTN) which is used to connect dial-up voice and data calls. The various switching centers (known as Central Offices, or C.O.s) route and switch the telephone call. You, as an end user, do not know (nor do you really care) how many of these offices your call traverses, or which connection paths they take. As long as the telephone call to the distant end goes through, you deem the process satisfactory. The same is true with internetworks using relay open systems. A number of these switching nodes could exist between source and destination hosts (e.g. Open Systems A and B). The data from the originating system (A) passes through the communication subnet on its way to the destination system (B). No alteration of the application data occurs within the subnet; it acts as a transparent pipe for that data.

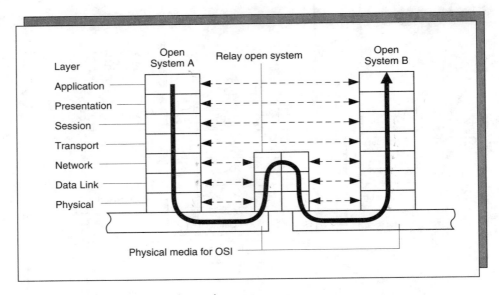

Figure 1-4. Communication involving relay open systems

What does all of this have to do with internetworking? Let's reserve that question for section 1.4, and look next at specific protocols defined by the ISO.

1.3   OSI Protocols for Internetworking

The ISO's development of the OSI Reference Model has resulted in the ongoing development of associated protocols (Figure 1-5). These protocols describe internetworking utopia—if all vendors used identical protocols at all layers, our internetworking problems would be solved. Unfortunately, the predominance of SNA, DECnet, and other proprietary networking architectures has slowed industry evolution towards a fully OSI-compliant architecture. In addition, the wide availability of openly-available solutions, such as the Transmission Control Protocol and Internet Protocol (TCP/IP), has also led some network architects to question the wisdom of implementing a fully-compliant OSI architecture. Let's see what each layer of an ideal internetworking environment would represent.

OSI Layer	Example ISO Protocols			
Application	ISO 9040/9041 VT	ISO 8831/8832 JTM	ISO 8571/8572 FTAM	ISO 9595/9596 CMIP
Presentation	ISO 8823/ITU-T X.226 Connection-Oriented Presentation Protocol			
Session	ISO 8327/ITU-T X.225 Connection-Oriented Session Protocol			
Transport	ISO 8073/ITU-T X.224 Connection-Oriented Transport Protocol			
Network	ISO 8473 Connectionless Network Service		ISO 8208/ITU-T X.25 Packet Level Protocol	
Data Link	ISO 8802-2			
	ISO 9314-2 FDDI	ISO 8802-3 CSMA/CD Bus	ISO 8802-4 Token Bus	ISO 8802-5 Token Ring	ISO 7776 ITU-T X.25 LAP/LAPB	ISO 7809 HDLC
Physical	Options from EIA, ITU-T, IEEE, etc.			

Figure 1-5. ISO Protocol examples

The Physical and Data Link Layer protocols offer a multitude of options for accessing LAN, WAN, and mini/mainframe systems. Many existing standards, such as IEEE 802, have ISO counterparts: ISO 8802-2, 8802-3, 8802-4, or 8802-5. Other ISO standards define connectors (e.g. the ISO 8877, the familiar 8 pin modular plug sometimes known as an RJ-45) or frame formats (e.g. ISO 7809—HDLC [High Level Data Link Control]) similar to IBM's SDLC (Synchronous Data Link Control). Other standards associations such as the Electronic Industries Association (EIA), American National Standards Institute (ANSI), or International Telecommunications Union (ITU) have also developed Physical and Data Link Layer standards that are widely accepted. An example of a Data Link Layer protocol is ISO 7776, which is also ITU-T X.25 LAP/LAPB. This standard defines the Link Access Procedure/Link Access Procedure Balanced protocol used within the X.25 protocol suite.

Network Layer standards can define either a connection-oriented (virtual circuit) or connectionless (datagram) service. ISO has defined a connectionless service with ISO 8473, "Protocol for Providing the Connectionless-Mode Network Service." The ISO Internet protocol (ISO IP) is similar to the Internet Protocol (IP), from the TCP/IP suite, that was originally developed by the U.S. Department of Defense (DoD). There are several interesting differences, however. First, ISO IP allows variable address lengths where most protocols usually define a fixed address length; a preliminary field in the ISO IP header defines the length of the field which contains the addresses themselves. Secondly, an options field is also included within the ISO IP header for specifying optional parameters, such as the quality of service or routing information. Another Network Layer standard is ISO 8208/ITU-T X.25, which specifies the Packet Layer Protocol, and is the subject of Chapter 4.

At the ISO Transport Layer, a number of protocol options are available depending upon the type of underlying network (i.e., the communications subnet) being used. Three different classes of networks—Types A, B, and C—are defined. Type A represents an optimum service, error-free, no-Network-Layer-reset (N-RESETS) network. Type B networks assure perfect packet delivery, but have N-RESETS due to network congestion or hardware/software failures. Type C networks provide unreliable service, possibly losing packets, and also have N-RESETS. Tanenbaum [1-1] cites LANs, Public Data Networks (PDNs), and packet radio networks as respective examples of Type A, Type B, and Type C networks. Within the three network types, there are five Transport Layer protocol classes:

⊗ Class 0: Simple class, used for network type A. No sequence or flow control.

⊗ Class 1: Basic error recovery class, used for network type B. Has sequencing to handle N-RESETS.

⊗ Class 2: Multiplexing class, used for network type A. Enhances class 0 to permit multiplexing.

⊗ Class 3: Error recovery and multiplexing class, used for network type B.

⊛ Class 4: Error detection and recovery class, used for network type C. Assumes the worst case (unreliable) network type, and necessarily the most complex protocol treatment.

Of the above protocols (designated TP0–TP4), TP4 bears the greatest resemblance to our familiar Transmission Control Protocol (TCP), and is the most frequently discussed. Two standards detail the Transport Layer protocols: ISO 8072 (Connection-Oriented Transport Service) and ISO 8073 (Connection-Oriented Transport Protocol). The ITU-T equivalent of ISO 8073 is X.224. Further details on the three network types and five Transport classes are found in Uyless Black's *OSI, A Model for Computer Communications Standards* [1-3].

The Session Layer provides four services. The first is to establish the connection, exchange data, and then terminate the connection. The second is to use tokens to manage the exchange of that data, synchronize the connection, and determine if half- or full-duplex transmission is required. The third service is to establish synchronization points within the data stream so that communication can be resumed from that point if interruptions occur. The fourth service interrupts the data transfer, continuing from a pre-determined synchronization point. At the Session Layer, standards ISO 8326 (Connection-Oriented Session Service) and ISO 8327 (Connection-Oriented Session Protocol) are employed. The ITU-T equivalent of ISO 8327 is X.225.

Rather than serving a communication function, the Presentation Layer deals in the realm of data representation. This layer preserves the semantics (or meaning) of the data being transmitted, regardless of the syntax (or form) that is used. The standards used at the Presentation Layer are ISO 8822 (Connection-Oriented Presentation Service) and ISO 8823 (Connection-Oriented Presentation Protocol). The data structure entitled Abstract Syntax Notation 1 (ASN.1) is also defined as ISO 8824. These standards relate to functions such as data encryption and compression.

The Application Layer of the Reference Model has standards for several specific functions. ISO 9040/9041 defines the Virtual Terminal Service/Protocol. ISO 8831/8832 defines Job Transfer and Management Service/Protocol for remote program execution. ISO 8571/8572 is the File Transfer Access and Manipulation Service/Protocol, which defines remote file manipulation services.

ISO 9595/9596 defines the Common Management Information Service/Protocol used for network management.

With this background in the OSI protocols, let's next explore how connectivity devices stack up.

1.4 Applying Connectivity Devices to the OSI Model

Let's explore how connectivity devices work with regard to OSI protocols. We'll return to the peer protocol model (Figure 1-2) and assume that the two open systems are connected with a physical transmission medium such as a twisted pair or fiber optic cable. What happens if the cable length is so long that the signal loses power? We can solve this by adding a repeater (Figure 1-6) that will amplify (or regenerate) the physical signal. Repeaters function at the Physical Layer and operate between like networks, such as token ring to token ring, or Ethernet to Ethernet. A repeater can be added to the internetwork to extend the range of the network; connected segments behave physically (and logically) as a single network.

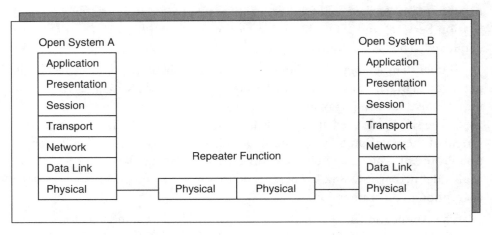

Figure 1-6. Comparing a repeater to OSI

When repeating a signal is insufficient for the existing network, a bridge adds the functionality of the Data Link Layer (Figure 1-7). The bridge logically separates two network segments by operating upon the address within the Data Link Layer (or IEEE Medium Access Control [MAC] Layer) frame. Information that is either stored at the bridge or provided within the transmitted frame assists the bridge in making a rather simple decision: pass the frame to the next segment (known as forwarding) or do not pass the frame to the next segment (known as filtering). Bridges operate on networks having compatible Data Link Layer addressing schemes (such as IEEE 802.3 to 802.3, or 802.3 to 802.5), but are transparent to the protocols of the Network and higher layers.

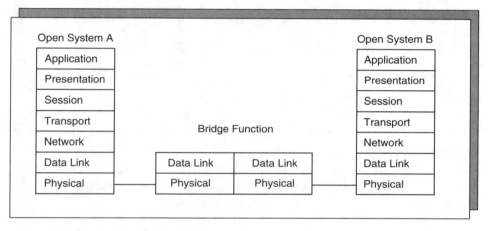

Figure 1-7. Comparing a bridge to OSI

Routers operate at the Network Layer, and may interpret either one or more protocols at that layer (Figure 1-8). Recall that the Network Layer makes a choice between available paths within the communication subnet, eventually connecting the source and destination hosts. A router performs similarly, reading information about the destination network address, and forwarding that packet to the appropriate destination network. (Bridges, as discussed above, make a simple binary decision to forward or not to forward a frame after examining the Data Link Layer address.) The router thus serves a network-wide connectivity function. Routers may operate on one Network Layer protocol, such as the Internet Protocol (IP), or multiple protocols such as IP, DECnet, and Novell's IPX (Internetwork Packet Exchange).

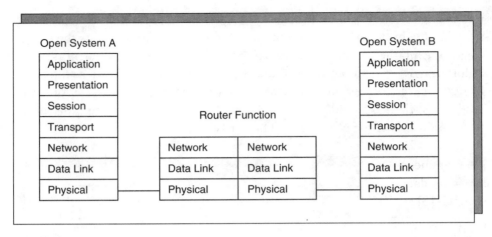

Figure 1-8. Comparing a router to OSI

Finally, gateways may operate at all seven OSI layers (Figure 1-9). Gateways are application-oriented, and may be responsible for connecting incompatible electronic mail systems, converting and transferring files from one system to another, or enabling interoperability between dissimilar operating systems. Chapter 10 will be devoted to various application-specific gateways.

Open System A	Gateway Function		Open System B
Application	Application	Application	Application
Presentation	Presentation	Presentation	Presentation
Session	Session	Session	Session
Transport	Transport	Transport	Transport
Network	Network	Network	Network
Data Link	Data Link	Data Link	Data Link
Physical	Physical	Physical	Physical

Figure 1-9. Comparing a gateway to OSI

A great deal of literature is available on the subject of LAN connectivity devices. Reference [1-8] looks at the connectivity design issues from an OSI perspective. Bridges and their applications are discussed in reference [1-9]; router architecture is explored in references [1-10] and [1-11]; gateways are profiled in [1-12].

1.5 IEEE Project 802

No reference on internetworking would be complete without information on LAN standards and associated frame formats. The companion volumes, references [1-13] and [1-14], discuss these issues in detail; a summary is provided here.

Recognizing a need for standards in the LAN market, the Institute of Electrical and Electronics Engineers (IEEE) undertook Project 802. Named for the month (February) and year (1980) of its inception, Project 802 addresses LAN standards at the Physical and Data Link Layers of the OSI model (Figure 1-10).

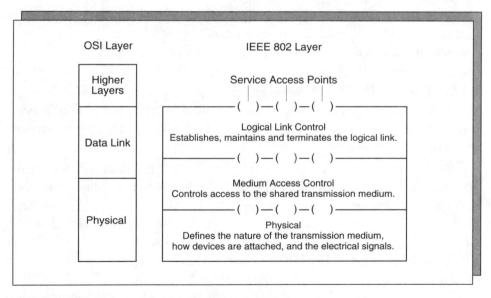

Figure 1-10. Comparing IEEE Project 802 with OSI *(© IEEE)*

1.5.1 Physical and Medium Access Control Layers

The Physical Layer of the IEEE LAN model is similar to its OSI counterpart. Its responsibilities include signal encoding and decoding, serial bit transmission and reception, and providing the physical connection to the transmission medium via twisted-pair, coaxial, or fiber-optic cable.

The IEEE Medium Access Control (or MAC) Layer extends below to the Physical, and above to the Data Link Layers. This layer, as its name implies, controls access to the transmission medium, and is further subdivided into other standards, such as:

802.3: Carrier Sense Multiple Access Bus with Collision Detection (CSMA/CD)

802.4: Token Passing Bus

802.5: Token Passing Ring

802.6: Metropolitan Area Networks

Each of these MAC standards defines a unique frame format, discussed in Section 1.6, and detailed in references [1-15] through [1-18], respectively.

1.5.2 Emerging MAC Layer Developments

Many other LAN standards, supporting both wireless media (802.11) and faster transmission technologies (100BASE-T and 100VG-AnyLAN), are in various stages of development.

One example of this continuing work is the 100BASE-T standard, designated 802.3u, which supports 100 Mbps transmission over both twisted pair and fiber optic media (see references [1-19] through [1-21]). Many data-intensive applications, such as imaging and multimedia, require data throughput higher than the current 802.3 products provide. A number of vendors, including 3Com, Intel, SMC, Sun Microsystems, Bay Networks (SynOptics), and others, formed the Fast Ethernet Alliance to address these high bandwidth requirements. Their work has resulted in the 100BASE-T architecture, which provides a smooth migration from existing 802.3 and Ethernet networks.

Fast Ethernet technology is based upon the same Medium Access Control (MAC) protocol, Carrier Sense Multiple Access with Collision Detection

(CSMA/CD), of existing 802.3 networks. The bit transmission time is reduced by a factor of ten, which allows an increase by a factor of ten in the transmission rate. The frame formats remain intact, so that no extensive changes to supporting systems, such as network management or protocol analysis tools, are required. Three Physical Layer options are available with 100BASE-T. 100BASE-T4 is a four-pair system over either voice or data grade unshielded twisted pair cable (UTP categories 3, 4, or 5). 100BASE-TX is a two-pair system that requires category 5 UTP or shielded twisted pair (STP) cabling. 100BASE-FX uses two strands of fiber optic cable.

A second emerging technology is 100VG-AnyLAN, which is defined as the 802.12 standard (see references [1-22] through [1-24]). The network is configured as a star topology, with a link connecting each node to the hub.

This network uses a new, centrally-controlled access method, called Demand Priority. In this network access method, nodes issue requests (or demands) for network service, and send their data to the hub. The hub continually scans its network ports. When a request for network service is received, the hub directs the incoming data to the port with the matching destination address. Requests for data service may be prioritized, allowing time-critical applications, such as video or multimedia, to have service before more routine applications.

Several Physical Layer options have been defined, using four pairs of category 3, 4, or 5 UTP. Future implementations with two-pair UTP or STP, and fiber optic cable, are under consideration. Each hub may be configured to support 802.3 or 802.5 frame formats, although all hubs on the same network must use the same frame format. This network offers message frame compatibility with existing 802.3 and 802.5 networks. This compatibility allows bridges to connect 100VG-AnyLAN networks and 802.3 or 802.5 networks, and routers to connect 100VG-AnyLAN networks to FDDI or ATM networks or WAN links.

These fast LAN architectures are just two examples of the ongoing work of Project 802, which will continue to make significant contributions to networking technologies.

1.5.3 Logical Link Control

The highest layer of the IEEE LAN Model is the Logical Link Control (LLC) Layer, defined by the IEEE 802.2 standard [1-25]. While the LLC bears a close resemblance to the OSI Data Link Layer, there are also some important differences. Both

Data Link and LLC must reliably transmit frames of information between adjacent stations. In the LAN model, however, there is no need for the Network Layer functions of routing and switching. Since there is only one available "route" (the cable), the addressing defined in the MAC Layer frame is sufficient for delivery of the frame. Other functions, such as flow control (which assures that a fast sender does not overwhelm a slow receiver) and error control, are also handled by the Data Link Layer.

The major difference between the OSI Data Link Layer and the IEEE 802.2 LLC Layer is that multiple endpoints to the data link can exist in the IEEE model. With a LAN, communicating between one source and multiple SAPs (or Service Access Points) is often required. SAPs function in a manner somewhat analogous to ports. Thus, a workstation that has one MAC Layer address (provided by the hardware or Network Interface Card [NIC]) can communicate with several higher layer processes. Each of these processes would have a unique SAP address. Both Source (SSAP) and Destination (DSAP) addresses are specified in the 802.2 LLC Protocol Data Unit (Figure 1-11).

DSAP address	SSAP address	Control	Information
8 bits	8 bits	8 or 16 bits	M*8 bits

DSAP Address = destination service access point address field

SSAP Address = source service access point address field

Control = control field (16 bits for formats that include sequence numbering, and 8 bits for formats that do not)

Information = information field

* = multiplication

M = an integer value equal to or greater than 0. (Upper bound of M is a function of the medium access control methodology used.)

Figure 1-11. The Logical Link Control (LLC) Protocol Data Unit (© IEEE)

Three types of LLC operations are defined:

⊚ Type 1 (unacknowledged, connectionless services): the sending and receiving of frames in a datagram fashion. Point-to-point, multipoint, and broadcast transmissions are supported by Type 1.

⊚ Type 2 (connection-oriented services): a logical connection between SAPs providing sequence control, flow control, error control, and acknowledgments.

⊚ Type 3 (acknowledged connectionless services): a datagram, point-to-point service with acknowledgments.

For further information, see reference [1-25].

1.6 LAN Frame Formats

Four major LAN architectures—Ethernet, token ring, ARCNET, and FDDI (Fiber Distributed Data Interface)—have different transmission formats for their Data Link Layer frames. We'll look at these individually.

1.6.1 Ethernet

The Ethernet frame format (reference [1-26]) was developed by DEC, Intel Corporation, and Xerox Corporation, and is slightly different from the IEEE 802.3 format. The specific fields are shown in Figure 1-12. The Ethernet frame begins with a Preamble (eight octets) that is an alternating 1010 pattern ending in 10101011. The Preamble provides synchronization. The Destination Address is a six-octet field that can either define a Physical Layer address or a multicast address, which is determined by the LSB (least significant bit) of the first byte of that field. A Physical Layer address (usually burned into a ROM chip) sets LSB to 0, and is unique across all Ethernet networks. A multicast address can go to a group or be broadcast to all stations, and has LSB=1. In the case of a broadcast address, the destination field is set entirely to 1's—that is, FFFFFFFFFFFFH. (Throughout this text we will use a capital "H" to designate hexadecimal notation.)

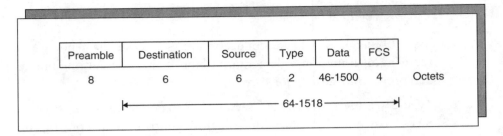

Figure 1-12. The Ethernet frame format

The address fields are further subdivided: the first three octets are assigned to a manufacturer in blocks (formerly by Xerox, but now assigned by the IEEE), and the last three octets are assigned by the manufacturer. Should the NIC become defective but the node address need to remain consistent (such as a well-known address for a gateway), the ROM chip containing the original address can be removed from the old board and inserted on the new board, or the address can be set in a register using the NIC diagnostic disk. Regardless of the technique used, care should be taken when human intervention is needed to replace the automated address administration safeguards.

The Source Address—the address of the station originating the frame—is the next field specified.

The Type field, sometimes referred to as the Ethertype, is a two-octet field that specifies the higher layer protocol used in the Data field. Some familiar Ethertypes would be 0800H (TCP/IP) and 0600H (XNS).

The Data field is the only variable-length field, and can range from a minimum of 46 to a maximum of 1500 octets. The contents of this field are completely arbitrary, and are as determined by the higher-layer protocol in use.

The last field is an FCS that is a 32-bit CRC based upon the contents of the Address, Type, and Data fields.

The allowable frame length, not including the Preamble, ranges from 64 to 1518 octets. Frames outside that range are considered invalid.

1.6.2 IEEE 802.3

The IEEE 802.3 frame format is shown in Figure 1-13. This frame begins with a Preamble (seven octets) that is an alternating 1010 pattern. The Start Frame

Delimiter (SFD) is next, defined as 10101011. Note that if the 802.3 Preamble and Start Frame Delimiter fields are combined, a pattern identical to the Ethernet Preamble will result.

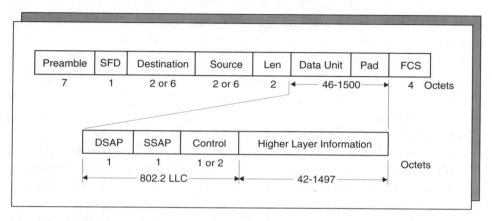

Figure 1-13. The IEEE 802.3 MAC frame format (© *IEEE*)

The SFD is followed by the Destination Address field, which can be either two or six octets in length, although a six-octet length is most common. The Individual/Group (I/G) field corresponds to the Physical/Multicast designation of Ethernet; the Universal/Local (U/L) field indicates whether the address is administered universally (by the IEEE) or locally (by the network administrator). The Source Address comes next, and must match the Destination Address field in length (either two octets for Destination and two for Source, or six octets for Destination and six for Source, but not two and six).

The Length field is two octets long and indicates the number of LLC octets in the Data field. A minimum of 46 octets of data is required; when the LLC data is less than 46, the Pad field is used. Maximum length of the Data and Pad fields combined is 1500 octets. Note that the 802.2 LLC PDU would be completely encapsulated within the Data Unit of the 802.3 MAC frame.

Finally, the FCS, which is based upon a 32-bit CRC, is computed according to the contents of the Destination Address, Source Address, Length, Data, and Pad fields (see reference [1-15] for further details).

Again referring to Figures 1-12 and 1-13, note the differences between the Ethernet and IEEE 802.3 frames. To start with, 802.3 replaces the Type field with a Length field. This difference has two implications. First, the frames are the same length at the Data Link Layer, but are incompatible at the Network and higher layers. Second, if the length of the data must be specified within an Ethernet frame, some parameter defined by the Network Layer (and contained within the Data Link Layer Information field) must convey that quantity. In addition, Ethernet has no provision to pad the data to its required 46-octet minimum, but 802.3 does. Thus, in Ethernet, the Network Layer will consider this parameter and pad the length.

1.6.3 IEEE 802.5

Because of the nature of token ring network operation, three different frame formats are required. The three-octet Token, shown in Figure 1-14a, circulates around the ring, passing network access control to the various workstations. The multi-octet Frame, shown in Figure 1-14b, contains either user data or ring-management data. The two-octet Abort Sequence in Figure 1-14c is used for correcting error conditions, such as errors internal to the workstation. We'll review each transmission type.

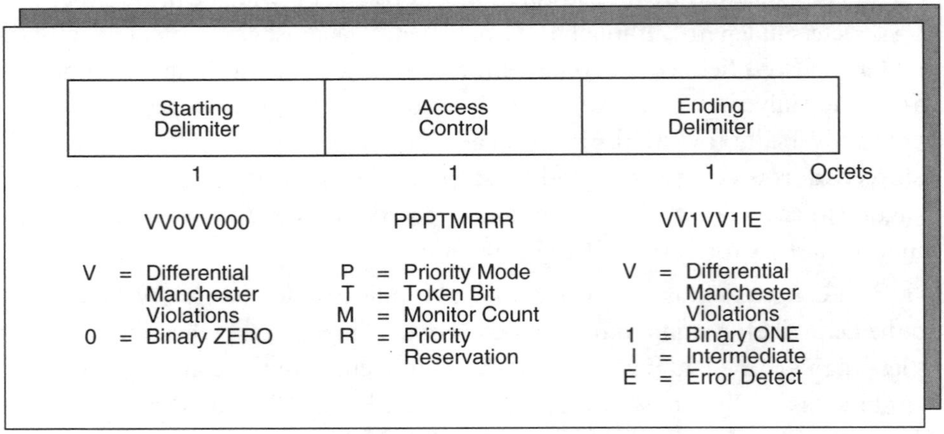

Starting Delimiter	Access Control	Ending Delimiter	
1	1	1	Octets
VV0VV000	PPPTMRRR	VV1VV1IE	

V = Differential Manchester Violations
0 = Binary ZERO

P = Priority Mode
T = Token Bit
M = Monitor Count
R = Priority Reservation

V = Differential Manchester Violations
1 = Binary ONE
I = Intermediate
E = Error Detect

Figure 1-14a. The IEEE 802.5 token format (© IEEE)

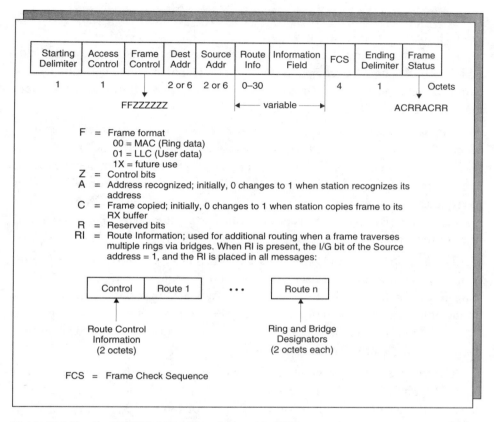

Figure 1-14b. The IEEE 802.5 MAC frame format *(© IEEE)*

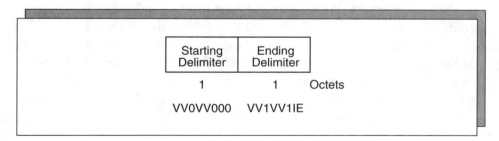

Figure 1-14c. The IEEE 802.5 Abort Sequence format *(© IEEE)*

The 24 bits of the token (Figure 1-14a) are divided into three octets: the Starting Delimiter, which contains violations to the Differential Manchester Code (thus indicating a unique data sequence) plus binary 0's; the Access Control field, which grants network access; and the Ending Delimiter, which contains Differential Manchester Code violations, binary 1's, and two additional bits—Intermediate and Error Detect—described below.

The Access Control field starts with three Priority (P) bits that set the priority of that Token. The Token (T) bit delineates either a token (T=0) or a Frame (T=1). Each workstation is assigned a priority for its transmissions, 000 being the lowest and 111 being the highest. The Reservation (R) bits can be used by a workstation to request the reservation of the next token as a transmission passes by. In order for a workstation to transmit, its priority must be greater than or equal to the priority of that token.

The Monitor Count (M) bit is used to prevent high-priority tokens or any frames from continuously circulating around the ring. It is set to M=0 by the transmitting station, and set to M=1 by the Active Monitor. If the monitor sees an incoming priority token or frame with M=1, it assumes that the transmitting station did not remove the token or frame after one round trip, and removes that token or frame, purges the ring, and issues a new token.

The Ending Delimiter includes Differential Manchester Code violations and binary 1's; an Intermediate frame (I) bit which, when set, indicates that this frame is part of a multi-frame transmission; and an Error Detect (E) bit that is set when a frame contains an FCS error, a non-integral number of octets, or a Differential Manchester code violation between Starting and Ending delimiters.

The variable-length frame shown in Figure 1-14b is transmitted by the workstation following the successful capture of the token. The first two octets of the frame, the Starting Delimiter and Access Control, are taken from the token format described above. The Frame Control field defines two types of frames—either LLC frames that carry user data, or MAC frames that carry ring-management data. The Destination and Source Address fields, either two or six octets in length, follow the same format as the 802.3 address fields.

An optional Routing Information (RI) field precedes the variable-length Information field. The RI field is used when the transmitting frame must go between multiple rings via bridges. A source-routing protocol, which we will discuss in Section 1.7.2, defines route control information as well as ring and bridge designators, and is used for these multiple ring topologies.

For LLC frames, the Information field contains the LLC Protocol Data Unit (PDU). The PDU includes the DSAP and SSAP addresses and Control information, plus the data from the higher layers (Network and above). For MAC frames, the Information field contains Commands and Parameters for ring management.

A Frame Check Sequence (FCS) follows the Information field. The Ending Delimiter field is taken from the token frame. The Frame Status field ends the 802.5 frame. It includes the Address Recognized (A) and Frame Copied (C) bits that verify that the receiving station has properly processed MAC frames. These bits do not have meaning for LLC frames in multiple ring topologies.

The Abort Sequence format shown in Figure 1-14c is used when certain error conditions occur. The Starting and Ending Delimiter fields are identical to the corresponding fields in the token.

1.6.4 Sub-Network Access Protocol

An extension to the IEEE 802.2 LLC header, known as the Sub-Network Access Protocol or SNAP [1-27], has been defined by the Internet community. This extension was made in order to encapsulate Internet Protocol (IP) datagrams and Address Resolution Protocol (ARP) requests and replies within an 802.X (802.3, 802.4, 802.5, etc.) frame.

The SNAP header immediately follows the 802.2 header, and is encapsulated within the 802.X frame (see Figure 1-15). For the 802.2 header, both DSAP and SSAP fields are set to AAH, and the Control field is set to 03H (for Unnumbered Information). The Protocol ID or Organization Code is three octets, and is specified in RFC 1042 [1-27] as all ZEROs. The Ethertype (two octets) completes the SNAP header. By using 802.2 and SNAP within the same 802.X MAC frame, both SAP addresses and Ethertypes can be specified.

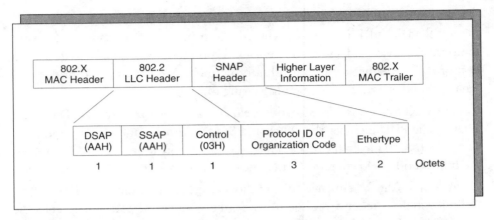

Figure 1-15. Sub-Network Access Protocol (SNAP) header encapsulated within an IEEE 802.X frame

1.6.5 ARCNET

ARCNET, originally developed by Datapoint Corporation, is not part of the IEEE Project 802 standards. It bears some resemblance to the IEEE 802.4 Token Passing Bus architecture, but a comparison of specifics such as node addressing reveals incompatibilities. An enhanced version, called ARCNETPLUS, operates at 20 Mbps, but likewise is not IEEE 802-compatible. For example, the original 2.5 megabits per second (Mbps) ARCNET uses eight-bit addresses, while the IEEE standard uses 48-bit addresses.

ARCNET has five frame formats, as depicted in Figure 1-16. The Invitation to Transmit (ITT) is the token that passes control of the network from one workstation to another. The Free Buffer Enquiry (FBE) is a query from a station desiring to transmit to determine if the intended receiver has sufficient buffer space available to hold the incoming frame. The Packet (PAC) is the frame itself, and can contain a system code (1 octet) plus up to 507 octets of data. An Acknowledgment (ACK) confirms the receipt of a packet or offers a positive response to an FBE. The Negative Acknowledgment (NAK) indicates a refusal to accept a packet or a negative response to an FBE. For further information on the ARCNET protocols, see reference [1-28].

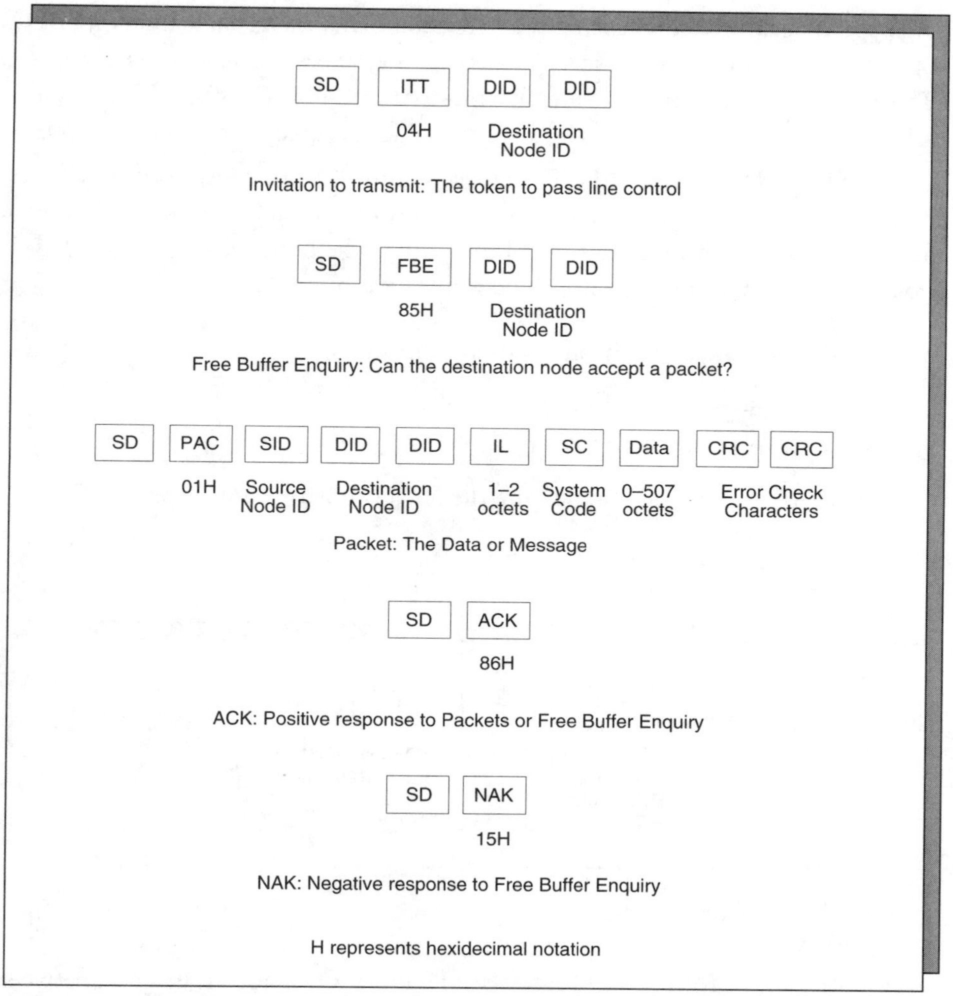

Figure 1-16. The ARCNET frame formats

1.6.6 FDDI

The Fiber Data Distributed Interface (FDDI) is a 100-Mbps network developed by the American National Standards Institute (ANSI). It has a number of standards (see references [1-29] through [1-32]) and is designed for both LAN and MAN (Metropolitan Area Network) configurations. A popular LAN application using FDDI as a high-speed backbone will be explored in Section 2.3.3. As its name implies, FDDI's physical topology is a fiber optic token passing ring, somewhat similar to IEEE 802.5. The FDDI frame formats also resemble those defined in IEEE 802.5. The encoding scheme used with FDDI defines a "symbol" which is equal to four bits.

The first FDDI format, the Token (see Figure 1-17a), consists of four fields. The Preamble (16 symbols) is used for synchronization. The Starting Delimiter, SD (2 symbols), indicates the start of the frame. The Frame Control, FC (2 symbols), defines the frame type and function. The subfields are:

C: Frame class (asynchronous or synchronous)

L: Frame address length (16 or 48 bits)

F: Frame format (defines LLC or MAC data)

Z: MAC control bits (indicating the MAC control frame type)

The Ending Delimiter, ED (2 symbols), indicates the end of the frame.

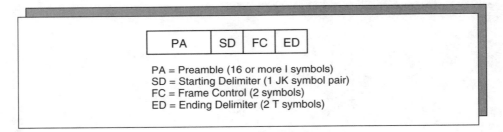

Figure 1-17a. FDDI token format

The second FDDI format, the Frame (see Figure 1-17b), adds four fields between the FC and ED:

DA: Destination Address (4 or 12 symbols, same format as IEEE 802)

SA: Source Address (must match DA in length)

INFO: Information (variable)

FCS: Frame Check Sequence, a 32-bit Cyclic Redundancy Check (8 symbols)

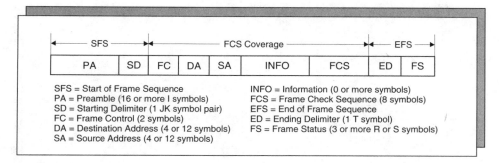

Figure 1-17b. FDDI frame format

The Ending Delimiter (1 symbol) indicates the end of the frame. The Frame Status, FS (at least 3 symbols), includes Error Detected (E), Address Recognized (A), and Frame Copied (C), as in IEEE 802.5.

1.7 IEEE Bridging Standards

As we studied in Section 1.4, a bridge is an internetworking device that relays frames of data from one network segment to another, making the multiple segments appear as one contiguous LAN. Figure 1-18 shows an architectural model of a bridge, with the protocol relationships between the various peer processes indicated by horizontal lines. Several design issues are worth noting [1-33]. First, each segment (left or right) may have its own Physical (PHY) and Medium Access Control (MAC) layers. No requirement exists for consistency on each side. Second, Logical Link Control (LLC) and higher-layer protocols pass transparently through the bridge; the bridge is independent of higher-layer protocols. Third, bridges do not provide data flow control; therefore, congestion within them is possible. When this occurs, any frames that were discarded or lost must be recovered by a higher layer protocol process.

Since some frames will be forwarded (or passed across the bridge relay) and others will be filtered (not passed across the bridge), another question arises: How does the bridge make its relaying decision? The two predominant methods of bridging have been Transparent Bridging (TB) and Source Routing (SR). The IEEE 802 committee has also adopted a Source Routing Transparent (SRT) method that provides both Transparent Bridging and Source Routing. We'll look at these three methods individually.

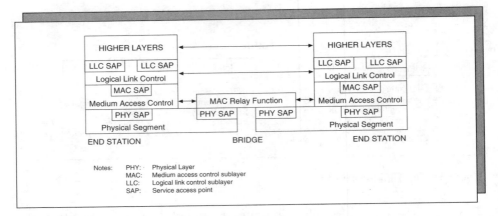

Figure 1-18. Protocol flows for bridged local network *(© 1988 IEEE)*

1.7.1 Transparent Bridging Method

The Transparent Bridging Method is so-named because the intelligence necessary to make the relaying decision exists in the bridge itself, and is thus transparent to the communicating workstations. Backes [1-34] describes three distinct functions of the Transparent Bridge:

1. Frame forwarding
2. Learning workstation addresses
3. Assuring that no topological loops exist

The first function, frame forwarding, is best described with a diagram (Figure 1-19). Traffic on LAN 1 (e.g. workstation A to B) remains on LAN 1 and is not relayed to LAN 2. Traffic from LAN 1 to LAN 2 (e.g. workstation B to C) is relayed by Bridge 1, but ignored by Bridge 2. Traffic from LAN 1 to LAN 3 (e.g. workstation A to E) is relayed by both Bridge 1 and Bridge 2.

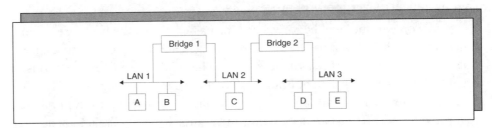

Figure 1-19. Bridge forwarding *(© 1988 IEEE)*

The second function of the TB, learning workstation addresses, is done by monitoring both incoming and outgoing ports (Figure 1-20). A database of workstations (on either side of the bridge) is developed by listening to all transmissions—a process known as learning. The bridge keeps a list of which stations transmit to each port, thereby allowing the forwarding or filtering decision to be made based upon the MAC-Layer address read.

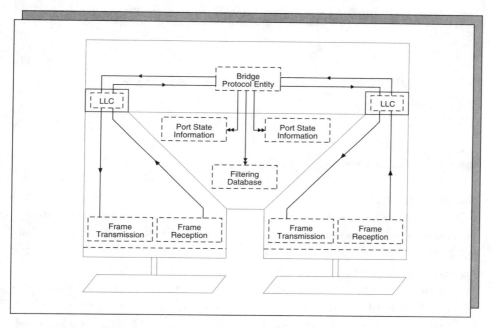

Figure 1-20. Operation of Inter-Bridge Protocol *(©IEEE)*

The TB bridge's third function is to provide overall control of the relaying operation—described in Figure 1-20 as the Bridge Protocol Entity. The topological assumption required by the TB bridge is that the network has formed a spanning tree. Backes describes the spanning tree as a network in which "there is only one path of bridges and LANs between any two LANs in the entire bridged LAN." In other words, there is only one (not two or more) path from LAN 1 to LAN 2 so that the possibility of a loop (Figure 1-21) does not exist. If workstation A were to broadcast a frame having an unknown destination address, both Bridge 1 and Bridge 2 would forward that frame.

A loop could cause frames to pass from LAN 1 to LAN 2 ad infinitum, giving new meaning to the phrase "you can't get there from here!" To eliminate the loop, one of the bridges must be (logically) disconnected, thereby making only a single path from LAN 1 to LAN 2 available.

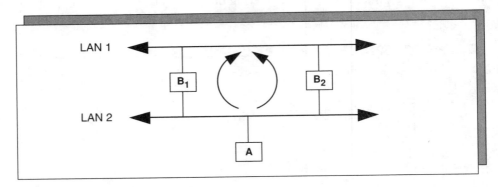

Figure 1-21. Loop of bridges *(© 1988 IEEE)*

The algorithm that takes the physical network topology and creates a logical Spanning Tree is known as the Spanning Tree algorithm. Bridges communicate with each other through messages known as Hello Bridge Protocol Data Units (BPDUs). One bridge becomes the "root" and all bridges transmit frames in the least-cost direction of that root. The root port is the port of each bridge which is communicating to or from the root. The root is selected depending upon transmission of Hello BPDUs, and the minimum-cost path decision. An example from IEEE 802.1D [1-35] shows a physical topology (Figure 1-22) that becomes a logical topology (Figure 1-23) after the Spanning Tree algorithm is used. The resulting Spanning Tree is shown in Figure 1-24. Note that Bridge 1 has been selected as the root, and Bridges 3 and 5 have been logically disconnected. The Spanning Tree algorithm defines the logical topology: Bridge 1 connects LAN 1 and LAN 2; Bridge 2 connects LAN 1 and LAN 3, as well as LAN 1 and LAN 4; and finally, Bridge 4 connects LAN 2 and LAN 5. Details of the algorithm are found in the standard [1-35].

The Spanning Tree algorithm has been widely used in IEEE 802.3 networks, and is supported by a large number of internetworking vendors.

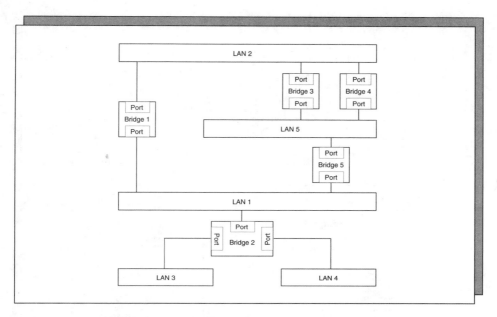

Figure 1-22. Bridged local area network *(© IEEE)*

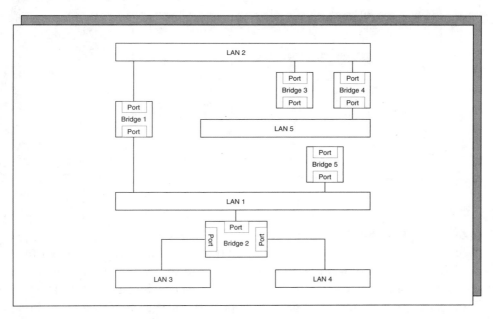

Figure 1-23. Active bridged network topology *(© IEEE)*

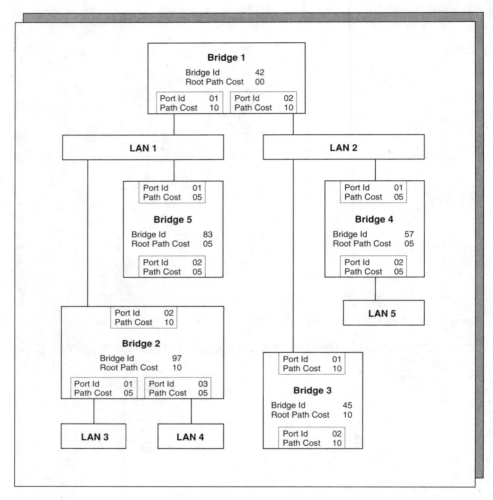

Figure 1-24. Spanning Tree *(© IEEE)*

1.7.2   Source Routing Method

While the TB Bridging Method depends on bridge intelligence, the Source Routing Method (SR) requires that the workstation (a source) determine the frame route. Interestingly enough, the SR algorithm was developed by IBM. The SR-compliant bridge requires less processing power, since much of its work is done for it by the originating workstation.

The key to the SR Method is the optional Routing Information field (RI) shown in Figure 1-14b, and the I/G bit of the Source Address field, known as the Routing Information Indicator (RII). When RII=1, RI is present, indicating that this frame can be source routed through source routing bridges. Frames with RII=0 will not be forwarded by source routing bridges; i.e., they will remain on the local ring. The operation of a source-routed bridge is described in IEEE 802.1D, Annex C, and illustrated in Figure 1-25.

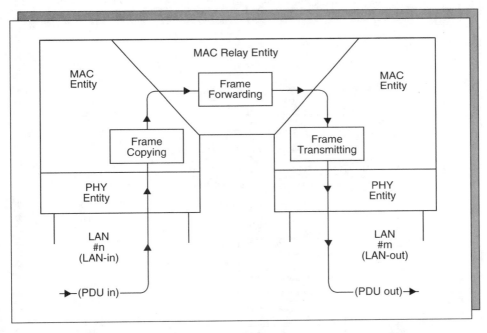

Figure 1-25. Elements of a source-routed bridge (© 1993 IEEE, Std 802.1D-1990)

The format of the RI field is shown in Figures 1-26a and 1-26b, and consists of a Routing Control field (two octets) followed by up to 14 two-octet Route-Designator pairs. The Route-Designator pair consists of a ring number (12 bits) and a bridge number (4 bits). A total of 14 route segments is possible, making the largest internetwork span 13 bridges (or hops). The RI field is determined by a discovery process originating at the workstation. A "discovery" frame is circulated to the various rings via the bridges until the intended destination station is located using a Spanning Tree. On its way back to the originator, each bridge adds its designator (ring ID and bridge number) until the reply finally reaches the transmitting station. The route from source to destination is thus selected from the RI fields shown on the returning frames.

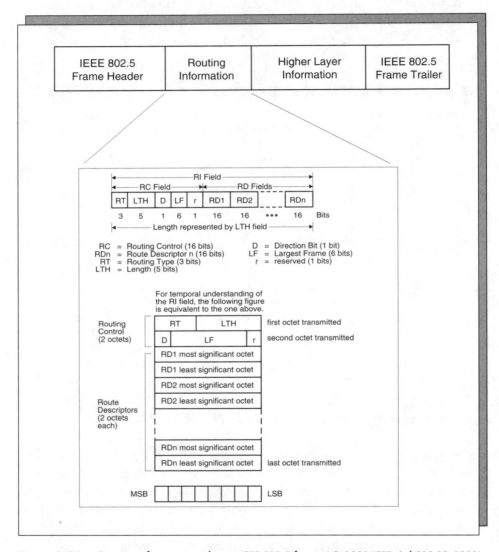

Figure 1-26a. Routing information within an IEEE 802.5 frame (© *1993 IEEE, Std 802.1D-1990*)

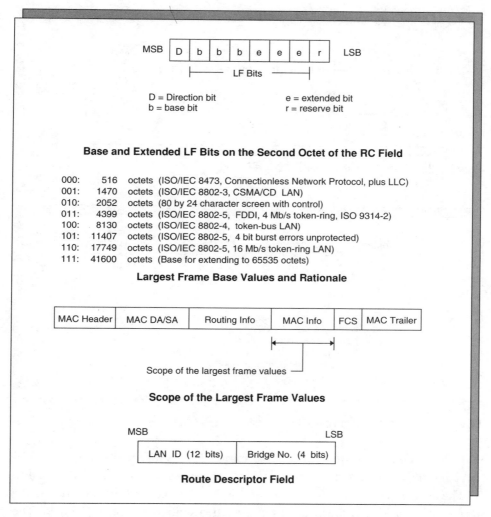

Figure 1-26b. Routing information field details *(© 1993 IEEE, Std 802.1D-1990)*

An example of this process, taken from reference [1-36] (also described in reference [1-37]), is shown in Figure 1-27. Workstation A wishes to communicate with Workstation B, which is not on its ring. The discovery process yields the RI Field 0830 AA03 AA14 AA20H. As shown in Figure 1-27a, workstation A is attached to ring number AA0, then to ring AA1 via bridge 3. Ring AA1 attaches to ring AA2 via bridge 4. The complete RI field is shown in Figure 1-27b.

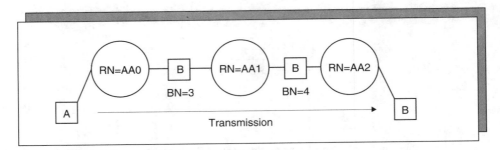

Figure 1-27a. *Source routing example (© 1988 IEEE)*

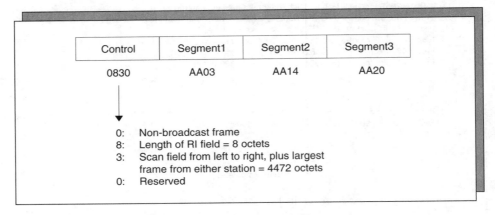

Figure 1-27b. *Routing information field example (© 1988 IEEE)*

In order to communicate with B, Workstation A thus inserts 0830 AA03 AA14 AA20H in the RI field, and sets the I/G bit of the Source Address (RII) equal to 1. The completed frame (including data) is then placed on the network. As the frame passes bridge 3, the bridge first sees RII=1, and looks for the RI field. The bridge recognizes its address (3) in the concatenated segment list, since it knows it is connected to both ring AA0 and ring AA1. Bridge 3 then copies the frame, and places it on ring AA1, which is copied by bridge 4. Bridge 4 in turn places the frame on ring AA2, where workstation B is located. The response from B to A might follow the same (reverse) route, or take some other route on a more complex network topology.

Because the discovery process and the insertion of the RI field is done by the source workstation, the term "source routing" is used. While this technique places more processing responsibility on the workstation, the bridge's job is simpler—look for RII, decode the RI field, copy the appropriate frames, and forward to the next ring.

1.7.3 Source Routing Transparent Method

As we have studied, the TB Method has been widely used in IEEE 802.3 networks, and SR was designed for IEEE 802.5. What happens if you need to connect a TB-based network to an SR-based network? A solution, described in IEEE 802.1D, Annex C, is known as the Source Routing Transparent (SRT) method. As the name implies, the SRT algorithm combines both methods:

Source Routing (SR) is performed when a frame is received with the RII=1 (indicating the presence of the RI field).

Transparent Bridging (TB) is performed when a frame is received with the RII=0 (indicating the absence of the RI field).

IEEE 802.1D, Annex C defines operation on two network types, both having an RI field defined:

Token Ring (ISO/IEC 8802-5)

FDDI MAC (ISO 9314-2)

Operation of the SRT algorithm is illustrated in Figure 1-28. Two sections of logic exist within the bridge's MAC Relay Entity: SR and TB. Frames entering the MAC entity with RII=0 (non-source routed) are either forwarded or discarded according to the TB Method we discussed in Section 1.7.1. If the received frame has RII=1 (source routed), then the SR logic is used. The SR logic depends on the type of frame received.

The SRT algorithm has several distinct advantages [1-38]. The ability to mix SR and TB on the same LAN eliminates the previous interoperability between the two techniques. As a result, SR stations and TB stations can now communicate, and connectivity is assured. Finally, since SRT applies to both the ANSI

FDDI and IEEE 802 standards, an upward migration path to the faster FDDI backbone is guaranteed. Two other good references for comparisons between the SR and TB methods are [1-39] and [1-40].

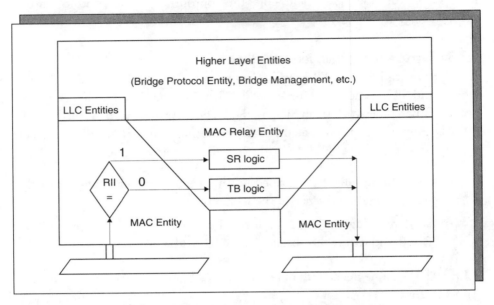

Figure 1-28. SRT bridge operation logic *(© 1993 IEEE, Std 802.1D-1990)*

Those of you who have successfully made it through all of this theory are about to be rewarded. In the next ten chapters, we will take off our "standards" hat and replace it with our "implementation" hat. We'll begin in Chapter 2 by looking at devices that solve the LAN-to-LAN connectivity issue.

1.8 References

[1-1]   Tanenbaum, Andrew S. *Computer Networks*. 2d ed. New York: Prentice-Hall, 1989.

[1-2]   Stallings, William. *Data and Computer Communications*. 4th ed. New York: Macmillan, 1994.

[1-3]   Black, Uyless. *OSI, A Model for Computer Communications Standards*. New York: Prentice-Hall, 1991.

[1-4]   McConnell, John. *Internetworking Computer Systems*. New York: Prentice-Hall, 1988.

[1-5]   Rose, Marshall T. *The Open Book*. New York: Prentice-Hall, 1990.

[1-6]   International Organization for Standardization. *Information Processing Systems—Open Systems Interconnection—Basic Reference Model*, ISO 7498-1984.

[1-7]   Voelcker, John. "Helping Computers Communicate." *IEEE Spectrum* Vol. 23, No. 3 (March 1986): 61–70 (also published in *Computer Communications: Architectures, Protocols and Standards*. 2d ed., IEEE Computer Society Press, 1987: 9–18).

[1-8]   Perlman, Radia, et al. "Choosing the Appropriate ISO Layer for LAN Interconnection." *IEEE Network* (January 1988): 81–86.

[1-9]   Koshy, George T. "Understanding Multiple LANs: The Why and How of Linking Up." *Data Communications* (May 1986): 221–227.

[1-10] Boulé, Richard and John Moy. "Inside Routers: A Technology Guide for Network Builders." *Data Communications* (September 21, 1989): 53–66.

[1-11] McQuillan, John M. "Routers as Building Blocks for Robust Internetworks." *Data Communications* (September 21, 1989): 28–33.

[1-12] Mier, Edwin E. "LAN Gateways: Paths to Corporate Connectivity." *Data Communications* (August 1989): 72–84.

[1-13] Miller, Mark A. *LAN Troubleshooting Handbook*, 2nd ed. New York, NY: M&T Books, 1993.

[1-14] Miller, Mark A. *LAN Protocol Handbook*. New York, NY: M&T Books, 1990.

[1-15] Institute of Electrical and Electronics Engineers. *Information technology—Local and metropolitan area networks—Part 3: Carrier sense multiple access with collision detection (CSMA/CD) access method and physical layer specifications*. ISO/IEC8802-3: 1993 (ANSI/IEEE Std 802.3–1993).

[1-16] Institute of Electrical and Electronics Engineers. *Information technology—Local and metropolitan area networks—Part 4: Token-passing bus access method and physical layer specifications*. ISO/IEC8802-4: 1990 (ANSI/IEEE Std 802.4–1990).

[1-17]   Institute of Electrical and Electronics Engineers. *Information technology—Local and metropolitan area networks—Part 5: Token ring access method and physical layer specifications.* ISO/IEC8802-5: 1992 (ANSI/IEEE Std 802.5-1992).

[1-18]   Institute of Electrical and Electronics Engineers. *Information technology—Telecommunications and information exchange between systems—Local and metropolitan area networks—Specific requirements—Part 6: Distributed Queue Dual Bus (DQDB) Subnetwork of a Metropolitan Area Network MAN).* ISO/IEC8802-6: 1994 (ANSI/IEEE Std 802.6–1994).

[1-19]   Flynn, David. "100BASE-T, the High-Speed Migration Path for 10BASE-T Networks." *3TECH, the 3Com Technical Journal* (October 1994): 3–10.

[1-20]   Melatti, Lee. "Fast Ethernet: 100 Mbit/s Made Easy." *Data Communications* (November 1994): 111–116.

[1-21]   Institute of Electrical and Electronics Engineers. *100BASE-T Fast Ethernet Draft,* 802.3u, 1995.

[1-22]   Hewlett-Packard Company. *100VG-AnyLAN: A Technical Overview.* Document 5963-6682E, 1995.

[1-23]   Rauch, Peter and Scott Lawrence. "100VG-AnyLAN: The Other Fast Ethernet." *Data Communications* (March 1995): 129-134.

[1-24]   Institute of Electrical and Electronics Engineers. *Information Technology—Local and Metropolitan Area Networks—Part 12: Demand-Priority Access Method, Physical Layer and Repeater Specifications for 100 Mb/s Operation.* P802.12 Draft, December 1994.

[1-25]   Institute of Electrical and Electronics Engineers. *Information technology—Telecommunications and information exchange between systems—Local and metropolitan area networks—Specific requirements—Part 2: Logical Link Control.* ISO/IEC8802-2: 1994 (ANSI/IEEE Std 802.2–1994).

[1-26]   Digital Equipment Corp. *Ethernet Data Link Layer and Physical Layer Specifications.* Document no. AA-K759B-TK, November 1982.

[1-27]   Postel, J.B. and J.K. Reynolds. *A Standard for the Transmission of IP Datagrams Over IEEE 802 Networks.* RFC 1042, February 1988.

[1-28] Datapoint Corp. *ARCNET Designer's Handbook*. Document 61610, 1988.

[1-29] American National Standards Institute. *Fiber Distributed Data Interface (FDDI)—Token Ring Media Access Control (MAC)*. ANSI X3.139, 1987.

[1-30] American National Standards Institute. *Fiber Distributed Data Interface (FDDI)—Token Ring Physical Layer Protocol (PHY)*. ANSI X3.148, 1988.

[1-31] American National Standards Institute. *Fiber Distributed Data Interface (FDDI)—Token Ring Physical Layer Medium Dependent (PMD)*. ANSI X3.166, 1990.

[1-32] American National Standards Institute. *Fiber Distributed Data Interface (FDDI)—Single-Mode Fiber Physical Layer Medium Dependent (SMF-PMD)*. ANSI X3.184, 1991.

[1-33] Dixon, Roy C. and Daniel A. Pitt. "Addressing Bridging and Source Routing." *IEEE Network* (January 1988): 25–32.

[1-34] Backes, Floyd. "Transparent Bridges for Interconnection of IEEE 802 LANs." *IEEE Network* (January 1988): 5–9.

[1-35] Institute of Electrical and Electronics Engineers. *Information Technology—Telecommunications and information exchange between systems—Local area networks—Media Access Control (MAC) bridges*. ISO/IEC 10038: 1993 (ANSI/IEEE Std 802.1D–1993).

[1-36] Texas Instruments. TMS380 *Adapter Chipset User's Guide Supplement*. Document SPWU003, 1987.

[1-37] Hamner, M. Claire and Gerald R. Samsen. "Source Routing Bridge Implementation." *IEEE Network* (January 1988): 33-36.

[1-38] Pitt Daniel and Kirk Preiss. "SRT Bridging." *IBM* (July 10, 1990).

[1-39] Soha, Michael and Radia Perlman. "Comparison of Two LAN Bridge Approaches." *IEEE Network* (January 1988): 37-43.

[1-40] Zhang, Lixia. "Comparison of Two Bridge Routing Approaches." *IEEE Network* (January 1988): 44–48.

2 LAN to LAN Internetworking

Now that we've discussed the various standards for both LANs and internetworking devices, it's time to examine some of the products that enable those connections. Before we dive in, allow me to present a road map for this and related chapters. In this chapter, we will focus on LAN to LAN internetworking devices, and will discuss, in order, repeaters, bridges and switches, bridge/routers, and routers. In Chapter 6, we will discuss LAN to MAN and WAN hardware, including asynchronous communication servers, analog and digital leased line-compatible bridges and routers, and hardware to access T1 facilities and broadband networks such as frame relay and ATM. In Chapter 9 we'll look at the internetworking and interoperability of networking software. In Chapter 10, we will complete the product reviews by looking at application-specific gateways. Appendix F lists selected manufacturers of internetworking products.

Admittedly, many products would fit equally well in any of these four chapters; however, an attempt has been made to place them in the category that seems most appropriate from an internetwork-design point of view. Let's begin our review of products by discussing the design of the internetwork itself.

2.1 Designing the LAN-to-LAN Connection

Many interesting events that have had an impact on the job of the network manager and/or designer have occurred in American business in the last few years. First, the proliferation of personal computers has fostered a tremendous growth in the number of workstations connected to a single LAN. An annual growth of 100–200 percent per year of workstations per network is not uncommon. Second, a number of business mergers and acquisitions have forced system growth, and forced it on an instantaneous basis. Third, in a development that relates to the first two, there is a need to connect users and/or networks in different geographical areas. These geographical challenges may be imposed upon single users, such as telecommuters working from home, or upon branch offices that need to connect to the headquarters location. These requirements add another variable—the Wide Area Network (WAN) transmission facility—to the design.

Hopefully, your reason for needing a LAN-to-LAN connection falls into one of the above three categories: growth, major addition/merger, or WAN requirements. Several internetworking devices are available for these applications. You must decide which one is most appropriate.

2.1.1 Repeating, Bridging, Switching, or Routing?

Let's establish some general guidelines for the selection of the internetwork hardware and software. We'll assume that the need for internetworking is driven by the need to address one (or more) of the following situations: multiple transmission media types, dissimilar LAN architectures, several protocols, or incompatibility between different application programs. We'll also assume that the LAN started out relatively small (i.e. less than 100 nodes) and that growth has significantly increased the network's size. We could use four types of devices to handle this growth: repeaters, bridges, switches, and routers.

Repeaters are used to extend the physical cable length, or the number of workstations allowed per segment. For example, a thin Ethernet/IEEE 802.3 network can support 30 attachments per 185 meter segment. If either the number of attachments or the length is exceeded, a repeater can be installed between the two segments. Token ring and ARCNET networks have similar constraints on cable length and the number of attachments used. (We will explore repeater usage in Section 2.2.)

Bridges are used to segment networks based upon network traffic. Segmentation divides the network into logical subsets, keeping traffic from workstations that frequently communicate on a common LAN. This traffic segmentation is based upon filtering algorithms internal to the bridge, which operate on the source and/or destination addresses, upper layer protocol information contained within the bridged frame, or other criteria. Switches are similar to bridges, but typically with more ports. Each of these ports may be dedicated to a segment or an individual device, such as a server. Transmitting devices are allocated the full network bandwidth on a demand basis. In many cases, the switch also provides interfaces with differing transmission rates, such as many 10 Mbps Ethernet ports (for connections to segments or servers) and a few 100 Mbps fast Ethernet ports (for connections to a backbone). (We'll look at bridge and switch examples in Section 2.3.)

Bridge/Routers are also traffic-sensitive devices—however, they include the capacity to logically segment the network based upon the routing algorithm, higher layer protocol, or WAN facility in use. In many cases, a software upgrade changes a bridge into a router. (Section 2.4 is devoted to bridge/routers.) Routers segment network traffic based upon the Destination Network Layer address (not the workstation Data Link Layer or hardware address) of interest. As such, routers are heavily dependent upon the Network Layer Protocol (e.g. IP or Novell's IPX) in use. We'll study router examples in Section 2.5. Gateways are application specific devices that connect different network architectures. We'll look at gateways in Chapter 10.

Figure 2-1 summarizes the functions of these five devices. References [2-1] and [2-2] are excellent tutorials on the subject of internetwork device selection and applications.

2.1.2 Analyzing the Network

As an example, let's assume that cable distance is not the issue, and that a WAN facility is not required. Traffic on the network, however, has increased over time, and with that, users are now complaining of longer delays or higher response times. Without becoming mathematicians, let's describe pictorially what is occurring, aided by research done on CSMA/CD networks by bridge and router manufacturer Retix [2-3].

Repeater
    Operates at OSI Physical Layer
    Regenerates or repeats physical signals
    Used to extend LAN range
Bridge / Switch
    Operates at OSI Data Link Layer
    Logically separates network segments
    Independent of higher layer protocols
    Used for LAN traffic management
Bridge / Router
    Operates at OSI Data Link and Network Layers
    Combines the protocol transparency of a bridge with the ability to route
      certain protocols
    Used for networks with mixed-protocol traffic
Router
    Operates at OSI Network Layer
    Logically separates subnetworks
    Dependent upon Network Layer protocol
    Must obtain knowledge of network topology
    Used for internetwork communication
Gateway
    Operates at OSI Higher Layers (Session through Application)
    Dependent upon user application
    Used for application-to-application communication

Figure 2-1. Comparing internetworking devices

CSMA/CD networks operate quite efficiently under light to medium traffic loads. As more workstations attempt to access the network, however, network throughput declines, as shown in Figure 2-2. As additional workstations are added, their traffic increases the aggregate network traffic accordingly. At a certain point (shown as the red zone in Figure 2-2), the total throughput actually declines. This is caused by frame collisions. When two stations collide, the CSMA/CD algorithm requires that both back off and attempt the transmission later. More traffic creates more collisions, which creates more stations that have data to send and are waiting to transmit on a clear channel. Since more stations are waiting to send, more collisions occur and the actual throughput declines. The collisions thus waste network time that could otherwise be used to transmit data.

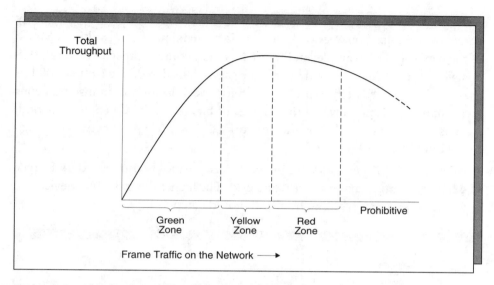

Figure 2-2. CSMA/CD throughput as a function of network traffic *(Courtesy of Retix)*

A second approach to analyzing the network is to measure network delay—the time required to access the network and complete a transmission to a distant node. Retix's research (see Figure 2-3) indicates that this delay is rather stable at less than 20 percent of CSMA/CD network capacity.

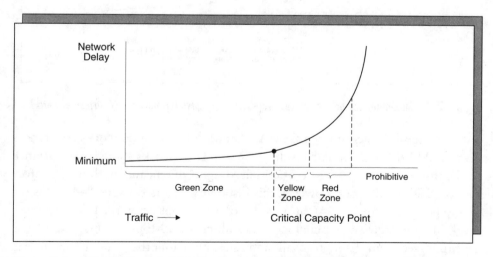

Figure 2-3. CSMA/CD Network Delay as a Function of Network Traffic *(Courtesy of Retix)*

This should not be confused with two other benchmarks: network capacity and network utilization. Network capacity is the maximum bandwidth (in Mbps) of the network. For example, an Ethernet has a maximum capacity of 9,922,048 bps when the 9.6 microsecond interframe gap is considered, not 10,000,000 bps as one might immediately expect [2-4]. Network utilization is an instantaneous measurement, a ratio between the number of bits transmitted in a given period, such as one second divided by the network capacity. A typical network utilization would be 20–30 percent.

For CSMA/CD networks, the network performance is also related to the type of device generating that traffic (Figure 2-4). The higher the traffic per device, the fewer devices of that type can be allowed on the network.

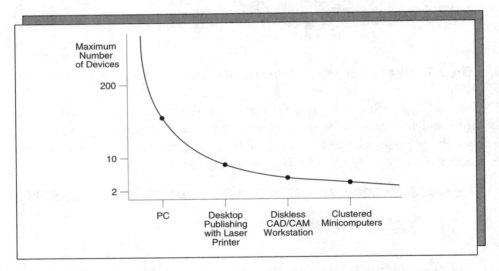

Figure 2-4. Maximum number of devices supported on a CSMA/CD network *(Courtesy of Retix)*

IBM's research has compared CSMA/CD and token ring networks (references [2-5] and [2-6]) with similar results. CSMA/CD networks show some variance in the instability point (Figure 2-5a) based upon the mean length of the Information field. In all cases, however, this instability occurs between 2–4 Mbps (or 20–40 percent of maximum) throughput for a 10 Mbps network. Token ring networks demonstrate similar characteristics for either 4 Mbps (see Figure 2-5b) or 16 Mbps (see Figure 2-5c) transmission rates. Note that the instability point has shifted to approximately 80 percent of maximum throughput.

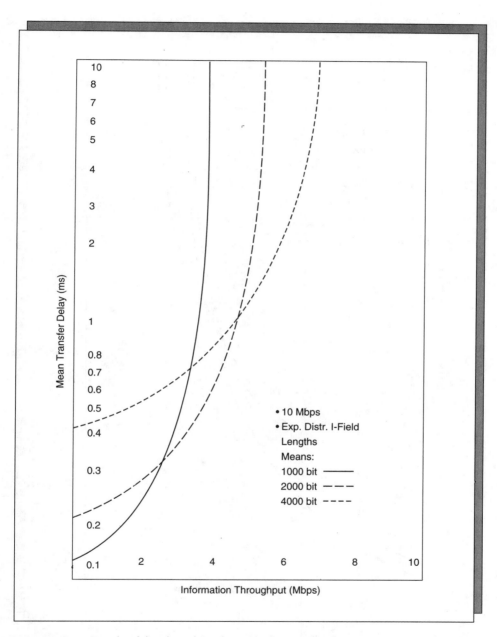

Figure 2-5a. CSMA/CD delay-throughput characteristics: 10 Mbps transmission rate *(Reprinted by permission of International Business Machines Corporation)*

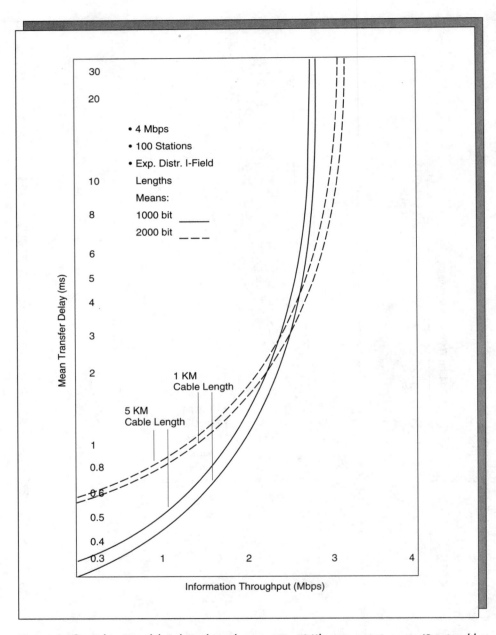

Figure 2-5b. Token Ring delay-throughput characteristics: 4 Mbps transmission rate *(Reprinted by permission of International Business Machines Corporation)*

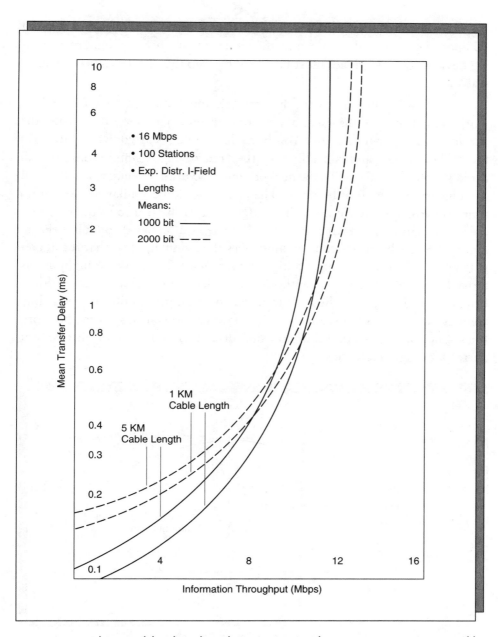

Figure 2-5c. Token ring delay-throughput characteristics: 16 Mbps transmission rate *(Reprinted by permission of International Business Machines Corporation)*

We can conclude that neither a throughput nor a network utilization of 100 percent is attainable. When traffic increases on a network, internetworking devices such as bridges must be added to keep the network's performance stable.

Let's now assume that you, the network administrator, have used a network management tool such as a monitor or protocol analyzer to measure the network traffic or utilization. You have determined that your network is in the "yellow zone" and is heading for the "red zone." A simple solution will avoid sleepless nights: divide the network into two distinct segments, and install a bridge (or a switch) in between. The result should be similar to the configuration shown in Figure 2-6. The bridge isolates the traffic of the two segments, thus allowing each segment to operate at a higher throughput. From Figure 2-6, the bridge effectively multiplies the throughput so that the aggregate peak utilization occurs at a higher traffic load. The peak throughput has moved from traffic level A (without the bridge) to traffic level B (with the bridge). The bridge has thus reduced the collision probability by providing some isolation between segments. With fewer workstations on the network (or segment), the likelihood of collision decreases and network throughput correspondingly increases.

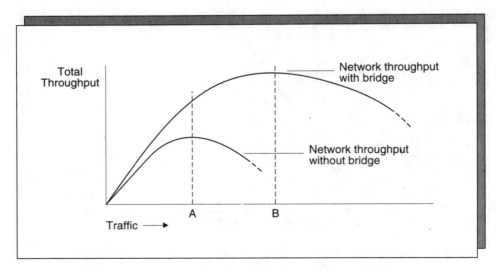

Figure 2-6. CSMA/CD network throughput with and without a bridge *(Courtesy of Retix)*

Where do we place the bridges for greatest efficiency? How do we decide which stations (e.g. workstations, hosts, and servers) are to be placed on either side of the bridge? A network management tool for recording the traffic between pairs of stations (often called pair counts) is invaluable here. Stations that communicate with each other on a frequent basis should be placed on the same side of the bridge. A rule of thumb (also from reference [2-3]) suggests that the 80/20 rule be followed: 80 percent of the traffic should remain on the local segment, and 20 percent should cross the bridge(s) to other segment(s).

Note that an important assumption has been made here: the bridge has somehow acquired the intelligence to know which of the frames that it examines should be forwarded across the bridge. This decision is based either upon a table lookup within the bridge (for Transparent Bridges, discussed in Section 1.7.1) or information sent along within the frame (for Source Routed Bridges, discussed in Section 1.7.2). It is also important to note that the addresses referred to here are Data Link Layer addresses, which have a flat (i.e. non-hierarchical) nature. In other words, each address is a unique entity, unrelated to the other addresses. (We'll look at hierarchical addressing in Section 2.5.) Thus far, we have only discussed solving the internetworking problem for like-topology systems such as Ethernet to Ethernet. Let's look now at internetworking dissimilar architectures.

2.1.3 Connecting Dissimilar LANs

Let's throw another variable into the network design formula, and now assume that we have LANs of two (or more) different architectures, such as Ethernet and token ring. How can we connect these? Three approaches are commonly used: a LAN-to-LAN bridge, internal bridging (or routing) at a server, or using a common-denominator protocol such as TCP/IP.

The LAN-to-LAN bridge for dissimilar networks is probably the most limiting solution, as it requires additional hardware that is specific to the LAN protocols in use, such as Ethernet and FDDI. We'll study the technical challenges of this alternative in detail in section 2.3.2.

In contrast to the hardware solution, internetworking at the server offers a software solution to the problem of connectivity. Network Operating Systems (NOSs)—such as Novell's NetWare and Banyan Systems' VINES—have an architecture that facilitates an internetworking solution. The NOS can be divided into three general components: a driver for the Network Interface Card

(NIC) hardware (operating on the OSI Physical and Data Link Layers); internetworking protocols (operating on the Network and Transport Layers); plus application program support (operating on the Session, Presentation, and Application layers).

Suppose that at the server, you install two (or more) dissimilar NICs. Each NIC has a unique hardware address, and receives its higher layer information from a NOS driver. In other words, an Ethernet driver talks to the Ethernet NIC with hardware address A, and a token ring driver talks to a token ring NIC having hardware address B. If all the higher layer (Network through Application) protocols are the same, internetworking between these dissimilar architectures is automatic. (We'll study this concept more fully in Chapter 9, which is devoted to the internetworking capabilities of such popular network software as those by Novell, IBM, Banyan, and Apple.)

Our third option for connecting dissimilar networks is to find a common-denominator protocol to facilitate internetworking. One obvious example is the TCP/IP (Transmission Control Protocol/Internet Protocol) suite, which was developed specifically for this purpose. If both dissimilar systems can access the common denominator (TCP/IP), then communication between the two becomes possible. A requirement for application program (e.g. electronic mail) compatibility may still exist, and must be addressed. (We will study the TCP/IP and related protocols in Chapter 7, and application-dependent gateways in Chapter 10.)

2.2 Repeaters

A repeater, as the name implies, performs the function of signal amplification (i.e., repeating). This permits the originally-transmitted signal to go further than the attenuation limits of the transmission media (e.g., twisted pair, coaxial) will allow. Repeaters used thus depend on two variables: the network architecture (token ring, Ethernet, or ARCNET) and the media type being used. In this section, we'll look at examples of repeater products available for three LAN architectures. Let's start with token ring.

2.2.1 Andrew TRR 8120, 8416, and TRx 9416

Andrew Corporation of Torrance, California, is one of the major vendors of token ring/IEEE 802.5 networking hardware. Andrew manufactures several token ring repeaters with advantageous design features. The TRR 8416 Copper Media Repeater operates at 4/16 Mbps. It supports IBM Types 1 and 2 (shielded twisted pair) plus Type 3 (unshielded twisted pair). While the typical hermaphroditic (or data) connectors are used for Types 1 and 2, Andrew also offers modular RJ-45 connectors for the unshielded cable, making installation somewhat easier. A second advantage is that fewer repeaters are required. Most token ring networks are wired with a primary and a backup transmission path. With other vendors a total of four repeaters would be required: two at each end for both primary and backup paths. Andrew Corporation combines the primary and backup circuits into a single repeater, thus saving hardware expense. The third advantage of Andrew's products is the built-in diagnostics LEDs which indicate a normal signal, unusable (noisy) signal, or signal loss, as well as active stations.

The TRx 9416 Jitter Doctor has enhanced jitter attenuation in a token ring repeater. When installed in a token ring network, a pair of TRx 9416 repeaters will substantially minimize the impact of signal jitter, thus improving reliability and performance at an economical cost. The TRx 9416 uses phased-lock loop (PLL) technology to re-time and regenerate the token ring signal, thus providing the greatest possible transmission distance.

The TRR 8120 Fiber Optic Repeater also operates at 4 Mbps, and is used to connect geographically-separated multi-station access units (MSAUs) via fiber optic cables. Four different cable types are supported: 62.5/125 micron, 50/125 micron, 85/125 micron, and 100/140 micron. Bayonet-type ST connectors are used for attachment to the fiber optic cable.

Sample applications of the token ring repeaters are shown in Figure 2-7a for both copper and fiber optic cable designs. A second application (Figure 2-7b) shows the repeaters being used to extend the maximum lobe distance to a single workstation. This configuration would eliminate the need for an MSAU and a second repeater at the remote location.

To summarize, Andrew's token ring repeaters are extremely user-friendly, adding a choice of media types, connectors, and diagnostics to an otherwise fundamental device.

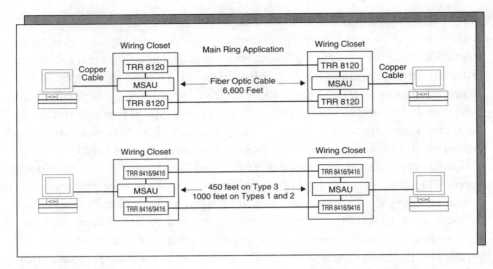

Figure 2-7a. 16 Mbps taken ring repeater application *(Courtesy of Andrew Corporation)*

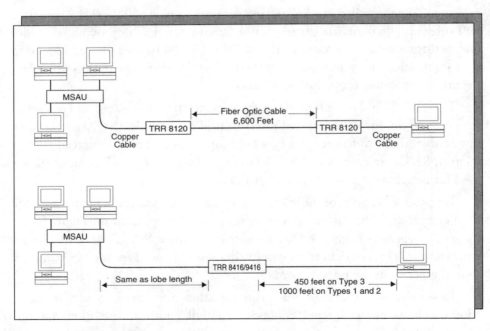

Figure 2-7b. Token ring lobe extension application *(Courtesy of Andrew Corporation)*

2.2.2 *Cabletron Systems MMAC*

Cabletron Systems, Inc. of Rochester, New Hampshire, develops, manufactures, and markets standards-based Ethernet/IEEE 802.3, token ring, FDDI, and ATM solutions. Cabletron's product offerings include intelligent hubs, interconnection equipment, bridges, repeaters, transceivers, test equipment and transmission media, components and accessories. The company also offers Spectrum 3.0, an industry-leading management platform that provides protocol independence and multivendor management for complete enterprisewide systems integration. What is unique to Cabletron hardware is the number of media choices available, including unshielded and shielded twisted pair, fiber optic, and thin or thick Ethernet cables.

The heart of Cabletron's System is a family of Multi Media Access Centers (MMACs), shown in Figures 2-8a and 2-8b. The MMAC is a modular chassis allowing a combination of Ethernet/IEEE 802.3, token ring, FDDI, LocalTalk, SNA, or WAN connectivity. The MMAC chassis comes in three sizes, with eight, five, or three slots to fit any network demand. Modules slide easily into the hub to interconnect via Cabletron's exclusive Flexible Network Bus (FNB), a protocol independent backplane that provides flexibility, interoperability, and fault tolerance.

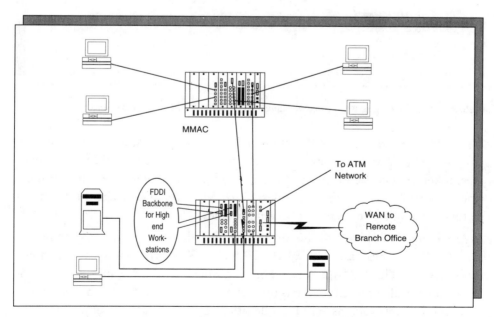

Figure 2-8d. Ethernet multi channel connectivity *(Courtesy of Cabletron Systems Inc.)*

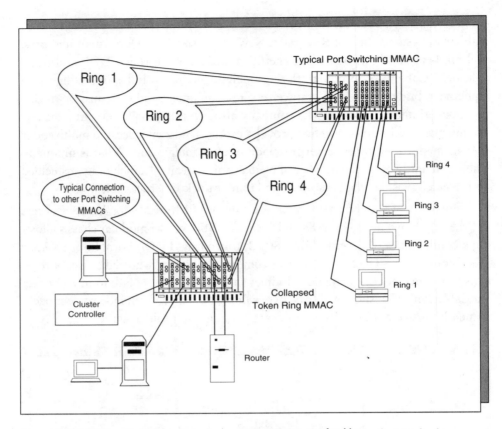

Figure 2-8b. Token ring multi channel connectivity *(Courtesy of Cabletron Systems Inc.)*

The MMAC modules offered include intelligent repeaters, unshielded twisted pair, twisted pair, and fiber optic connectivity; several multichannel Ethernet modules; token ring concentrators, repeaters, bridges and management for multiple rings; SNA/LAN integration modules; FDDI Management/Bridges and concentrators; Localtalk and Network Server Modules.

Included in Cabletron's line of standalone solutions are the MicroMMAC remote office solution, as well as the HubSTACK SNMP manageable connectivity devices. The MMAC-Plus, Cabletron's next generation modular switching system, is also housed in a modular chassis. It provides a migration path to new technologies such as ATM, while offering switching and connectivity for traditional technologies in a single hub.

To summarize, Cabletron's MMAC family provides the ultimate intelligent hub, integrating a number of current media types and protocols, and providing for future requirements such as ATM LANs.

2.2.3   SMC Active Hubs

SMC (Standard Microsystems Corporation) of Hauppauge, NY, was the first manufacturer of ARCNET controller chips, and has long been known as a premier ARCNET hardware vendor. The topology of ARCNET, which can either be a bus, a star, or a combination, yields itself to a great deal of flexibility. SMC has capitalized on this by offering numerous media choices, including RG-62/U coax, shielded and unshielded twisted pair, and duplex fiber optic cables. Obviously, each type has advantages and disadvantages. Twisted pair is low in cost and easy to install, but limits the transmission distance. Coaxial cables have longer distance limits, but are more expensive and bulky. Fiber optic cables have the advantage of grounding and lightning protection, as well as security, but they are also more expensive.

Active Hubs (see Figure 2-9) are used in star-topology ARCNETs to connect individual workstations. At this writing, SMC manufactures two types, supporting both coax and twisted pair cabling, and continues to support fiber optic ARCNET. (Demand for fiber optic ARCNET has dwindled in deference to faster fiber optic technologies such as FDDI, and therefore SMC discontinued manufacture of that technology as of January 1995). All three types are cascadeable and may be interconnected. Active links (not shown) are used to extend one coax segment or to connect a coax segment to a twisted pair segment. Twisted pair repeaters are used to connect two daisy-chained twisted pair segments, thus extending the maximum point-to-point distance.

The beauty of the ARCNET architecture is its ability to interconnect different media types. If you want to run terminals in the computer room on RG-62/U coax, PCs in the accounting department on twisted pair, and workstations in the factory on fiber optic, ARCNET active links do this with elegance. SMC has taken great advantage of this architectural strength in the design of their hub, link, and repeater hardware products.

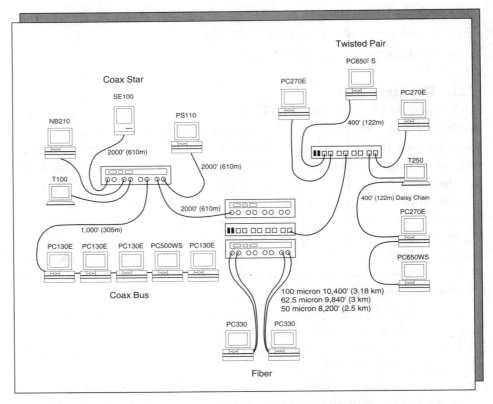

Figure 2-9. ARCNET connectivity *(Courtesy of Standard Microsystems Corporation)*

2.3 Bridges and Switches

Bridges are devices which operate at the Data Link Layer and relay or forward frames between networks. Most bridges operate on networks of similar architecture, such as token ring to token ring, or Ethernet to Ethernet. This is not necessarily a hard and fast rule, however, since the IEEE 802.X standards contain a common denominator in the 802.2 LLC format and the use of either two- or six-octet addressing. Given these assumptions, therefore, a bridge can be constructed between dissimilar 802.X LANs. In this section, we will look at four examples of bridges: the Retix NETXchange bridge family, the IBM 8229 token ring to Ethernet bridge; and the UB Networks' FDDI to Ethernet bridge, and GeoRim/E Ethernet switch and the Solectek AIRLAN wireless networks. Because of their popularity, bridging and switching products and their operation have been profiled in a number of recent articles. References [2-7] through [2-13] are examples worth reading.

2.3.1 Retix Local and Remote LAN Bridges

As we discussed in Section 2.1, Retix of Santa Monica, California, has made a number of contributions to Ethernet internetworking. This company manufactures both local and remote bridges—we'll look at the Retix NETXchange series of local bridges first (see Figure 2-10). All members of the NETXchange family are dual port, MAC-layer bridges. They have a maximum frame filtering rate of 29,000 frames per second (fps), and a maximum forwarding rate of 13,650 fps for frames between 64 and 1518 octets in length. The two ports can connect to thin or thick Ethernet/IEEE 802.3 backbones or to an FOIRL (Fiber Optic Inter-Repeater Link) network via an optional adapter.

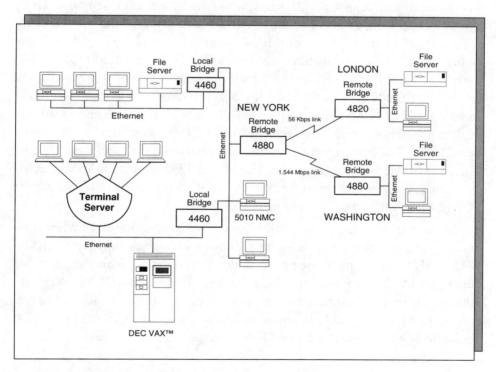

Figure 2-10. Retix local and remote bridge configuration *(Courtesy of Retix)*

Two models are available. The NETXchange 4460 local bridge is suggested for networks where equipment from multiple vendors is in use, because the bridge is transparent to higher-layer network protocols. The NETXchange 4460 has a filtering rate of 29,000 packets per second (pps), with a forwarding rate of nearly wire speed—13,650 pps. It also features the Simple Network Management Protocol, Spanning Tree protocol, and flash memory for easy management, installation, and upgrades. The NETXchange 4560 is a local bridge/router with TCP/IP routing functionality. The 4560 can partition networks based on IP addresses. In environments where the average Ethernet frame is small, but there are frequent bursts of traffic, the 4560 will manage the data flow without missing a single packet. The NETXchange 4560 filters at 14,880 pps and forwards at 7,800 pps. It also supports SNMP, Spanning Tree, and flash memory.

For internetworks requiring remote connections, Retix 4800 series bridges connect Ethernets via WAN facilities. Models 4810/4850 support one or two links operating at 56, 64, or 128 Kbps, while the Model 4880 supports one or two links operating at 1.544 or 2.048 Mbps. Both bridges offer a single LAN port, and can connect to thin or thick Ethernet/IEEE 802.3 networks (review Figure 2-10). These models filter and forward at 9000 and 1,200 fps, respectively. The Model 4880, designed for high throughput, filters at the maximum Ethernet/IEEE 802.3 rate of 14,880 fps, and forwards at 8000 fps. Two high-speed LAN-WAN-LAN links can thus be fully utilized. Both models support the PC-based Retix Network Management Center (NMC) or a RISC workstation-based NMC. The NMC compiles statistics on network traffic, and remotely controls each bridge and its filter tables. The Model 4942 remote bridge/router has the same interfaces and throughput as the 4880, but it also offers routing for TCP/IP, Novell IPX, and DECnet networks.

In summary, the Retix Ethernet/IEEE 802.3 bridges provide an excellent combination of simplicity for low-end applications with high throughput for LAN-WAN-LAN connections. These products also fit into Retix' broader product line which includes other internetworking devices, such as the ROUTERXchange 7000t multi-protocol router with versions for central site and remote office networks, the FIBERring 100 fiber-optic transport system, the SWITCHStak 5000 stackable Ethernet switch, and the LINKXchange ISDN access devices.

2.3.2 IBM 8229 LAN Bridge

IBM has gone out of its way to open up its token ring products for internet-working applications. One example is the IBM 8229 LAN Bridge, which allows communication between Ethernet/IEEE 802.3 LANs and token ring (IEEE 802.5) LANs.

Bridging these dissimilar networks is not an easy task. To begin with, the frame sizes of Ethernet/IEEE 802.3 are different, with Ethernet transmitting up to 1500 octets of data per frame, and token ring transmitting 4,500 octets (at 4 Mbps) or 17,800 octets (at 16 Mbps) per frame. Data throughput, which is typically measured in frames per second, becomes more difficult to bench-mark [2-13].

A second issue affecting bridge operation (not the end user) is the bit order of the network addresses. Ethernet/IEEE 802.3 and IEEE 802.5 represent the Medium Access Control (MAC) addresses in different manners. The LSB of each octet of an Ethernet/IEEE 802.3 address has the same meaning as the MSB of an IEEE 802.5 address. Thus, when identical Ethernet/IEEE 802.3 and IEEE 802.5 addresses are displayed in hexadecimal, they would appear different. When either type is transmitted, however, the Individual/Group (I/G) address bit is sent out first. Information within the Data Field is not a problem, since the same hardware (e.g. token ring and token ring) exists on both ends of that side of the bridge. The Address fields, however, require bit swapping before a frame can be forwarded from one side of the bridge to the other.

Third, the bridge must be prepared to handle the Source Routing (SR) method on the token ring port (developed by IBM and submitted to IEEE as part of IEEE 802.1D) or the Transparent Bridging (TB) method on the Ether-net/IEEE 802.3 port (developed by DEC—see reference [2-13]). As we studied in Section 1.4, the SR method requires the originating station to specify the path to the destination via intermediate bridges. As a result, bridges require less processing to forward frames. The TB method, in contrast, places the process-ing responsibility on the bridge, and it makes the forwarding (i.e. send across the bridge) or filtering (i.e. do not send across the bridge) decision based upon tables that have either been manually loaded into, or dynamically discovered by, the bridge itself.

Thus, the token ring-to-Ethernet bridge problem is what engineering professors call a "non-trivial problem." IBM, however, has solved these problems in the design of the 8229, which supports either a 4 or a 16 Mbps token ring and another connection to an Ethernet/IEEE 802.3 network (see Figure 2-11a). The 8229 can also be used in networks with other token ring-to-token ring bridges (see Figure 2-11b).

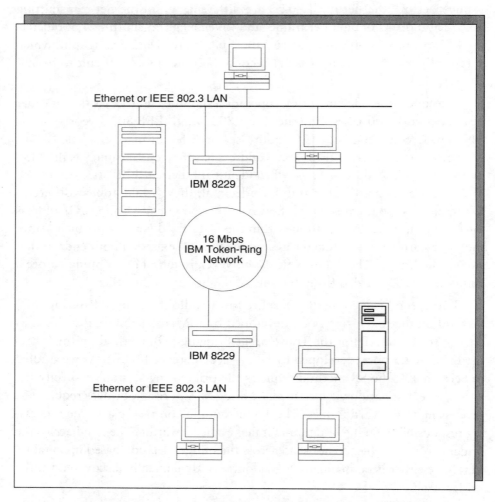

Figure 2-11a. IBM 8229 LAN Bridge in Token Ring Backbone Configuration *(Reprinted by permission of International Business Machines Corporation)*

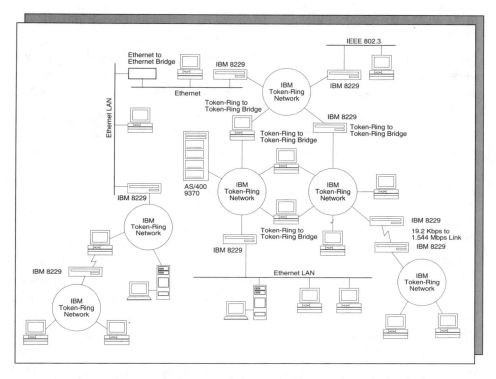

Figure 2-11b. Connecting multiple LANs with the IBM 8229 LAN Bridge and other bridges (Reprinted by permission of International Business Machines Corporation)

Two modes of 8229 operation support different protocols. Mode 1 is used for Ethernet version 2.0 LANs, and supports TCP/IP, SNA 802.2 LLC, and NetBIOS traffic. Mode 2 allows connection to IEEE 802.3 LANs, and supports 802.2 LLC, TCP/IP, NetBIOS, and SNA traffic. An "auto-detect" selection is available that supports both Mode 1 and Mode 2 on a dynamic, switchable basis.

Three models of the 8229 are currently available. Model 001 connects two local token ring segments. Model 002 connects a local token ring segment and a local Ethernet segment. Model 003 connects a local token ring segment with a remote token ring segment via a WAN link operating at the T1/E1 rates or below.

Parallel bridges are allowed between token ring and Ethernet. Only one of the bridges can be active at a time, however, to eliminate the possibility of a frame that loops between the LANs. Workstations on the token ring side treat the 8229 as a standard SR-compliant bridge. Workstations on the Ethernet side treat the 8229 as a transparent bridge, with all workstations on the token ring side appearing as if they were on the near side of the bridge. As a final detail, the 8229 is supported by IBM's LAN Network Manager, the network management program, or an SNMP-compliant management console, such as IBM's AIX NetView/6000.

To summarize, the IBM 8229 LAN Bridge solves many network managers' worst nightmare: how to connect token ring and Ethernet architectures without a third party server (such as Novell's) or a major redesign of the internetwork.

2.3.3   UB Networks' FDDI Bridges and Switches

Ungermann-Bass (UB) Networks, Inc. of Santa Clara, California, is well-known as an innovator in both networking hardware and software products. Most bridged networks connect LANs having similar architectures but with different transmission media types or speeds. One example of this would be multiple thin-Ethernets bridged to a single thick-Ethernet backbone. Many campus environments use this type of architecture. A second example would be a 16 Mbps token ring backbone, with multiple 4 Mbps rings connected via bridges. UB Networks' products demonstrate an improvement on this technique by using a backbone technology (FDDI) that is dissimilar to that of the connecting LANs. Before we examine the UB product in detail, let's take a quick look at the FDDI architecture upon which their design is based.

Recall from our discussion in Section 1.6.6 that FDDI (Fiber Data Distributed Interface) is a token passing ring network, operating at 100 Mbps over fiber optic cable and adhering to the ANSI X3T9.5 standard. The topology of a four-node FDDI network is shown in Figure 2-12a (note the dual-ring topology). The primary ring is the data path, while the secondary ring provides redundancy or additional bandwidth. Up to 500 stations can exist on the network, with up to 2 Km of cable between stations. The current standard uses 62.5/125 micron fiber optic cable, with a wavelength of 1300 nanometers (nm). The fiber optic cables are called duplex cables because there are actually two of them: one for the transmitting path, and one for the receiving path.

Since the ring architecture would become disabled if one of the stations lost power, an external optical bypass relay (OBR) is used (see Figure 2-12b). The OBR connects the inbound and outbound cables, thus assuring network integrity.

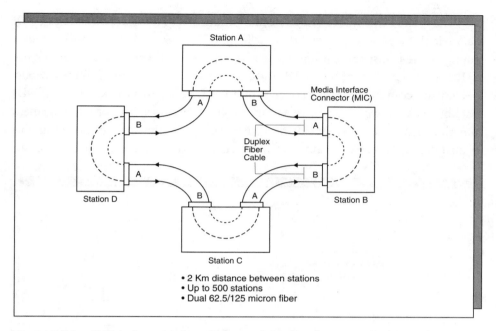

Figure 2-12a. FDDI dual-ring topology *(Courtesy of UB Networks)*

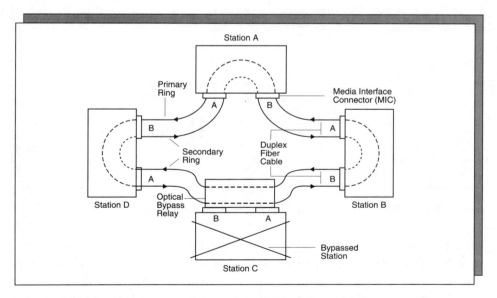

Figure 2-12b. FDDI ring with optical bypass relay *(Courtesy of UB Networks)*

The Access/One FDDI Bridge/Router product (see Figure 2-12c) utilizes FDDI as a backbone, and supports Ethernet/IEEE 802.3 networks. The bridge/router supports the transparent bridging, plus IP, IPX, and DECnet routing. As Figure 2-12c illustrates, two of the FDDI bridges can exist on the same FDDI backbone, permitting communication between multiple Ethernet networks via the FDDI backbone. A Network Resource Monitor (NRM) provides network management functions from the Ethernet side of the network. Statistics such as the amount of transmitted and received data, collisions, corrupted frames, etc., are measured.

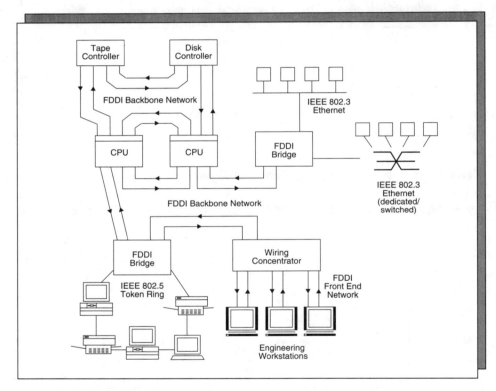

Figure 2-12c. FDDI as a network backbone *(Courtesy of UB Networks)*

Another UB Networks' product the GeoRim/E Ethernet switch, provides uplinks to FDDI, fast Ethernet, or ATM networks. The GeoRim/E may be configured with up to 12 switched Ethernet ports in any combination of BNC, 10BASE-T, or fiber optic connections. The backbone port options include FDDI, 100BASE- TX, and

ATM. Three separate processors combine their power to support a throughput of over 100,000 pps without data loss. This modular architecture allows legacy LANs to be connected to FDDI networks today, with a migration path to ATM in the future.

To summarize, UB Networks has made several advances with its FDDI bridges and switching hubs, providing an upgrade path for greater bandwidth, with a guarantee against network obsolescence.

2.3.4 Solectek AIRLAN Wireless Networks

Solectek Corporation, of San Diego, California, designs, develops, and markets an extensive line of wireless Ethernet products. Just as with traditional cabled networks, Solectek's wireless products allow users to share files, documents, and printers, but without the need to physically link computers with cabling. As a result, the company's products provide flexibility and mobility in establishing and maintaining network connections. There are three well-accepted uses for wireless networks: adding workstations to an existing wired network, applications which require PC mobility, or applications where network cable is difficult or impossible to install [2-14].

Solectek's products, which use spread spectrum radio technology, fit into two categories: wireless roaming and wireless bridging. The AIRLAN/Access is a wireless access point that creates a 50,000 square foot "cell" area of connectivity. Using AIRLAN/PCMCIA or AIRLAN/Parallel network adapter cards, mobile users can roam freely from Access cell to Access cell, while maintaining seamless connectivity to the network. A third type of adapter, called the AIRLAN/Internal, supports the PC ISA architecture, and is used for desktop systems that move within the network from time to time. These adapters, which are IEEE 802.3 compatible, allow the attached computers to roam within a virtually unlimited area, as long as they are within 800 feet of an AIRLAN/Access.

When networking coverage within a campus area network (CAN) is required, the AIRLAN/Bridge Plus is used (Figure 2-13). AIRLAN/Bridge Plus provides a wireless backbone linking the major structures. Reliable links up to three miles and beyond are possible, depending upon the environment. The bridge is compatible with all major network operating systems, and is manageable using the Simple Network Management Protocol (SNMP). Other features of the bridge include protocol and address filtering, and broadcast storm protection.

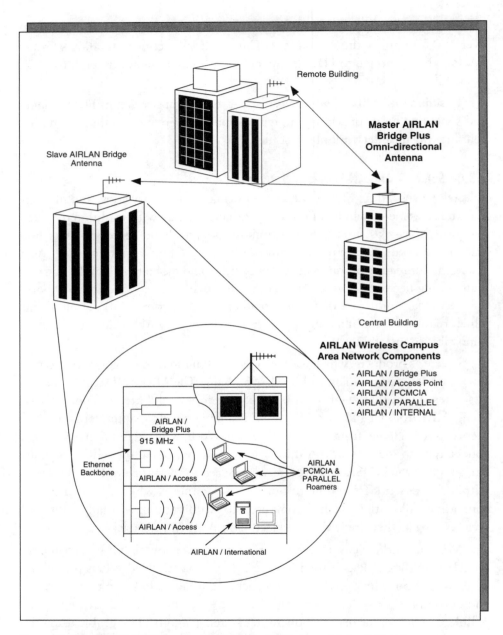

Figure 2-13. AIRLAN Wireless campus area network *(Courtesy of Solectek Corp.)*

In summary, the AIRLAN products cut the tie to the physical cabling system, which for many users is a serious impediment to efficient networking. Reference [2-15] discusses other capabilities of the emerging wireless networking marketplace.

2.4 Bridge/Routers

The bridge/router, sometimes called a brouter, is designed to provide the processing speed of a bridge, but with the internetworking capabilities of a router. Bridges are protocol-independent devices which make a forwarding or filtering decision based upon the Data Link Layer address of the frame. Routers, on the other hand, choose the outgoing path based upon the Network Layer address. A router is therefore protocol dependent and must understand the particular Network Layer protocol in use, such as IP, IPX, DECnet, or ISO. The brouter is a hybrid of the bridge and the router: it provides the protocol independence of a bridge while adding the ability to direct LAN traffic to one of a number of other networks, depending upon the Network Layer Protocol being used. In this section, we'll look at 3Com Corporation's NETBuilder II family, and the Advanced Computer Communications series.

2.4.1 3Com NETBuilder II Bridge/Router

3Com Corporation of Santa Clara, California, is a company that most network managers would identify as a significant contributor to Ethernet technology. The company was, in fact, founded by Robert Metcalfe, the inventor of Ethernet. In recent years, however, 3Com has expanded to contribute to all areas of networking technology—from Ethernet, token ring, and FDDI network interface cards (NICs), hubs, and switching hubs to ATM switches and bridge/router platforms—all integrated by 3Com's design philosophy, known as High-Performance Scalable Networking (HPSN), and managed by 3Com's Transcend family of network management software. Within the bridge/router arena, 3Com has continued its tradition of designing innovative solutions with the NETBuilder family of hardware and software products—from low-cost, fixed-port devices designed specifically for small remote office environments to flexible, scalable, high-end systems.

The flagship of 3Com's family of bridge/routers is the NETBuilder II platform (Figure 2-14a). The NETBuilder II system begins with a choice of three modular chassis—the 4-Slot, 8-Slot, and 8-Slot Extended—offering a range of total port capacities and reliability features. All three chassis employ the same central processor and interface modules, allowing any combination of Ethernet, Fast Ethernet, token ring, FDDI, ATM, and WAN connections. WAN options include both leased and dial-up lines, X.25, frame relay, SMDS, and ISDN connections, supporting data rates from 1200 bps up to T3/E3 and OC1/STS1 at 52 Mbps. A wide range of physical/electrical interfaces provide connection via V.35, RS-232, RS-449, RS-530, X.21, G.703, HSSI, and others.

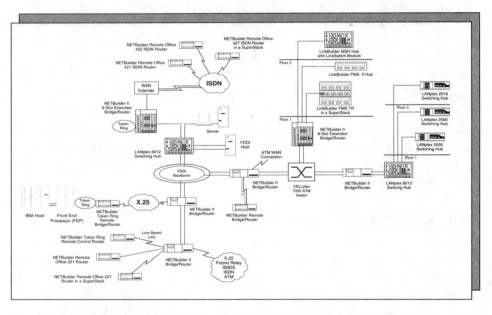

Figure 2-14a. NETBuilder II bridge/router applications *(Courtesy of 3Com Corporation)*

Any of 3Com's NETBuilder family can function as a bridge, a router, or as a bridge/router, simultaneously bridging some protocols while routing others. As a bridge, each system supports three different bridging methods. Translation bridging provides communication between end stations on different types of LANs, such as Ethernet to FDDI. Transparent bridging, defined in IEEE 802.1D for Ethernet to Ethernet connections, plus Source Routing Transparent bridging, supporting both source routing and non-source routing (transparent) devices, are also available.

As a router, NETBuilders support all major routable protocols, including TCP/IP, Novell's IPX, IBM's APPN, AppleTalk Phase II, Banyan VINES, DEC-net Phases IV and V, OSI, and XNS. SNA environments are further supported with Data Link Switching (DLSw) and Local Address Administration (LAA). Sophisticated inter-router protocols, including Open Shortest Path First (OSPF), Border Gateway Protocol (BGP) IV, Novell's NLSP, and OSI's Intermediate System to Intermediate System (IS-IS), are also supported.

On the hardware side, 3Com's NETBuilder II gives network managers tremendous flexibility for their designs, offering high reliability options, scalable performance, and modularity to accommodate future expansion. Reliability features include optional dual power supplies, redundant cooling fans, Flash memory-based booting, and hot-swappable modules, guaranteeing maximum up-time. The modular, chassis-based approach accommodates easy integration of new technologies such as 100BASE-T Fast Ethernet and ATM.

Scalable performance is provided by NETBuilder II's MP (multiprocessor) architecture. Each NETBuilder II employs a RISC-based central processor, custom ASICs, and an 800 Mbps backplane to provide balanced performance across each standard interface installed. Additional processing power is provided by NETBuilder II's line of MP interface modules, each of which carries its own additional RISC processor on-board, allowing the user to add processing power as he grows his network.

Other key capabilities of the NETBuilder software family optimize the management and administration of the internetwork to reduce cost and complexity. 3Com's Boundary Routing System architecture facilitates expansion of routed networks to include a large number of small offices by simplifying router installation and administration at remote offices, transferring complexity to the corporate LAN where administration is more economical. Bandwidth-on-Demand automatically activates a dial-up line when traffic needs dictate, then automatically disconnects that line when traffic returns to normal levels. Data compression reduces the size of packets sent over the serial lines by a factor of two to four, reducing the usage charges on those links.

Further, NETBuilders can be managed by a variety of management tools. Each NETBuilder comes with built-in management software—offering either command-line or menu-driven interfaces—which is accessible via a directly attached console, a modem, or through Telnet from any station on the network.

Next, NETBuilders can be managed by any Simple Network Management Protocol (SNMP)-compliant console. Lastly, 3Com offers its Transcend Network Management System, a family of graphical management applications that not only manage the NETBuilder bridge/routers, but also integrate management of the various network infrastructure components, including hubs, switches, and even adapters. Transcend applications are available for Hewlett-Packard's OpenView, Sun Connect's SunNet Manager, and Microsoft's Windows management platforms.

Finally, one of the great strengths of the NETBuilder product line is its integration into 3Com's High-Performance Scalable Networking (HPSN) architecture (Figure 2-14b). The philosophy of HPSN is to recognize the need for an organization's network, be it local or global, to be a single, cohesive, infrastructure. Each component can stand on its own, but a manager will get the best value from his investments by smoothly integrating all of the key network elements, including the workgroup, personal office, remote office, building or campus backbone and the WAN. At the core of HPSN is the Transcend family of management applications. From here, the thrust of HPSN is to both extend the reach and scale the performance of the network.

Extending the reach means offering low-cost, easy-to-manage solutions for including all of an organization's resources in the internetwork—including remote offices, personal offices, and even mobile users —The NETBuilder Remote Office family of bridge/routers is a key to this side of HPSN. Scaling performance means both accommodating manageable, high-performance designs such as collapsed backbones and server farms and providing smooth growth paths to future high-speed technologies. NETBuilder II plays a key role in this approach. A collapsed backbone reduces cost, centralizes complexity, and increases performance by replacing backbone-connected internetworking devices on each LAN with a single, multi-port, high-performance device such as NETBuilder II. The server farm concept furthers this design by concentrating all of an organization's servers in a location at the center of the network, simplifying management and facilitating lower-cost migration to high-speed technologies such as FDDI.

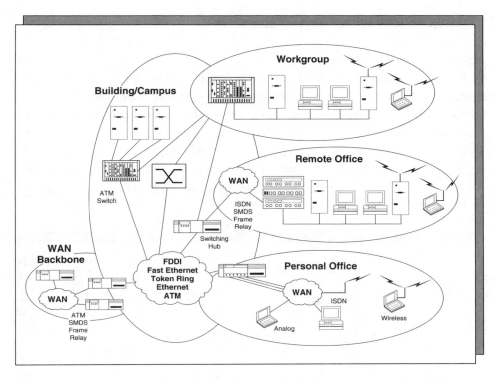

Figure 2-14b. High Performance Scalable Networking Connectivity Systems *(Courtesy of 3Com Corporation)*

In summary, 3Com's philosophy, as articulated in HPSN, is to help the network manager extend the reach and scale the performance of his network, providing access to everyone and performance for all. The NETBuilder family of bridge/routers is at the heart of this philosophy, whether it's NETBuilder II and NETBuilder Remote Office platforms providing low-cost, easy-to-manage connections to all locations in the global WAN, or NETBuilder II supporting manageable, scalable, high-performance designs for building and campus LAN designs. The flexibility of NETBuilder II's modular design, the reliability provided by redundant boot and power systems, and the scalable performance of its multiprocessor architecture make it an ideal platform for the centerpiece of mission-critical network infrastructures, ready to meet today's needs and to adapt to tomorrow's new requirements.

2.4.2 ACC Multi-Protocol Bridge/Routers

Advanced Computer Communication (ACC) of Cupertino, California, manufactures internetworking products that are used to create integrated local and wide area networks that incorporate multivendor and multiprotocol computer equipment. Its strategy is to provide internetworking solutions that offer a low cost of ownership, a high degree of reliability, an excellent price/performance ratio, and interoperability in multivendor environments. To accommodate a wide variety of networking protocols and topologies, ACC combines bridging and routing functions simultaneously in a single, cost-effective system (Figure 2-15). Leading-edge bridging and routing technologies are employed to give users the best internetworking techniques available.

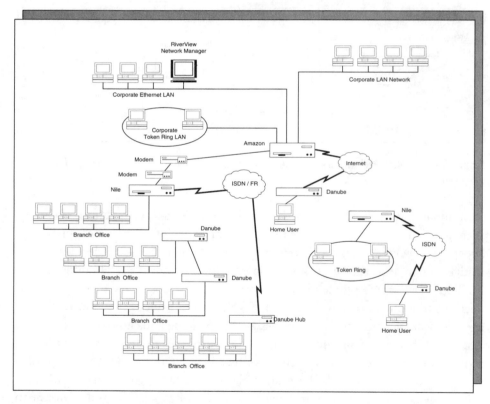

Figure 2-15. ACC bridge/router applications *(Courtesy of Advanced Computer Communications)*

ACC is unique in offering an integrated set of powerful software features designed to optimize the utilization of wide-area bandwidth, reduce operating costs, and enhance wide-area networking flexibility [2-16]. This suite of software features provides a cost-effective internetworking solution that minimizes lifetime operating costs while maximizing connectivity, performance, and flexibility. This feature set is available across all members of ACC's bridge/router product line.

Each of ACC's bandwidth optimization features provides cost-cutting and performance benefits. All of these competitive advantages are also available in ACC's sophisticated frame relay implementation—including data compression, a unique feature of the ACC bridge/router line:

- Data Compression: reduces the size of messages by converting data into an alternative format that is smaller than the original message. Data compression can typically reduce the data sent across WAN links by a factor of 4:1, improving the response time to users and increasing utilization of low-speed lines to avoid expensive upgrades. Currently, ACC is the only bridge/router company to offer data compression over frame relay networks.

- Express Queuing: offered only by ACC, automatically allocates WAN bandwidth fairly or according to priorities established by the network administrator. Express Queuing stabilizes network behavior during congested periods and results in increased speed and reduced overhead costs.

- Dial on Congestion: provides for automatic dial up of a second WAN link when the primary link is heavily congested or is experiencing an unacceptable error rate, thereby ensuring predictable throughput on congested WAN links.

- Dial Backup: provides for automatic dial up of a secondary WAN link to temporarily replace a failed primary link, virtually eliminating network downtime and maintaining mission-critical connectivity.

- Dial on Demand: establishes a data link when data for a given destination is waiting and a physical connection doesn't exist, reducing the cost associated with dedicated links and allowing a connection to be made only when needed.

ACC's internetworking products are designed to offer best-of-class internetworking functions. Its software runs on a variety of ACC hardware platforms designed to accommodate diverse user connectivity requirements, including remote routing at speeds up to 2 Mbps, local routing at media speed, and hub routing over a high-speed bus (320 Mbps). Both Transparent (IEEE 802.1d) and source route bridging protocols are supported. On the routing side, TCP/IP, DECnet, IPX, XNS, and AppleTalk protocols are supported.

ACC's hardware platforms support a wide range of port density, from two up to a maximum of 41 ports, with such advanced features as fault tolerance, hot-card insertion, RISC technology, and FDDI routing. A wide variety of hardware interfaces is available as well, including Ethernet and token ring on the LAN side, plus EIA-530, RS-232, RS-422/449, V.35, X.21, DSX-1, G.703, and ISDN for WANs.

The Amazon Regional Office bridge/router is the cornerstone of ACC's remote access internetworking solution. Amazon is designed for larger regional locations in need of connectivity to corporate headquarters or as a WAN concentrator at regional or corporate sites. As a WAN concentrator, Amazon acts as a remote site "groomer" bringing remote branch offices, home users, and smaller regional locations into the regional or corporate LAN backbone.

ACC's Nile remote office bridge/router is ideal for branch offices that have higher traffic demands and require redundant connectivity to a regional site or smaller regional offices in need of connection to a corporate location. Nile is available with one Ethernet or token ring LAN interface and up to two WAN interfaces for added flexibility.

ACC's Danube is ideal for small branch offices in need of connectivity to regional or corporate locations. This model contains one WAN port and one LAN port. Attractively priced, small in size, and high in functionality, it is also an ideal solution for home office workers or home users wanting an efficient and cost-effective way to connect to the Internet "Superhighway".

A true remote bridge/router, Danube offers an extensive suite of features. It also supports ACC's exclusive bandwidth optimization features, which dramatically reduce the lifetime operating costs of your network. The Danube is available in two models: with a single autosensing Ethernet interface that can accommodate either 10BASE-T or AUI network connections; or with an integrated 8-port 10BASE-T hub. Both models of Danube use the same WAN interface cards available for ACC's Nile, and can support either RS-232 (V.24), V.35, RS-422, X.21, or ISDN BRI modules. Wide area protocols supported include frame relay, HDLC/LAPB, X.25, PPP, and ISDN. These quick-change WAN modules provide maximum configuration flexibility so that remote sites can be linked via dedicated leased lines, or via dial-up links for occasional use applications. With its robust set of bandwidth optimization features, the Danube is particularly useful in applications with link speeds at or below 64 Kbps. Danube's software is stored in Flash Memory for convenient remote upgrades.

ACC's RiverView for Windows is a complete network management package designed to maximize performance and control of the internetwork. This easy to use, cost effective platform provides a comprehensive set of graphic point-and-click monitoring and management tools. Functions of RiverView include network mapping, Real Time and Long Term Graphical Data Analysis, Health Meters, Alarms and Event Management, Flash Configuration, and Application File support. Ping and TraceRoute features are included to facilitate network troubleshooting.

In summary, ACC offers a broad spectrum of products to fit enterprise networking needs. Significant features include a low price per port, cost cutting bandwidth optimization technology, and support for virtually all types of WAN transmission services.

2.5 Routers

Routers operate at the OSI Network Layer and determine the correct network address to which they forward the data packet. Because of a router's additional functionality, it is more complex. The router is a protocol-dependent device, and operates with a hierarchical address that is defined by that protocol. Recall that while bridges operate at the Data Link Layer and use flat addresses, routers operate at the Network Layer and use hierarchical addresses. (A good example of a hierarchical addressing system is a telephone number, which is divided into four sections: country code, area code, central office code, and line number.) Thus, an IP (Internet Protocol) router would necessarily have difficulty understanding an address scheme that did not match its own format, such as one used by ISO protocols. We'll explore two protocols for router address recognition, the Routing Information Protocol (RIP), and Open Shortest Path First (OSPF), in Section 7.4.4.

Figure 2-16 (taken from reference [2-17]) illustrates how router addresses are used. Consider three networks, designated 1, 2, and 3; three host computers, A, B, and C; and two gateways (actually IP routers), R and S.

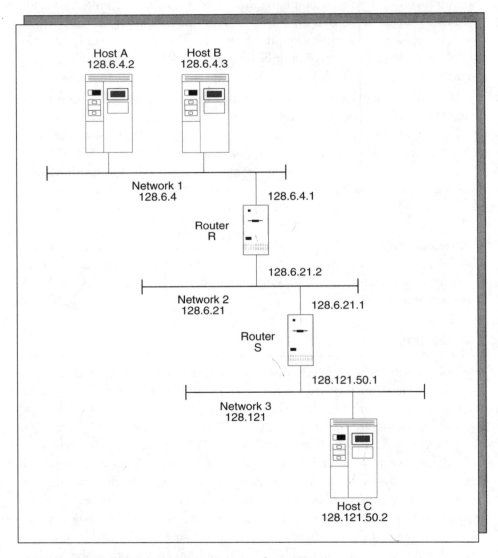

Figure 2-16. Internetwork addressing *(Courtesy of Rutgers University)*

The 32-bit IP addresses are expressed in a shorthand notation, known as dotted decimal (see Section 7.4), with each number representing 8 bits. Each portion of the address can take on a value from 0–255. Networks 1, 2, and 3 have unique addresses, 128.6.4, 128.6.21, and 128.121, respectively. Hosts attached to those networks reflect a network ID and a host ID in their address (e.g. host A is attached to network 128.6.4 and has address 128.6.4.2). Gateways (IP routers) have multiple addresses which represent the two networks which they connect. Thus Gateway R contains addresses 128.6.4.1 and 128.6.21.2, and connects network numbers 128.6.4 and 128.6.21. Communication between host A (on network 1) and host C (on network 3) must traverse two gateways, R and S.

Host A must contain a routing table based upon these hierarchical addresses:

Network	Gateway	Hops
128.6.4	none	0
128.6.21	128.6.4.1	1
128.121	128.6.4.1	2

The hop count indicates how many gateways must be traversed between Source and Destination Network Address. Destinations beginning with 128.6.4 require no further processing; the host suffix (128.6.4.3) is sufficient. Destinations beginning with 128.6.21 must be routed to gateway 128.6.4.1 (1 hop). Destinations beginning with 128.121 must go to gateway 128.6.4.1 and then access a similar table at Gateway R before reaching their final destination (2 hops).

A layered architectural model of a router (see Figure 2-17, from reference [2-18]) makes this process a little more clear. The router does not need consistent Physical or Data Link Layer protocols on an end-to-end basis, as long as each router-half communicates with its respective side. Protocol consistence in the Network Layer at both Source, Router, and Destination is required for addressing consistence. Higher-layer data (e.g. TCP) communicate on an end-to-end basis and are not affected by the router processing.

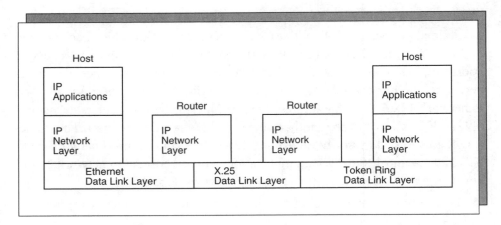

Figure 2-17. Layered router architecture *(Reprinted from September 21, 1989, Data Communications Magazine © 9/21/89 McGraw-Hill, Inc. All rights reserved.)*

References [2-18] through [2-25] discuss router selection requirements. Reference [2-20] is a good product comparison guide for shoppers.

2.5.1 Proteon CNX 500/600 Routers

Proteon, Inc. of Westborough, Massachusetts, which developed the first independent token ring network as well as the first fiber optic token ring, is recognized as a leader in token ring technology. In 1985 they developed the first multi-protocol internetworking router, and in subsequent years were the first to implement DECnet, 4/16 Mbps 802.5 connectivity, and the Open Shortest Path First (OSPF) protocol in a router. The CNX 500/600 series routers are products that support 16 Mbps token ring backbone connectivity and IBM source routing bridging in multi-protocol, multi-network internetworks. They were developed to provide an enterprise-wide solution for internetworking both IBM and non-IBM traffic over a variety of media—fiber optic cable, shielded twisted pair (STP), and unshielded twisted pair (UTP) (see Figure 2-18a).

At the LAN interface, the CNX 500/600 support IEEE 802.5 4/16 Mbps token ring, IEEE 802.3 Ethernet, ProNET-10, and Apollo token ring. WAN interfaces are available for DDS (at 64 Kbps), T1 (1.544 Mbps), X.25, and frame relay. Multiple higher-layer protocols can be routed, including TCP/IP, Novell's IPX, XNS, DECnet, Apollo DOMAIN, OSI, and AppleTalk.

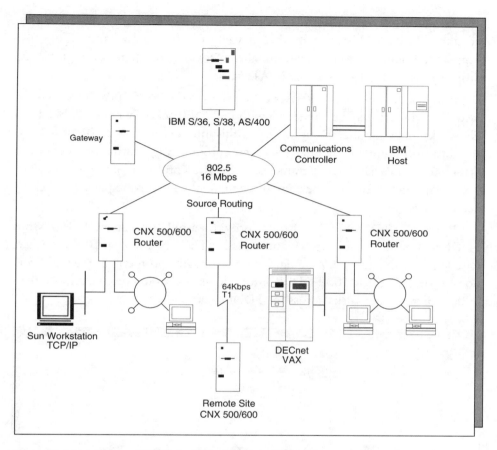

Figure 2-18a. Proteon Multivendor Token Ring Connectivity *(Courtesy of Proteon)*

Proteon routers support a number of protocols for router information exchange along the internetwork. For TCP/IP internetworks, the IGP (Internal Gateway Protocol), EGP (Exterior Gateway Protocol), and OSPF protocols are available. (Proteon led the working group which developed the OSPF standard, which provides fast convergence, load sharing, decreased routing traffic, and least cost routing.) Other supported protocols include the Multicast Open Shortest Path First (MOSPF), Data Link Switching (DLSw), and BGP-4. (BGP-4, the Border Gateway Protocol, is a routing protocol used in the Internet to exchange routing information among autonomous systems. BGP-4 is particularly important in large networks where dozens—or even hundreds—of routers are attached to the Internet.)

The CNX 500/600 offer IBM-compatible source routing bridging for connecting IBM PC LANs to each other as well as to IBM mainframes. They also support the spanning tree algorithm, which provides transparent bridging of all protocols as well as carrying DEC LAT traffic.

Another example of LAN/WAN connectivity is the CNX 500/600 X.25 Interface. Two routers may be connected with PSPDN (Packet Switched Public Data Network) lines. An interesting feature of this interface is its X.25 National Personality Configuration menu. This menu automatically configures the critical Data Link and Packet Layer parameters of the X.25 protocol for the specific PDN in use. Parameters can also be configured manually for private packet-switching network designs.

Proteon's CNX 600 FDDI Router provides a fully interoperable 100 Mbps FDDI backbone solution (see Figure 2-18b). The CNX 600's FDDI interface, based on the ANSI X3T9.5 standard, routes the same protocols as the CNX 500 does. Proteon's CNX 600 FDDI Router allows you to interconnect more than 1000 individual networks across the FDDI backbone.

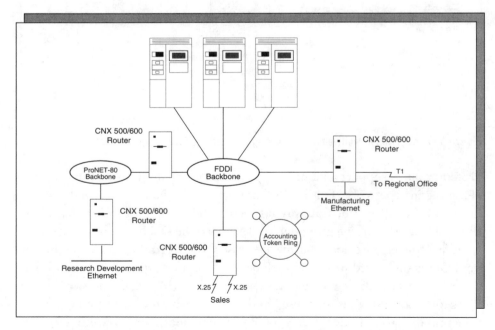

Figure 2-18b. Proteon FDDI backbone router attachment *(Courtesy of Proteon)*

Both the CNX 500/600 routers have an additional feature available to the user: standards-based network management. Proteon's OneVIEW is an icon-based network management system that supports SNMP (Simple Network Management Protocol). OneVIEW runs in a stand-alone 80486 PC or Sun UNIX workstation, and may be placed at any location in the internetwork. The SNMP engine provides equipment status and performance data for all hardware elements and transmission facilities within the internetwork. OneVIEW displays all of the Internetwork devices as icons and assigns a particular color—such as green for normal operation— to each. The health of any SNMP-compatible node can be queried at any time. OneVIEW maintains an error-log noting the critical events that might affect the health of the Internetwork.

To summarize, Proteon's CNX 500 Bridging Router and CNX 600 FDDI Router provide product value with optimization around token ring internetworking and backbones. Their multiple LAN/WAN interfaces and SNMP-based network management capabilities make them excellent choices for complex internetworks.

2.5.3 Cisco Systems 7000 Router

Cisco Systems, Inc., headquartered in San Jose, California, is a global supplier of enterprise networks, including routers, LAN and ATM switches, dial-up access servers, and network management software. These products, integrated by Cisco's Internetwork Operating System (IOS), found in more than 300,000 installed Cisco units and in the products of more than 20 partners, link geographically dispersed LANs, WANs, and IBM networks.

Cisco's 7000 family of high-end routers anchors some of the largest, most highly available internetworks in the world. High availability and port density make the Cisco 7000 series particularly appealing to telecommunications companies, brokerage firms, banks, large manufacturing companies, and other organizations that require multiple, highly reliable internetwork connections.

The 7000 series—which includes the high-end Cisco 7000 and the compact Cisco 7010—offers users connectivity to Asynchronous Transfer Mode (ATM) networks, channelized T1/E1 connections, mainframe attachment, and a unique packet-switching architecture that easily handles the demands of large internetworks running many diverse protocols and applications (Figure 2-19).

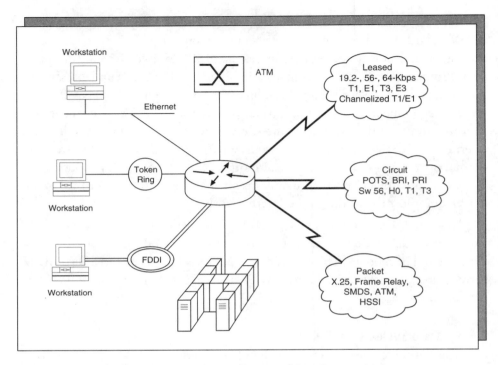

Figure 2-19. Cisco 7000 series connectivity *(Courtesy of Cisco Systems, Inc.)*

The Cisco 7000 architecture achieves state-of-the-art performance because the data bus, the switch processor, the route processor, and each interface processor operate independently. The Cisco 7000 series parallel processing architecture can perform both real-time operations, such as switching, and background operations, such as route calculation. Further, each processor is optimized for the unique operations it performs. The resulting architecture delivers scalable performance of more than 250,000 packets per second and the ability to expand as the network grows.

In addition, a broad range of support for media access and network layer protocols is available. For example, the Fast Serial Interface Processor (FSIP) is the highest-density serial card on the market, supporting eight T1 or E1 serial ports at full wire speed in both directions. A six-port Cisco Ethernet interface processor supports Ethernet wire speeds and offers exceptional port density for cost-effective connectivity to a large number of Ethernet users. The Cisco 7000 series' four-port Token Ring processor card delivers the highest token ring throughput on the market with the lowest latency. This card is based on the IBM 4/16 Mbps Token Ring chipset and an enhanced interface driver co-developed by Cisco Systems and IBM.

Multiprotocol routing, translational bridging between Ethernet networks and FDDI rings, remote source-route bridging (RSRB), transparent bridging, and encapsulation bridging are all supported by Cisco's FDDI interface processor.

A high-speed serial interface processor supports the High-Speed Serial Interface (HSSI) specification developed by Cisco Systems and its business partners. Standardized as EIA/TIA-612, HSSI supports serial communication at speeds up to 52 Mbps, allowing the efficient LAN-to-WAN connectivity required by distributed processing and database systems. To satisfy the requirements for ever-increasing bandwidth to support both the campus and WAN environments, Cisco Systems has developed an ATM Interface Processor (AIP). This interface card enables high-speed communications between the Cisco 7000 series routers and ATM switches and is initially capable of 155 Mbps throughput. The Cisco AIP supports both methods of converting data packets into ATM cells and back again— ATM Adaptation Layers 3/4 and 5—giving the user maximum flexibility. The AIP card uses two FRED (Fragmentation Device) ATM segmentation and reassembly chip sets, and two MIPS RISC processors for full simultaneous flow in both sending and receiving directions. In addition, AIP users will be able to select from among physical-layer daughter cards supporting TAXI (the Transparent Asynchronous Receiver/Transmitter Interface) 4B/5B on multimode fiber, SONET/SDH on single- or multimode fiber, DS3, or E3. Equipped with the AIP, the Cisco 7000 series, along with the Cisco family of ATM switches, form the core of emerging switched internetworks.

By combining the power and redundancy of the Cisco 7000 series with a direct mainframe channel attachment, the Cisco 7000 and 7010 also can provide high-speed network access to the mainframe. Using the Channel Interface Processor (CIP), IBM and IBM-compatible mainframes gain internetwork access by connecting directly to the mainframe channel. The CIP supports both IBM mainframe cabling standards: parallel channel (also called Bus and Tag), and Enterprise Systems Connection (ESCON) architecture. It can be used in conjunction with any Cisco 7000 interface processor.

In this chapter, we have studied some of the mathematics behind network operation, as well as various LAN-to-LAN internetworking devices that permit the extension, segmentation, or interconnection of these networks. An excellent source for those who would like further information on the mathematics behind LAN traffic models is reference [2-26]. In the next three chapters, we will extend our discussion of internetwork designs to include the WAN cases as well.

2.6   References

[2-1]   3Com Corporation. *Internetworking Design Guide*. Document No. DOC-IDG2, September 1994.

[2-2]   3Com Corporation. *Bridging and Routing—Technologies, Strategies and Benefits*, 1994.

[2-3]   Retix. *Local Bridge Application Guide*. Document 1040187-00, 1989.

[2-4]   Hewlett-Packard Co. *LAN Performance Analysis Product Note*. Document 5952-5103, 1986.

[2-5]   Bux, Werner. "Performance Issues in Local-Area Networks." *IBM Systems Journal,* volume 23, no. 4 (1984): 51–374.

[2-6]   Irwin, David R. "Second-Generation Token Ring LANs: Evaluating the Need for High Speed." *Data Communications* (March 21, 1989): 47–50.

[2-7]   Miller, Mark A. "Bridging Over Troubled Waters." *Network World* (August 30, 1993): 53–61.

[2-8]   Tolly, Kevin. "Testing Remote Token Ring Bridges." *Data Communication* (April 1994): 93–104.

[2-9]   Tolly, Kevin. "Token Ring Switching: The Design Challenge." *Data Communications* (February 1995): 97–104.

[2-10] Parnell, Tere'. "The Mystery of the Missing Bandwidth." *LAN Times* (February 13, 1995): 71–86.

[2-11] Axner, David. "Getting Tuned in to Ethernet Switches." *Network World* (February 13, 1995): L6–L7.

[2-12] Wittman, Art. "The Switching Hub Era Begins." *Network Computing* (September 1, 1994): 62–72.

[2-13] Mick, Colin. "Bridging Token-Ring, E-net LANs No Easy Task." *Network World* (June 18, 1990): 49–59.

[2-14] Solectek Corporation. *How to Get Smart About Wireless LANs*, May 1994.

[2-15] "Wireless Networks—Separating Fact from Fiction." *Network World Special Focus* (November 7, 1994): 43–54.

[2-16] Advanced Computer Communications. *Bandwidth Optimization Technology—An Overview*. Document 1700076, August 1994.

[2-17] Hedrick, Charles L. "An Introduction to the Administration of an Internet-based Local Network". Rutgers University, 24 July 1988. Copyright Charles Hedrick, used with permission.

[2-18] Boulé, Richard and John Moy. "Inside Routers: A Technology Guide for Network Builders." *Data Communications* (September 21, 1989): 53–66.

[2-19] McQuillan, John M. "Routers as Building Blocks for Robust Internetworks." *Data Communications* (September 21, 1989): 8–33.

[2-20] Miller, Mark A. "Routers: Poised to Make the Transition." *Network World* (September 12, 1994): 77–94.

[2-21] Wittman, Art. "State of the Router: Evolving or Dissolving?" *Network Computing* (February 1, 1995): 52–65.

[2-22] Gerber, Barry. "OSPF Routing: Coming Soon to a TCP/IP Router Near You." *Network Computing* (October 15, 1994): 16–26.

[2-23] Baker, Fred. "OSPF Fundamentals." *LAN Magazine* (December 1994): 71–78.

[2-24] Snyder, Joel and Ehud Gavron. "Fast Packets, Easy Routers." *LAN Magazine* (July 1994): 42–54.

[2-25] Hewlett-Packard Company. *HP Routing Services and Applications*, Document 5962-8770E, July 1994.

[2-26] Fortier, Paul J. and George R. Desrochers. *Modeling and Analysis of Local Area Networks*, CRC Press, Inc. Boca Raton, FL, 1990.

3 Analog and Digital Data Transmission Facilities for Internetworks

These days, it's rare to go to any LAN or internetworking seminar, conference, or tutorial where the presenter doesn't show a picture of a "cloud diagram" (see Figure 3-1). The cloud is used to explain the need for data transmission facilities. It is assumed that an end-user's terminal feeds data into the cloud, which mysteriously routes and switches that data to a distant location such as a host computer. The data arrives with no errors or retransmissions, and the internetwork manager lives happily ever after.

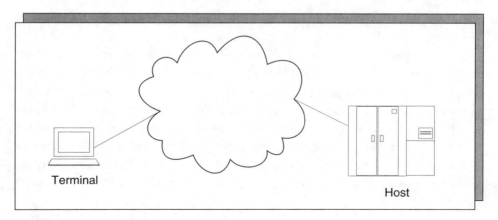

Figure 3-1. Generic data communications cloud

We all know that the cloud does not appear magically to transport data. We, the internetwork designers, must specify and order the communication facility from one of a multitude of providers. This chapter will discuss typical design requirements and the different choices available. We will begin with the easiest alternative, the dial-up telephone network, and work our way up to higher speed circuits. (As a reference, Appendix E lists North American carriers providing private line, public data networks and broadband services.)

3.1 Dial-Up Telephone Network Facilities

The dial-up telephone network, also known as the Public Switched Telephone Network (PSTN), is undoubtedly the data communication facility with which we are most familiar. In North America, users have often been accused (and rightfully so) of taking basic telephone service for granted. Other areas of the world—especially some of the third-world countries—do not enjoy the reliable service that we've come to expect from the Local Exchange Carriers (LECs) and Inter-Exchange Carriers (IXCs). There are several hundred million telephone lines in the United States, and the various switching systems that connect the voice and data calls do so with remarkable reliability. Let's begin our study of this network by looking at the characteristics of the basic telephone channel itself.

A telephone channel is defined as a "frequency band, or its equivalent in the time domain, established in order to provide a communications path between a message source and its destination" (reference [3-1], Volume 1). The telephone channel is therefore a specific frequency band that has been optimized for voice communication. For a number of reasons (described in references [3-1] and [3-2]), the required channel—called a passband—must pass frequencies that range from approximately 300 to 3300 Hertz (Hz). (Figure 3-2 and other figures in this chapter will plot the signal gain or loss on the vertical y-axis as a function of frequency, which is measured in Hz and shown on the horizontal x-axis.) The bandwidth is the width, measured in Hz, of the passband, and is found by subtracting the upper and lower frequency limits (thus equalling 3000 Hz). The passband is determined by the electrical inductance and capacitance of the cable itself, and by filters connected to every analog telephone line in the telephone company's Central Offices (C.O.s).

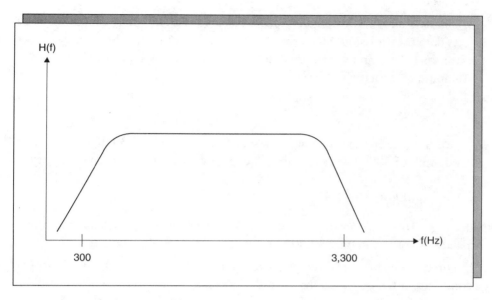

Figure 3-2. Analog telephone line passband

If all we wanted to transmit was an audio signal, it's easy to see that the telephone channel characteristics would define the frequencies of interest. Frequencies below 300 Hz or above 3,300 Hz would be attenuated, and not be transmitted with as great an amplitude as those frequencies within the passband.

Data communication signals, however, are measured in terms of bits per second (bps), not Hz, and therefore some mechanism must be employed to associate the transmission channel characteristic (in Hz) to the data rate (in bps). This relationship is established using two theorems that were also derived from early telegraph and telephone research (references [3-1], Volume 1, and [3-3]).

In 1928 Harry Nyquist, a researcher in the area of telegraph transmission efficiency, published an equation—called the Nyquist Rate—that measured the transmission signaling rate in baud. The Nyquist Rate equaled 2B symbols (or signals) per second, where B is the bandwidth of the transmission channel. Thus, using this equation, a telephone channel bandwidth of 3000 Hz can support up to 2 x 3000, or 6000, baud.

Claude Shannon furthered Nyquist's research with his study as to how noise affects data transmission. Shannon took into account the signal-to-noise ratio of the transmission channel (measured in decibels or dB) and derived what is known as Shannon's Capacity Theorem:

$$C = B \ log_2 \ (1 + S/N) \ bps$$

A typical voice telephone channel has a signal-to-noise ratio of 30 dB (1000:1) and a bandwidth of 3000 Hz. If we substitute these values into Shannon's Theorem:

$$C = 3000 \ log_2 \ (1 + 1000)$$

Since log_2 (1001) is approximately equal to 10, the theorem yields a maximum capacity of approximately 30,000 bps.

Three points are worth emphasizing. First, the terms "baud" and "bits per second" are often confused. Modem designers, and others who must deal with the actual signal that is placed on the telephone channel, will speak of those signals in terms of "baud." Those of us who wish to use those same channels to transfer a file, for example, will speak in terms of "bits per second." Second, upper limits to the data transmission characteristics of the telephone channel exist. These limits are 6000 baud and 30,000 bps. Thus, while it is possible to transmit data at rates greater than 30,000 bps over twisted pair transmission media, it is not possible to do so using the PSTN.

Third, it is correct to say, "I need a 9600 bps modem" instead of "I need a 9600 baud modem." Because of the Nyquist Theorem, we know that a 9600 baud modem could not transmit over the dial-up telephone network. What is probably meant when someone says "9600 baud modem" is a modem that transmits 2400 signals per second (baud) and represents each signal with 4 bits. The resulting data rate is 9600 bps (2400 signals per second x 4 bits per signal = 9600 bps).

Current modem technology, such as the V.34 standard which transmits at 28.8 Kbps, is pushing the upper limit of Nyquist's theorem. If faster data rates are required, two options are available. The first option is to compensate for the signal degradation caused by the transmission channel through a process known as conditioning. The second is to use a digital, instead of analog, transmission facility. We will study both of these techniques in the following sections.

3.2   Analog Leased Line Facilities

As we saw in the last section, dial-up transmission facilities are the most ubiquitous transmission option available. As we have all experienced, dial-up connections have a varying degree of quality—sometimes you get a circuit that is noisy, and sometimes you get one that sounds like the other party is next door. In other words, switched facilities have a randomness associated with them, and this is due to the switched nature of the connection itself. Every time a dial-up circuit is established, a different path is chosen. Some of those paths are noisy, some are not, and, as Shannon's Capacity Theorem illustrates, the amount of noise has a direct relationship to the maximum data rate.

An obvious improvement on this method of transmission would be to establish a constant transmission path. This path is known as a leased line or private line. The end user has access to a telephone line (either a 2-wire or 4-wire circuit) that is terminated at each end of the transmission path. The terminations could exist within the same city or across the country, connecting different LECs via one IXC. When the transmission path is fixed, the user is guaranteed predictable transmission parameters. Conditioning, or correction for transmission abnormalities, can be done on this fixed path.

A leased line has an economic advantage over the dial-up facility. Let's say that a leased line between two cities costs $500.00 per month. At a typical cost of $0.25 per minute, this translates to 2,000 minutes or 33.3 hours of dial-up usage. Thus, if a network requires use of the transmission facility for more than 33.3 hours per month, economics would dictate that a leased line be chosen instead of a dial-up line.

To begin our study of leased lines, let's look at the different transmission parameters that affect the quality of analog leased circuits.

3.2.1   Leased Line Transmission Parameters

A number of factors affect the quality of a leased line, and thus contribute to data transmission errors. We'll briefly summarize them here. For further details, see the AT&T standards that describe specific parameters (references [3-4] through [3-7]).

Noise is defined as any signal that impairs or interferes with the information that we wish to convey. There are several categories of noise. Impulse noise is energy that lasts for a short duration (perhaps only a few milliseconds) and then disappears. Sources of impulse noise include lightning, power surges, and switching systems such as electromechanical C.O. switches. Gaussian noise, or white noise, is the background "hiss" that often accompanies voice telephone transmissions. Crosstalk occurs when the electromagnetic field of one transmission circuit interferes with another, similar circuit. The carrier, such as AT&T, sets limits on the amount of each type of noise allowable on each type of leased line.

Attenuation is the loss of signal strength as it travels down the telephone line. Because attenuation is measured over an analog transmission facility, the loss is always determined at a specific frequency, such as 1000 Hz. Attenuation is measured in decibels (dB).

Several frequencies are contained within the data signal. The transmission line does not react to each of these frequencies in the same manner, as a result attenuating some more than others. Envelope Delay Distortion is a measurement (usually given in milliseconds, or ms) of the amount of delay between these various frequency components.

Phase Jitter occurs when all the zero crossings (those points, measured in the time domain, where the signal crosses the zero axis from a negative to a positive amplitude, or vice versa) of the transmitted signal are not in phase. If viewed on an oscilloscope, the signal would appear to wiggle (or jitter) horizontally instead of showing a clean, crisp trace. Amplitude Jitter is similar to Phase Jitter, occurring when the signal amplitude is not constant. A vertical movement would be seen on the oscilloscope.

Nonlinear Distortion is noticed when the harmonics (or multiples) of the fundamental signal frequency are not attenuated by the same amount.

Finally, transients occur when the signal abruptly changes amplitude, or drops out altogether. Transients are often caused by impulse noise, and may last a few milliseconds.

Section 4.3 of reference [3-5] provides an excellent summary of these transmission impairments. Reference [3-8] discusses the effects of these impairments on transmitted signals.

3.2.2 Leased Line Conditioning

As we have seen, all telephone lines experience noise and other transmission impairments. In the case of dial-up (PSTN) lines, there is little we can do, since every connection is a random selection between the various switching centers.

Leased lines are a different story, however, since the transmission path is a fixed constant. It is thus possible to "condition" that line, removing the negative effects of the various transmission impairments defined above.

Conditioning is defined by FCC tariffs 9,10, and 11, and specified by AT&T publication PUB 43202 [3-7]. These documents first identify the functional characteristics of different types of private lines. Ten different line types (1–10) are defined below:

Service Type	Description
1	Basic voice applications
2	Voice applications which require tighter control of performance specifications, i.e. tie trunks
3	Voice radio land lines that require tone control conditioning
4	Low speed data applications (less than 1200 bps)
5	Basic data applications
6	Voice and data applications on trunk circuits
7	Voice and data applications on private access lines
8	Voiceband data on intermachine trunks
9	Telephotographic or alternate voice/telephotographic transmission
10	Protective relaying applications, e.g., tone control systems

Type 5 (basic data applications) holds the greatest interest for internetwork applications. What is now called a Type 5 line was formerly defined in FCC tariff 260 as a 3002 unconditioned private line.

An unconditioned Type 5 line has no correction for the transmission impairments discussed in Section 3.2.1. To improve the line quality, five types of conditioning are available. C-conditioning corrects for attenuation distortion and Envelope Delay Distortion. D-conditioning corrects for signal-to-C-notched noise and harmonic distortion. International, Tone Control and Special Telephoto conditioning are used for specific applications. Of these options, C- and D- conditioned lines are most frequently used for internetwork communication channels.

Each type of conditioning specifies parameters for and limits of the correction. Figures 3-3, 3-4, and 3-5 (taken from reference [3-7]), provide the various specifications for Type 5, C-conditioned, and D-conditioned lines, respectively.

AT&T lists these specifications in tabular form. Motorola Information Systems Group (formerly Universal Data Systems), of Huntsville, Alabama, has reduced these specifications to the charts shown in Figures 3-6 and 3-7 [3-8]). These two figures describe the attenuation and Envelope Delay Distortion characteristics of C-conditioned lines. For the attenuation characteristics (see Figure 3-6), note that loss becomes less as the conditioning progresses from steps C1 to C2, and finally to C4 conditioning. The Envelope Delay Distortion characteristics (see Figure 3-7) show an additional improvement. Note that the frequency range of the minimum delay (which is close to 0 ms) becomes wider as the conditioning is increased. Notice also that C4 conditioning has almost no Envelope Delay Distortion over the range of 900–2500 Hz. (References [3-9] and [3-10] have good summaries of transmission impairments and channel conditioning.)

Performance Specification Limits Service Type 5	
Parameter	Immediate Action Limit
1 Loss Deviation (dB)	± 4.0
2 C-Notched Noise (dBrnCO)	51
3 Attenuation Distortion	
# (dB) between:	
504 & 2504 Hz	-2.0 to +8.0
404 & 2804 Hz	-2.0 to +10.0
304 & 3004 Hz	-3.0 to +12.0
4 Signal-to-C-Notched Noise Ratio (dB)	≥ 24
5 Envelope Delay Distortion (μs)	
between:	
804 & 2604 Hz	1750
6 Impulse Noise Threshold* (dBrnCO)	71
7 Intermodulation Distortion (dB)	
R2	≥ 27
R3	≥ 32
8 Phase Jitter (Degrees pk-pk)	
20 - 300 Hz	≤ 10°
4 - 300 Hz	≤ 15°
9 Frequency Shift (Hz)	± 3

Notes: #   (+) means more loss.
         *   15 counts in 15 minutes at specified threshold.

Figure 3-3. AT&T private line Type 5 specifications *(Reproduced with permission of AT&T)*

C-Conditioning
Immediate Action Limits

Conditioning	Attenuation Distortion Relative to 1004 Hz		Envelope Delay Distortion	
	Frequency Range (Hz)	Variation (dB)*	Frequency Range (Hz)	Variation (microseconds)
C1	1004-2404	-1.0 to +3.0	1004-2404	1000
	304-2704	-2.0 to +6.0	804-2604	1750
	304-3004	-3.0 to +12.0		
C2	504-2804	-1.0 to +3.0	1004-2604	500
	304-3004	-2.0 to +6.0	604-2604	1500
			504-2804	3000
C3 (access line)	504-2804	-0.5 to +1.5	1004-2604	110
	304-3004	-0.8 to +3.0	604-2604	300
			504-2804	650
C3 (trunk)	504-2804	-0.5 to +1.0	1004-2604	80
	304-3004	-0.8 to +2.0	604-2604	260
			504-2804	500
C4	504-3004	-2.0 to +3.0	1004-2604	300
	304-3204	-2.0 to +6.0	804-2804	500
			604-3004	1500
			504-3004	3000
C5	504-2804	-0.5 to +1.5	1004-2604	100
	304-3004	-1.0 to +3.0	604-2604	300
			504-2804	600
C7	404-2804	-1.0 to +4.5	1004-2604	550
C8	404-2804	-1.0 to +3.0	1004-2604	125

Notes: *   (+) means loss with respect to 1004 Hz.
(-) means gain with respect to 1004 Hz.

Figure 3-4. AT&T C-conditioned private line specifications *(Reproduced with permission of AT&T)*

D-Conditioning **Immediate Action Limits**	
Signal-to-C-Notched Noise Ratio	≥ 28 dB minimum
Intermodulation Distortion (4-tone) - Signal to second order modulation products - Signal to third order modulation products	≥35 dB minimum ≥40 dB minimum

D6 Channel Characteristics	
Parameter	Requirement
Intermodulation Distortion (4-tone) - Signal to second order (R2) - Signal to third order (R3)	≥ 45 dB ≥ 46 dB
Phase Jitter 20-300 Hz	≤ 7 Degree Pk-Pk
Signal to C-Notched Noise Ratio	≥ 32 dB
Envelope Delay Distortion 604-2804 Hz	1400 µsec
Attenuation Distortion 404-2804 Hz	-1.0 to +4.5 dB

Figure 3-5. AT&T D-Conditioned Private Line Specifications *(Reproduced with permission of AT&T)*

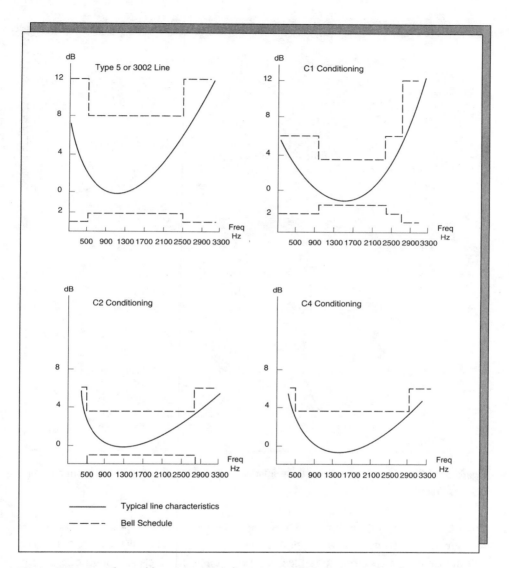

Figure 3-6. C-conditioned line attenuation characteristics *(Courtesy Motorola Information Systems Group)*

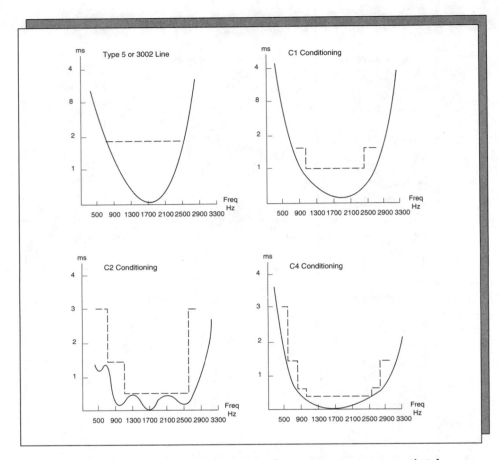

Figure 3-7. C-conditioned line envelope delay distortion characteristics *(Courtesy Motorola Information Systems Group)*

Fortunately, determining the means of conditioning is not always as complicated as it might sound. Transmission equipment, such as the synchronous modem, is designed to operate with a specific type of leased line, such as a C-2 conditioned line. Equipment specifications will indicate the line required, and the internetwork manager will include that information when ordering the line from the LEC and/or IXC.

Testing a private line for signal degradation and transmission impairment in order to determine conditioning is often more complicated. A device known as a TIMS (Transmission Impairment Measurement Set) is used (see Figure 3-8). The

TIMS is connected to the telephone line, and can thus measure circuit noise, attenuation, Envelope Delay Distortion and other parameters. A TIMS can be a valuable troubleshooting asset, and models are available ranging in price from a few hundred to several thousand dollars. The less expensive are manually-operated units, while the high-end devices automate the tests and provide hard-copy graphical outputs. Since all LECs and IXCs specify the noise level limits for the various types of lines, the TIMS will determine if the line is functioning properly. If not, the carrier should be contacted for repair. (Reference [3-11] includes an excellent checklist to use while making TIMS measurements.)

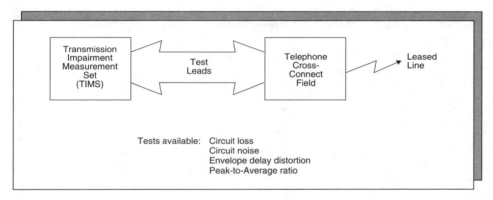

Figure 3-8. Testing the analog leased line with TIMS

3.3   Digital Leased Lines

As we saw in Section 3.2, analog leased lines are susceptible to impairments such as noise and attenuation. Digital leased facilities improve the overall channel performance by transmitting digital pulses, which are not as susceptible to those particular impairments. Digital lines are available from a number of LECs and IXCs, but are most commonly referred to by AT&T's name, DDS—short for Dataphone Digital Service or Digital Data System.

DDS is a synchronous, full- or half-duplex digital transmission facility operating at 2.4, 4.8, 9.6, 19.2, or 56 kilobits per second (Kbps). The actual DDS signals are carried inside T1 channels (discussed in section 3.4). Access to DDS facilities is available in most metropolitan locations, and connections to North

American, European, and Far East destinations are possible. Because of the digital nature of the transmitted signal, a modem cannot be used as the interface between the end user's Data Terminal Equipment (DTE) and the network. Instead, a device known as a DSU/CSU (Data Service Unit/Channel Service Unit) is employed. The DSU/CSU accepts the user data via a standard interface—typically EIA-232-E at the lower data rates and V.35 at 56 Kbps (see Figure 3-9).

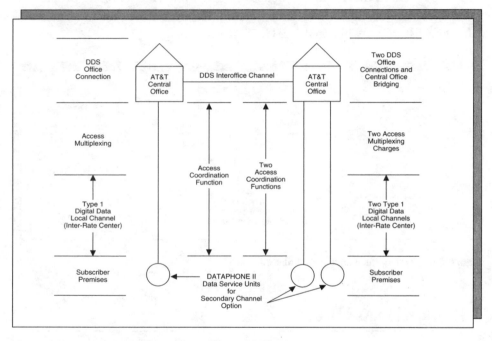

Figure 3-9. DATAPHONE Digital Service *(Courtesy of AT&T)*

DDS services are renowned for the high quality of their data transmission. AT&T quotes an average of 99.5% error-free seconds at 56 Kbps, and even better performance at the subrate (lower) speeds. Availability is quoted at a minimum of 99.9% on an annualized basis, resulting in an annual downtime of less than 0.1%. Transmission capabilities allow for remote loopbacks from the central office to the customer's premises, minimizing the Mean Time to Repair (MTTR) [3-12].

Switched digital services are also available from most LECs and IXCs. As the name implies, this service offering provides digital connectivity on demand, and is typically used for temporary circuits between three or more locations. The carrier's charge is based upon an access fee, plus a per-minute usage fee. Reference [3-13] compares switched services with other carrier alternatives; reference [3-14] compares the access methods and costs of switched digital services. For example, AT&T provides a number of switched digital options, including Switched 56, Switched 64, Switched 384, and Switched 1536 service. Many of these rates are available both domestically and on an international basis.

For users with requirements for lower data transmission rates (2.4, 4.8, 9.6, or 19.2 Kbps), AT&T provides a Subrate Data Multiplexing (SDM) service at their C.O.s. Multiplexing at the C.O. permits economies-of-scale by combining multiple lower-speed lines into one higher speed (56 Kbps) line. Three options are available: SDM-5 can multiplex a mix of five lower speed channels into one 56 Kbps channel; SDM-10 multiplexes up to ten 2.4 or 4.8 Kbps channels into one 56 Kbps channel; or SDM-20 can multiplex up to twenty 2.4 Kbps channels into one 56 Kbps channel [3-15].

As we have studied in the last two sections, a variety of analog and digital leased line options are available. This sector of wide-area networking is extremely competitive, and receives a great deal of attention in the press. References [3-16] and [3-17] are examples of recent WAN service comparisons. Appendix E lists names and phone numbers of many private line vendors.

3.4 T-Carrier Facilities

The T-carrier system was developed by Bell Telephone Laboratories in the 1960s as a means of multiplexing voice signals onto a digital transmission line. (Earlier systems such as the N-carrier multiplexed analog signals onto an analog transmission line.) The system was inspired by a telephone line capacity problem that developed in several metropolitan locations. Signals were carried between switching offices on individual pairs of copper wire, one pair per conversation. These pairs were bundled into a large cable, with up to 3000 pairs inside, and placed in a conduit under the city streets. As the city grew, so did the need for additional telephone circuits. Additional cables were placed, and conduit runs eventually became completely full of cables. When all the conduit ductwork became congested, the telephone company was left with two choices: dig up the street and place additional conduits, or figure out a way to get additional capacity out of the existing copper pairs. Bell System opted for the second alternative, and put their engineers to work to solve the problem. What we now refer to as the T-Carrier network was the result of their efforts.

The T1 circuit is a digital, full-duplex transmission facility operating at 1.544 Mbps. It can be used to transmit digital voice, data, or video signals. The complete circuit requires a 4-wire path (of copper) and is available only for point-to-point (not multi-point) connections. The T1 circuit, however, is not limited to copper-based, terrestrial communication channels. Many other transmission options are available, including 18- and 23-GigaHertz (GHz) microwave radio, fiber optics, infrared and coaxial cables.

At either end of the T1 circuit is a customer-provided Channel Service Unit, or CSU (see Figure 3-10). The CSU accepts the data from the Customer Premises Equipment (CPE), and encodes that data for transmission on the T1 circuit. Typical CPE would be a T1 multiplexer or a LAN bridge designed for T1 circuit rate transmission.

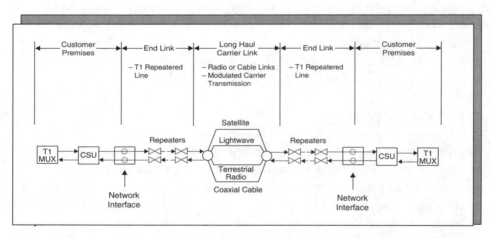

Figure 3-10. Typical T1 circuit configuration *(Courtesy Telecommunications Techniques Corporation)*

3.4.1   North American Digital Transmission Hierarchy

T1 circuits are only one of a number of digital transmission facilities that are available within North America. An existing hierarchy includes a number of different transmission rates. All of these facilities contain a specific digital signal level (abbreviated DS) and all are based upon the DS0 channel, which operates at 64 Kbps. The 64 Kbps channel is derived from a 4 KHz band limited channel that is sampled 8000 times per second. Each sample is then quantified at 1 of 256 levels (8 bits) resulting in the 64 Kbps rate (8000 samples per second x 8 bits/sample). This DS0 channel becomes the basic building block for ISDN (Integrated Services Digital Network) transmission, although the ISDN term for the 64 Kbps unit is a B (Bearer) channel. Note that the signal is referred to as "DS1," while the transmission channel (over a copper-based facility) is called a "T1" circuit. The various transmission rates used within the North American hierarchy are shown below:

Signal Level	Carrier System	Equivalent T1 Channels	Voice Channels	Data Rate (Mbps)
DS0	N/A	N/A	1	0.064
DS1	T1	1	24	1.544
DS1C	T1C	2	48	3.152
DS2	T2	4	96	6.312
DS3	T3	28	672	44.736
DS4	T4	168	4032	274.760

Figure 3-11a. Digital signals and data rates

The hierarchy is derived using a series of digital, time domain multiplexers (see Figure 3-11b, and reference [3-18]). The DS1 signal is generated by combining 24 of the individual DS0 channels. Two DS1s can be multiplexed into a DS1C, and two DS1Cs can become a DS2. Seven DS2s are combined for a DS3. Finally, six DS3s are multiplexed to generate a DS4 signal. The DS1 (1.544 Mbps) and DS3 (44.736 Mbps) rates are of greatest interest to LAN and WAN designers [3-19].

Those of you with calculators in hand will immediately notice that all the numbers, when multiplexed together, do not add up. For example, the DS1 rate contains 24 DS0 channels, but 24 x 64 Kbps yields 1.536 Mbps, not 1.544 Mbps. The numerical difference is in the framing information, which is the subject of the next section.

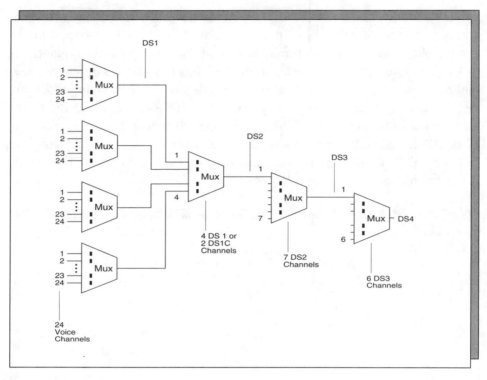

Figure 3-11b. Digital signal multiplexing hierarchy

3.4.2 DS1 Framing

All DS-level transmissions use Alternate Bipolar (ABP)—which is also called Alternate Mark Inversion (AMI)—signal encoding (see Figure 3-12). The signal has three different levels: a positive voltage (+V), a negative voltage (-V), and a ground reference (0). The signal is called "alternate" because successive "1"'s alternate in polarity. The first "1" is transmitted as a +V pulse, and the next "1" is transmitted as a -V pulse. Zeros are transmitted as a 0. The signal transmissions (+V and -V) are used to regenerate the timing information, since all T-carrier circuits are synchronous facilities and must be referenced from a master clock source. As a result, constraints may be placed on the data so that it contains enough 1s to regenerate the clock information. Those constraints are referred to as "pulse density" or "1s richness" requirements, and are often quoted at 12.5% (one 1 for every 8 bits). Since the pulse density is a requirement of the network (not the end equipment), users do not appreciate these constraints being placed on their data. As a result, carriers accept the user's data as is and modify its pulse stream to satisfy the 1s constraints. These modifications are done in such a way that they are transparent to the end user. The technique that is commonly used is B8ZS (Bipolar with 8 zero substitution), described in references [3-20] and [3-21]. With B8ZS, a special code is placed in and then removed from the pulse stream in substitution for a zero byte (all eight bits are equal to zero) that has been transmitted by the user's equipment.

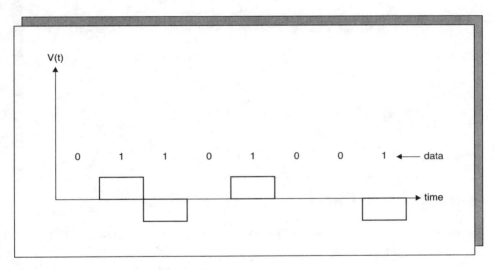

Figure 3-12. Alternate bipolar signal

After the format of the data is specified, a method of distinguishing between the individual channels (which may be distinct telephone conversations or data circuits) must be established. For DS1 signals, this framing is accomplished by adding one additional bit, dubbed the 193rd bit, to each frame (see Figure 3-13). The mystery of the DS1 transmission rate is solved thus:

24 DS0 channels at 64 Kbps	=	*1.536 Mbps*
1 framing bit at 8 Kbps	=	*0.008 Mbps*
Resulting DS1 data rate	=	*1.544 Mbps*

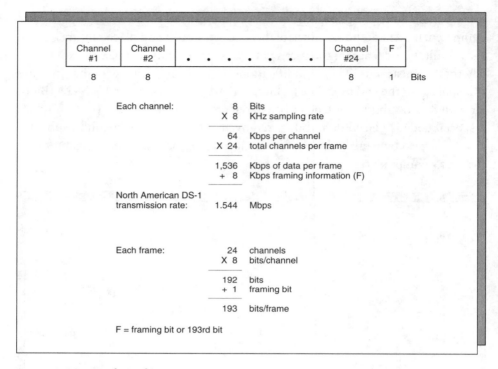

Figure 3-13. DS1 frame format

Two different framing techniques for DS-level transmission—D4 and ESF—are available. We'll look more closely at each.

3.4.2.1 D-4 Framing

D-4 framing (see Figure 3-14) uses the 193rd bit strictly for framing purposes. A total of 12 individual frames are combined into a D-4 "superframe." A pattern of the sampled 193rd bits (bit numbers 193, 386, 579, etc.) is used to identify individual DS0 channels within each DS1 frame. This framing pattern (100011011100) is repeated every 12 frames (or superframe). Signaling information (used for central office-to-central office messages) appears in bit 8 of frames 6 and 12. AT&T PUB 43801 (reference [3-22]) provides additional details.

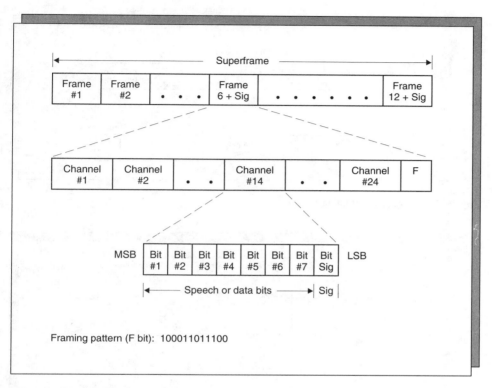

Figure 3-14. AT&T DS framing format

3.4.2.2 ESF Framing

In 1979, AT&T proposed a new DS1 framing format known as the Extended Superframe Format (ESF) (described in reference [3-23], and shown in Figure 3-15). ESF extended the superframe from 12 to 24 DS1 frames, which resulted in a total of 24 of the framing (or 193rd) bits. With 24 bits instead of 12 to work with, two additional capabilities became available (see Figure 3-16). The signaling capabilities were expanded to four options (T, 2, 4, 16) and are shown in the traffic and signaling columns in Figure 3-16. Signaling information (if used), is present in frames 6, 12, 18, and 24.

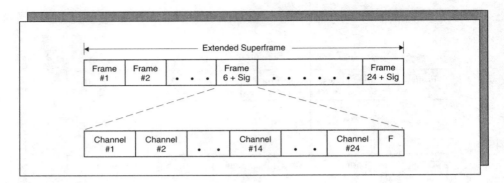

Figure 3-15. AT&T ESF framing format

Frame Number	S Bits			Bit Use In Each Channel Time Slot		Signaling-Bit Use Options			
	Fe	DL	BC	Traffic	Signaling	T	2	4	16
1	-	m	-	Bits 1-8					
2	-	-	C1	Bits 1-8					
3	-	m	-	Bits 1-8					
4	0	-	-	Bits 1-8					
5	-	m	-	Bits 1-8					
6	-	-	C2	Bits 1-7	Bit 8	-	A	A	A
7	-	m	-	Bits 1-8					
8	0	-	-	Bits 1-8					
9	-	m	-	Bits 1-8					
10	-	-	C3	Bits 1-8					
11	-	m	-	Bits 1-8					
12	1	-	-	Bits 1-7	Bit 8	-	A	B	B
13	-	m	-	Bits 1-8					
14	-	-	C4	Bits 1-8					
15	-	m	-	Bits 1-8					
16	0	-	-	Bits 1-8					
17	-	m	-	Bits 1-8					
18	-	-	C5	Bits 1-7	Bit 8	-	A	A	C
19	-	m	-	Bits 1-8					
20	1	-	-	Bits 1-8					
21	-	m	-	Bits 1-8					
22	-	-	C6	Bits 1-8					
23	-	m	-	Bits 1-8					
24	1	-	-	Bits 1-7	Bit 8	-	A	B	D

Notes:
Fe: Extended Framing (sequence...001011...)
DL: 4 kb/s Data Link (message bits m)
BC: Block-Check Field (check bits C1-C6)
Option T: Transparent (bit 8 for traffic)
Option 2: 2-State Signaling (channel 4)
Option 4: 4-State Signaling (channels A,B)
Option 16: 16-State Signaling (channels A, B, C, D)

Figure 3-16. AT&T ESF frame coding *(Reproduced with permission of AT&T)*

There are three uses for the framing function (shown as S in Figure 3-16): Framing itself (Fe); Data Link (DL); and Block Check (BC). The Data Link function provides a 4 Kbps communications link between circuit end points. Transmissions on this data link would typically consist of maintenance and performance messages. Two different standards exist for the use of these maintenance messages. The AT&T 54016 standard specifies that the CSU store up to 24 hours of statistics, and transmit those results over the Data Link to network management stations upon request. The ANSI T1.403 standard requires that the CSU transmit performance data on a continuous basis. Since the AT&T and ANSI standards govern the way the collected data is disseminated, not collected, both techniques can coexist on the same transmission facility. Reference [3-24] provides additional insight into the operation and advantages of ESF.

The Block Check framing function (BC) provides a six-bit Cyclic Redundancy Check (CRC-6), which is used to verify the accuracy of the entire superframe. Any individual line errors would cause a violation of the CRC-6, thus alerting the intermediate transmission equipment of the problem. The CRC-6 is 98.4% accurate (63/64) in detecting burst errors that occur on the transmission line.

The advantage of the ESF framing format over that of the D-4 is its ability to monitor the network and then notify a network management console of any difficulties. This communication path is often implemented via a serial (EIA-232) port on an intelligent CSU. Data from a number of CSUs can be accumulated and then presented in a centralized format.

3.4.3 Fractional T1

Fractional T1 (FT1), as its name implies, offers the network manager a range of digital bandwidth choices that are a fraction of a full T1 link. The service is designed for applications that have requirements greater than those provided by analog or DDS private lines, but perhaps less than a full T1 circuit. Fractional T1 circuits are thus configured in 64 Kbps segments, up to the maximum 1.544 Mbps.

Previously offered only by Canadian carriers, Cable and Wireless became the first U.S. IXC to offer the service in 1987. Since then, many IXCs and LECs have added FT1 services. The financial benefits of FT1 service, plus the ease in which bandwidth may be added as business needs increase, provide an alternative to voice-grade or digital private lines. References [3-25] and [3-26] provide economic comparisons and applications that illustrate these benefits.

As an example of FT1 service, AT&T offers ACCUNET Spectrum of Digital Services (ASDS), shown in Figure 3-17. This service offers transmission between an AT&T Point-of-Presence (POP) in one Local Access and Transport Area (LATA) and another AT&T POP in another LATA. Transmission speeds of 9.6, 56, or from 64 Kbps up to 768 Kbps in increments of 64 Kbps are available.

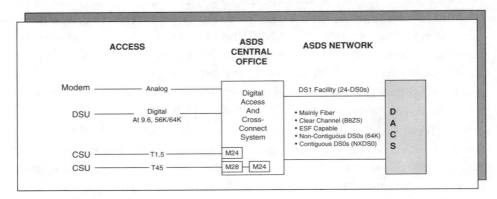

Figure 3-17. ACCUNET Spectrum of Digital Services *(Courtesy of AT&T)*

The ASDS facilities can be accessed via DDS or analog voice-grade lines, plus DS1-rate access with the M24 multiplexing option, or DS3-rate access with the M28 followed by the M24 multiplexing options [3-27]. The M24 Multiplexing office function combines or divides up to 24 voice-grade or 56 Kbps switched channels into one T1 circuit. The M28 Multiplexing Office function combines or divides 28 DS1 signals into a DS3. The M28 function can also be combined with the M24 function for a total T3 to T1 to subrate service connection.

3.5 Packet Switched Public Data Networks

Packet Switched Public Data Networks (PSPDNs), sometimes called Public Data Networks (PDNs) or Value Added Networks (VANs), have been popular data-transmission facilities since their inception in the early 1970s [3-28]. PSPDNs are often referred to as "X.25 networks." This statement (as we will study in Chapter 4) is clearly false. PSPDNs are, in fact, packet switched networks, and X.25 is the protocol of choice between most DTEs (Data Terminal Equipment) and the network.

The misconception lies in the fact that the X.25 protocols define an interface into the PSPDN, not the internal protocols within the PSPDN. This is a subtle but important point. The internal protocols and architecture of the PSPDN may be considered proprietary to the network provider, as well as the manner in which they route, switch and store their customer's packets of information. PSPDNs operate by accepting fixed-length packets of information (usually 128 octets in length) and routing these through the network to the desired location. To begin our discussion of PSPDNs, we'll look at the network access techniques and then discuss value-added services and pricing.

3.5.1 PSPDN Access

Network users can access the PSPDN "cloud" (see Figure 3-18) in several different ways. For high-speed applications, a synchronous leased line is provided between the customer's premises and the local PSPDN node. Typical transmission rates are 9.6, 14.4, 19.2, and 56 Kbps. Since most of the North American PSPDNs have access nodes in all major cities, the leased line becomes a local rather than a long-distance facility. Either the end user or the PSPDN can contract with the LEC for the leased line. The terminal equipment (synchronous modems or CSUs) required by the type of facility (analog or digital) must also be obtained.

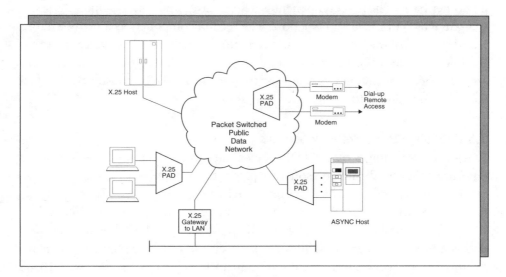

Figure 3-18. Packet Switched Public Data Network access options

Dial-up access is also available and can be provided in two different ways. The first method assumes that the user wishes to transmit asynchronous data, typically ASCII characters. The PSPDN publishes a list of access telephone numbers, along with the port speeds (1.2, 2.4 Kbps, etc.) associated with those ports. The user dials into the port with an asynchronous modem and then connects into another device, known as a PAD (Packet Assembler and Disassembler). The PAD functions similarly to a statistical multiplexer, taking the asynchronous characters and placing them into the appropriate length (e.g. 128 octet) packets. At the receiving end, the PAD performs the opposite function, decomposing the packet and generating characters.

The second alternative is dial-up access using the X.32 protocol, which provides synchronous X.25 service over dial-up lines. This alternative is often used when the traffic volumes don't warrant a dedicated connection, but the error control capabilities of the X.25 protocol are still required or desired.

3.5.2   PSPDN Rate Structures

PSPDNs have different rate structures for dial-up and leased access ports. Dial-up access charges are based upon connect time and are typically in the $5.00–10.00 per hour range. Leased line connections into a PSPDN are typically charged on a two-tier basis. The first component is a link charge and is based upon the speed (9.6–56 Kbps) of the leased line port. The second component is a traffic charge, based on the volume of data transmitted into the network. The typical metric is the kilocharacter (1000 characters) or kilopacket (1000 of the 128 octet packets). As pricing techniques vary among the various PSPDNs, consult the vendors listed in Appendix E for exact price quotations.

3.5.3   Value-Added Network Services

One of the advantages of a PSPDN is its ability to connect host computers that have dissimilar hardware and software platforms. A number of value-added network services, some of which are described below, are often incorporated into the PSPDN offering [3-29]. Speed and format conversion are fundamental, as PCs or Macintoshes transmitting ASCII characters at 14.4 Kbps may need to access a much faster IBM mainframe that uses the EBCDIC character formats. Protocol conversion is a frequent requirement for PSPDNs to offer, with IBM's 3270 and 5250 protocols among the most popular for access to IBM 30xx, 43xx,

93xx, AS/400 or S/3x processors. Electronic mail, a feature that allows users across the country to communicate with each other on a store-and-forward basis, is especially useful for those who travel and are difficult to reach. The public databases are also good features; they have capabilities for home shopping, airline reservations, and stock market quotations, and they provide access to research databases such as encyclopedias and magazine-article abstracts.

3.6 Integrated Services Digital Networks (ISDNs)

Integrated Services Digital Network standards were completed in the early 1980s. However, few user applications proved to be a good match for this technology. As a result of this lackluster beginning, many other meanings were coined for the letters "ISDN", including "I Still Don't Know", "Ideas Subscribers Don't Need", and "I See Dollars Now".

In the mid-1990s, ISDN service became sufficiently prevalent to become viable, and as references [3-30] to [3-31] attest, is currently a very popular transmission technology for LAN internetworking applications. One of the significant reasons for ISDN's rebirth has been Bellcore's work in establishing national consensus between carriers, switch developers, and terminal manufacturers for standards for ISDN that allow seamless connectivity between LECs and IXCs. These standards are known as National ISDN, and are described in references [3-32] and [3-33]. Prior to Bellcore's work, ISDN standards, although published from the ITU-T, were often implemented in proprietary ways. The National ISDN documents standardized vendor implementations, assuring compatibility in areas such as terminal and switching hardware, network connectivity, and operations, administration and maintenance (OA&M) functions.

As its name implies, the ISDN is an all-digital transmission facility that is designed to gradually replace the analog PSTN on a worldwide basis. ISDN service to residences and small businesses is known as the basic rate, offering a data throughput of 144 Kbps. The transmission pipeline is divided into two B (Bearer) channels offering 64 Kbps throughput each, plus one D channel operating at 16 Mbps. The B channels are for user information, carrying voice, data, or image communication. The D channel is used for signaling on behalf of the B channel, plus packet switched data transmission (Figure 3-19).

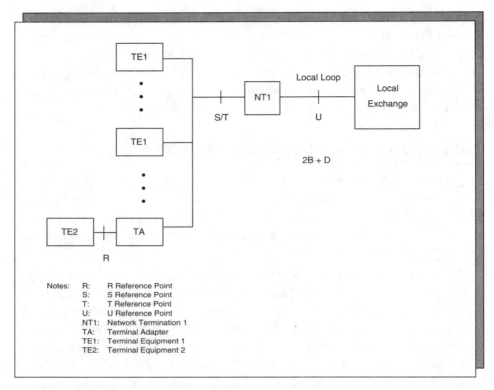

Figure 3-19. ISDN Basic Rate Interface (BRI)

The Primary Rate has a data throughput of 1.536 Mbps (Figure 3-20). It has the same structure as the DS1 frame, providing 24 of the 64 Kbps channels. In most configurations, 23 of the channels are B channels, with the last channel designated a D (signaling) channel. Primary rate interfaces are designed for businesses requiring higher bandwidth voice and data facilities.

The various devices that comprise an ISDN system have different functions, such as switching systems, end-user terminals, etc. Interfaces between these different devices are called reference points (review Figures 3-19 and 3-20). The Local Exchange, provided by the LEC or IXC, contains an ISDN switching system. In the United States, the U reference point is designated as the demarcation point (or boundary) between the local exchange and the customer premises. (Other countries may use the ITU-T's designated boundaries, the S or T reference points).

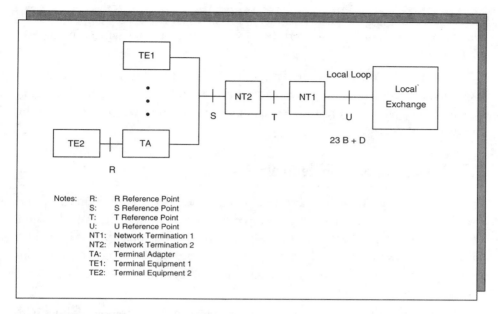

Figure 3-20. ISDN Primary Rate Interface (PRI)

Two types of network terminations are defined: type 1 (NT1) and type 2 (NT2). The NT1 physically connects the customer premises equipment to the digital transmission line. It would provide timing, multiplexing of the B and D channels, power conversion, etc. In the case of the PRI, the NT1 is a CSU/DSU-like device. For the BRI, the device is just typically called the NT1. NT2 devices provide customer premises switching, multiplexing or other forms of concentration, and are therefore used with the BRI. If a device performs both NT1 and NT2 functions, it may be referred to as an NT12.

The T reference point, which is between the NT1 and the NT2, supports point-to-point transmission. The S reference point is between the terminal equipment and the network termination (NT1 or NT2), and supports point-to-multipoint transmission. When an NT2 is not present in the system, this interface is called the S/T reference point.

Two types of terminal equipment (TE) have been defined: type 1 (TE1), and type 2 (TE2). A TE1 supports the ISDN protocols, while a TE2 supports other protocols, such as an analog telephone or an EIA-232-E compatible terminal.

When TE2 devices are used, a terminal adapter (TA), which is typically a stand-alone device, is required to convert the TE2's native protocol (such as analog telephone) to ISDN.

A wealth of information exists on this mature technology. Ameritech's Sketchpad document [3-34] illustrates many ISDN applications, while Gary Kessler's text on the subject [3-35] is an excellent resource for those needing the technical details.

3.7 The Future of WAN Technologies

Data-communication facilities can be a major expense of the total internetwork. Frequently, multi-year leases are required when the facility is installed, so the design decision has long-term implications. In view of the long term, it is vital for the internetwork manager to be aware of future trends in the telecommunications industry. Let's take a brief look into the broadband networks that are shaping the future of internetworking.

The first telecommunications trend is the replacement of analog facilities with digital facilities. The increased reliability of DDS, FT1, and T1/T3 circuits makes them an obvious choice, with all other factors (such as cost and existing equipment) being equal. A second, related trend is the increasing speed of transmission. We have seen LANs, such as the token ring, increase from 4 to 16 Mbps, and Ethernet migrate from 10 to 100 Mbps. When the speeds of the LAN backbones increase, the internetwork transmission facilities must increase in speed as well. We will look at these growth trends in more detail in Chapters 5 and 6.

To support the migration from analog to digital circuits, and the requirement for higher-speed transmission,new technologies have been developed in the last few years, which are now hitting their stride. First of these is SONET, the Synchronous Optical Network. Originally proposed by Bell Communications Research (Bellcore), SONET has also been adopted by the ANSI and the ITU-T. The basic signal is known as Synchronous Transport Signal Level One (STS-1), which operates at 51.84 Mbps. Higher transmission rates are obtained by interleaving the lower rates, which is similar to the North American T-carrier network hierarchy. SONET signals are transmitted via single mode fiber optic cables and have been tested by the various IXCs. Because of the high transmission speeds, SONET users will undoubtedly be internetworks with extremely high throughput requirements. Managers having a requirement in the DS3 (44.736 Mbps) range should investigate the possibilities of the SONET alternative.

Three other transmission systems have their roots in ISDN technology: frame relay, Switched Multimegabit Data Service, and Asynchronous Transfer Mode, or ATM.

Frame relay is a Data Link Layer protocol that is built upon the existing ITU-T X.25 and ISDN standards. Frame relay gets its name because it defines a method for efficiently relaying frames of information across a packet-switched network. Efficiencies are realized by reducing the overhead in each packet and making error calculations at source and destination, instead of at each individual switching node.

Switched Multimegabit Data Service (SMDS) was developed by Bell Communications Research, Inc. (Bellcore), the research and development organization that serves many of the Bell Operating Companies. SMDS is a connectionless subset of a metropolitan area networking (MAN) technology, the Distributed Queue Dual Bus (DQDB), defined by the IEEE 802.6 standard. Features of SMDS include any-to-any connectivity, group addressing and multicasting, and addressing defined by ITU-T Recommendation E.164, which is similar to telephone numbers. The analogies to analog telephone service have prompted some analysts to call SMDS "dialtone for data." Enhanced features include call blocking, call validation and call screening, which provide virtual private network services.

ATM is unique among the three broadband technologies, as a connection-oriented service for both LAN and WAN applications. The common denominator between all ATM applications is a foundation in cell switching, based upon 53-octet cells. A number of interfaces, operating between 25 and 622 Mbps have been defined, with the 100 Mbps interface for LANs, and the 45 and 155 Mbps for WANs, currently most popular. ATM products and services are currently under development by almost all of the major internetworking vendors, plus both the LECs and IXCs.

References [3-36] and [3-37] provide excellent surveys of these various broadband alternatives. Chapter 5 will discuss frame relay, SMDS, and ATM in greater detail.

3.8 Optimizing Transmission Facilities

A growing trend in the telecommunications arena is the use of software tools to simulate network performance and to calculate the optimum costs. In this section, we will look at two products that fulfill those requirements: the BONeS family of network simulation products, from Systems and Networks (Foster City, California); and the Distributed Network Design System, from Connections Telecommunications, Inc. (Brockton, Massachusetts).

3.8.1 Systems & Networks' BONeS

Performance analysis of today's computer networks is not a trivial task. The unpredictability of the performance of computer networks is caused by the decentralization trends in the information technology. As the mainframe environments migrate towards client-server configurations, the issues of capacity planning for LANs, WANs, routers, servers, and other network components become increasingly critical in the survival of networks. The constant addition of new client-server applications to networks raises a lot of tough questions such as the end-to-end performance of applications, the best methods of application distribution, and the thresholds on the scalability of the network components.

Unlike in centralized computing environments, network applications and components are supplied by a multitude of vendors in the client-server environments. As a result, no single vendor can predict the end-to-end performance of applications. These multi-vendor environments have also led to the introduction of new technologies by various vendors every day. Today's network designers have to choose the appropriate technologies for their environments based on very little (if any) personal experience with those technologies.

Traditional tools for planning and designing networks are too limiting and unreliable. Pencil-and-paper solutions cannot take into account the complex interaction of variables. Past experience does not apply to using new technologies. And physical lab tests are often too expensive and are not scalable.

A solution for these design challenges is found in modeling and simulation software. Using network simulation tools like BONeS, network planners and designers can solve their capacity planning problems for any type of network segment (LANs, WANs) and component (routers, servers, etc.). They can predict the end-to-end performance of applications, plan and justify capital investments before purchasing any equipment, and adapt the best technologies and architectures (Figure 3-21).

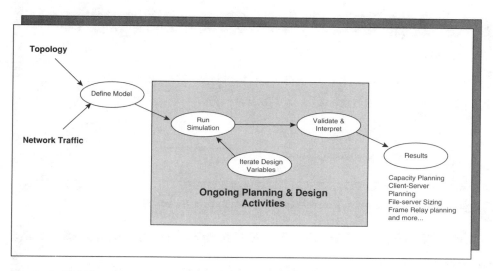

Figure 3-21. The BONeS process *(Courtesy of Systems & Networks)*

The simulation process begins by creating a virtual simulation model of the network (Figure 3-22). As this figure shows, the network architecture is one of the key elements of each simulation model. Every network component in the actual network is represented by an icon. Also, device characteristics have to be supplied, such as the amount of memory in the routers, the routing protocols installed on each port, and the traffic levels in different parts of the network. After this virtual model is created, the users perform a series of studies. Each simulation study reports the performance characteristics of the network for given sets of design parameters and network architectures. For example, a study comparing the mean packet delay with the number of users per floor is shown in Figure 3-23.

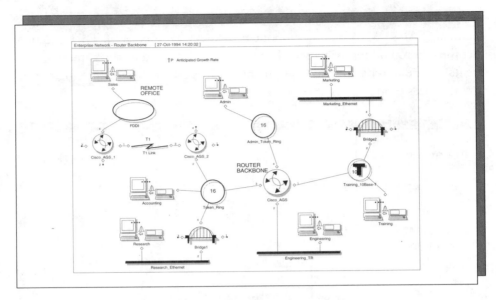

Figure 3-22. BONeS network model *(Courtesy of Systems & Networks)*

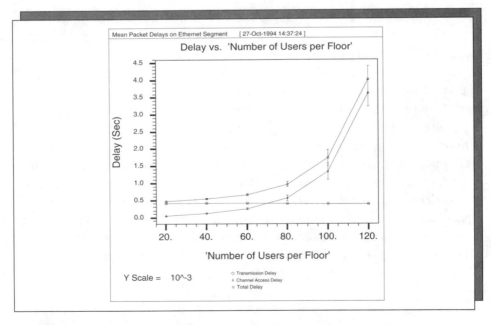

Figure 3-23. BONeS sample plot *(Courtesy of Systems & Networks)*

At the end of this process, users can:

⊗ Address key business concerns such as finding out the end-to-end performance of critical applications

⊗ Determine the impact of adding new applications/users to the network

⊗ Conduct accurate planning and scalability analysis based on a quantitative approach

⊗ Perform rapid "what-if" analysis of various alternatives before committing any money to purchasing equipment

⊗ Optimize cost/performance trade-offs for any network design

⊗ Perform baseline budget justification for capital equipment

The BONeS family of network simulation tools consists of three components (Figure 3-24):

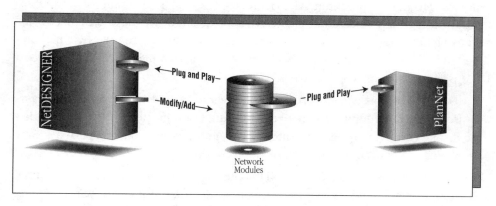

Figure 3-24. Key components of BONeS *(Courtesy of Systems & Networks)*

⊗ PlanNet is a graphical simulation engine which allows the user to specify network characteristics (topology, device parameters, network traffic, etc.) with Network Modules, to run simulations, and to analyze network performance.

⊗ Network Modules is an extensive library of simulation models of network hardware, software applications, and protocols. The modules include information on LAN segments, WAN segments, interconnect devices such as routers, and traffic models.

⊗ NetDESIGNER is a development environment for creating new Network Modules from scratch or by extending the capabilities of the existing Network Modules.

For network designers, this tool is a valuable resource for predicting network performance before investing in components.

3.8.2 Connections Telecommunications DNDS

If you have an existing WAN or LAN topology planned, defined, or otherwise underway, there are a number of transmission facility options available to the internetwork manager. However, keeping track of the changes in the rate and tariff structures of the various LEC and IXC carriers can be a monumental task.

The Distributed Network Design System (DNDS), from Connections Telecommunications, Inc. of Brockton, Massachusetts, is a PC-based design software package for integrated voice/data, packet switched, and other mesh-type networks. By using DNDS, you can easily and accurately evaluate alternative switch equipment, traffic routes, and transmission services, to determine the best possible cost and performance for your network.

DNDS operates with Microsoft Windows to provide an effective and easy-to-use interface with pull-down menus and full-color graphics. Network models are displayed on a map of the United States, and any portion of a network may be viewed in detail by zooming in or out as desired.

When designing a network, DNDS takes into account user-defined parameters for hardware, service classes, carriers, node details, traffic performance requirements, and topological constraints. You exert the degree of control necessary, either by using the tightly-defined design parameters or by allowing the software free rein in designing the network.

Among the various types of design tools are those that are used to create a network topology, typically built with a range of leased line services, or, with increasing frequency, with virtual service such as frame relay.

DNDS accomplishes the following:

- Creates the topology that interconnects all of the sites together.

- Determines how many circuits are needed between each site.

- Determines the bandwidth of network circuits.

- Selects the best type of switching hardware for each site.

- Based on a modified RIP routing protocol, it creates routing tables at each switch.

- Calculates the end-to-end delay of each traffic path.

- Calculates the network cost of hardware and circuits.

These tasks are accomplished in such a way as to meet certain design criteria entered by the user. The criteria include:

- A not-to-exceed end-to-end path delay

- Maximum allowable hops through the network

- Minimum number of alternate, or redundant, connections at each switch

- Protocol(s) to be used

- A selection of hardware types from a library of routers and switches

- Available leased line or virtual service options

- Available bandwidth options

- Average frame size

The user enters a list of sites according to the NPA/Nxx (or telephone area and exchange codes), which triggers a database search for V&H (vertical and horizontal) coordinates and circuit billing information. Afterwards, the user builds a traffic array from each site to each other site in the network. After selecting a subset of router types from the device library, the user enters the design criteria and a design ensues.

The design includes a topological map, and all of the design details described above. The user is presented with a series of reports which provide the design analysis.

In the following example, the user has defined a network with 30 site throughout the South, with seven sites selected as router sites for the backbone circuits (Figure 3-25). The user entered traffic in a traffic array, listing hourly traffic from each location to every other location (Figure 3-26). These traffic paths represent the applications that must be supported by the design.

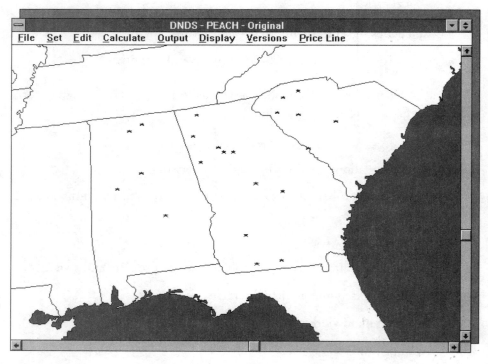

Figure 3-25. DNDS topological map *(Courtesy of Connections Telecommunications, Inc.)*

	Columbia	Conyers	Dalton	Decatur	Dublin	Gree
Albany	0.000	99.000	0.000	0.000	203.000	115
Anderson	0.000	72.000	0.000	0.000	0.000	90.
Atlanta	0.000	62.000	0.000	0.000	0.000	0.
Augusta	0.000	71.000	0.000	0.000	0.000	0.
Birmingham	0.000	251.000	0.000	225.000	0.000	0.
Carrollton	0.000	85.000	0.000	0.000	0.000	0.
Columbia		63.000	0.000	0.000	0.000	90.
Conyers	251.000		30319.000	177.000	36141.000	153
Dalton	0.000	43.000		0.000	0.000	0.
Decatur	0.000	73.000	0.000		0.000	0.
Dublin	0.000	116.000	0.000	0.000		0.
Greenville	36225.000	156.000	0.000	0.000	0.000	
Huntsville	0.000	319.000	0.000	0.000	0.000	0.
Macon	0.000	648.000	0.000	0.000	0.000	0.
Montgomery	0.000	1160.000	0.000	24015.000	0.000	0.
Rome	0.000	161.000	0.000	0.000	0.000	0.
Smyrna	0.000	364.000	330.000	0.000	0.000	0.
Spartenburg	0.000	184.000	0.000	0.000	0.000	90.
Thomasville	0.000	83.000	0.000	0.000	0.000	0.

Figure 3-26. DNDS traffic array *(Courtesy of Connections Telecommunications, Inc.)*

To meet the needs of the design, the user has built a new router type in the database called "IPROUTER" (Figure 3-27). This device will be selected by the software as the primary router at the seven backbone sites. Then the user is ready to enter design constraints. This design will use digital circuits, assign line speeds of 9.6 Kbps up to 1.544 Mbps, keep the circuits below 75% utilization, restrict the traffic to four or fewer hops across the network, provide at least three connections at each backbone router, meet a path delay of 0.250 seconds, use 1000-octet, frames and use the TCP/IP protocols (Figure 3-28).

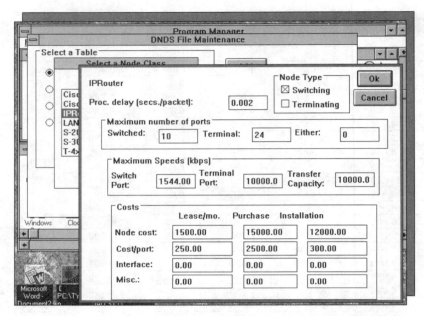

Figure 3-27. DNDS router parameters *(Courtesy of Connections Telecommunications, Inc.)*

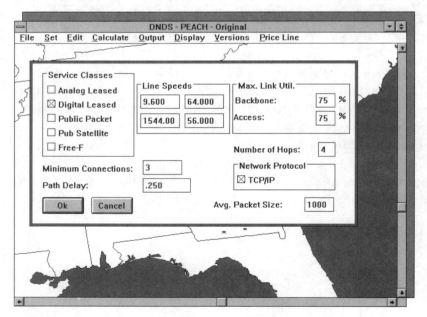

Figure 3-28. DNDS line parameters *(Courtesy of Connections Telecommunications, Inc.)*

These criteria allow the software to create a balanced network with guaranteed performance levels. The user then directs the software to select the minimum cost router or bridge type from the router and bridge library. Hardware constraints are set as variable to give the software the option of increasing ports and capacity at overloaded sites (Figure 3-29). By indicating that it is not an existing network, the user tells DNDS to design a completely new topology to meet the constraints. If "Yes" is chosen, the user can lock pre-existing links or services in place and add new sites or do a variety of exercises including failure analysis.

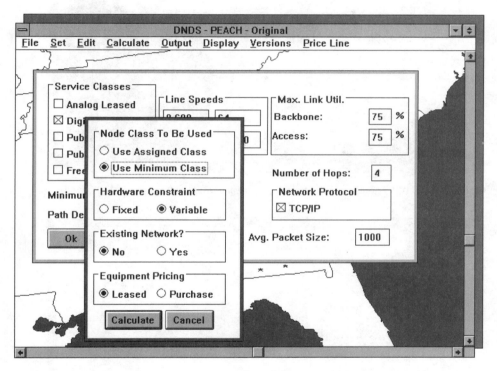

Figure 3-29. DNDS topology parameters *(Courtesy of Connections Telecommunications, Inc.)*

The resultant design provides a complete map as well as a series of reports including total Design, Link Pricing, Bandwidth, and much more (Figures 3-30, 3-31, and 3-32).

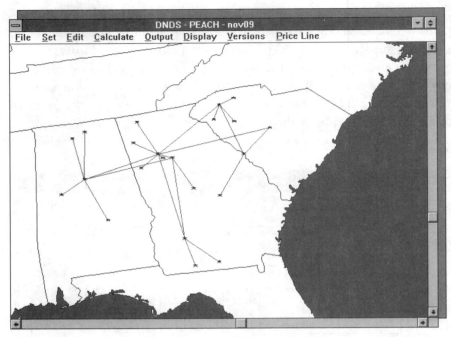

Figure 3-30. DNDS graphical output *(Courtesy of Connections Telecommunications, Inc.)*

```
---------------------------------------------------------------------
Network:  PEACH            Version:  1          Version Name: nov09
Created: 11/ 9/1994    9: 9.12         Modified: 11/ 9/1994   9:24.17
---------------------------------------------------------------------

                    Summary Link Cost Report: X- Albany

LINK:   X- Conyers / X- Albany LINK 13(s)
NPA-NXX: 404-482 / 912-432

Service Class: Digital   BST  LEC Access

  ACCESS                          Kbps  Mlg/Usage  Recurring  Nonrecurring

X- Conyers ACCESS COST (BSTGAFAT)  1544.0    6.00    520.00    1889.94
X- Albany ACCESS COST (BSTGAFAT):  1544.0    0.00    274.00    1733.94
TRANSPORT COSTS (ATTOOFTT):        1544.0  140.00   3873.00     680.00

TOTAL LINK COST                            146.00   4667.00    4303.88
.....................................................................
LINK:   X- Augusta / X- Greenvi LINK 3(s)
NPA-NXX: 404-650 / 803-234

Service Class: Digital   BST  LEC Access

  ACCESS                          Kbps  Mlg/Usage  Recurring  Nonrecurring

X- Augusta ACCESS COST (BSTGAFAT)  1544.0   10.00    624.00    1889.94
X- Greenvi ACCESS COST (BSTGAFAT): 1544.0    6.00    520.00    1889.94
TRANSPORT COSTS (ATTOOFTT):        1544.0   98.00   3707.10     680.00

TOTAL LINK COST                            114.00   4851.10    4459.88
.....................................................................
```

Figure 3-31. DNDS link cost report *(Courtesy of Connections Telecommunications, Inc.)*

```
----------------------------------------------------------------
Network:   PEACH                Version:  1        Version Name:
Created: 11/ 9/1994    9: 9.12                     Modified: 11/ 9/1994    9:24.17
----------------------------------------------------------------


                              Bandwidth Report
                              ----------------


Service Class: Digital Leased                  Link Speed: 56.0 Kbps

                         Miles  Link  Delays        Flow Kbps        Utilization
Node 1         Node 2    WC-WC  1->2    2->1      1->2     2->1       1->2  2->1
============   ========  =====  =====  =======   =======  =======    ====  ====

X- Conyers     X- Birmingham  152  0.159  0.165     2.362    4.491      0.04  0.09
X- Columbia    X- Smyrna      200  0.152  0.153     0.140    0.558      0.00  0.01
X- Smyrna      X- Albany      159  0.152  0.154     0.200    0.740      0.00  0.01


Service Class: Digital Leased                  Link Speed: 1544.0 Kbps

                         Miles  Link  Delays        Flow Kbps        Utilization
Node 1         Node 2    WC-WC  1->2    2->1      1->2     2->1       1->2  2->1
============   ========  =====  =====  =======   =======  =======    ====  ====

X- Augusta     X- Columbia     71  0.006  0.005    80.500    0.200      0.06  0.00
X- Augusta     X- Greenville   90  0.005  0.006     1.016  202.000      0.00  0.14
X- Conyers     X- Smyrna       26  0.008  0.006   418.542    3.393      0.29  0.00
X- Conyers     X- Albany      146  0.006  0.005   214.589    1.231      0.15  0.00
X- Greenville  X- Smyrna      141  0.005  0.006     2.064  123.509      0.00  0.08
X- Birmingham  X- Smyrna      131  0.000  0.006     0.000   66.867      0.00  0.05


    ************************ END OF REPORT ****************************
```

Figure 3-32. DNDS bandwidth report *(Courtesy of Connections Telecommunications, Inc.)*

The process uses a series of proprietary algorithms to create the topology as well as analytical modeling techniques to calculate end-to-end delay. DNDS includes a complete set of telephone company tariffs which are updated on a regular basis, freeing the network designer from keeping up with frequently-changing tariffs.

In summary, the challenges of network designs are simplified by using simulation or design software such as the two products described in this section. Reference [3-38] is an excellent book on network design techniques, and [3-39] provides a recent summary of available products.

Reference [3-38] is an excellent book on network design techniques, and [3-39] provides a recent summary of available products.

3.9 Remote Access to Internetworks

As the popularity and usage of LANs has increased, users have become more dependent on those systems. When users are traveling away from the central location, or working out of their home or a branch office, the need for remote access to a centralized LAN becomes a key design criteria. Remote workgroups need remote LAN access systems with flexible bandwidth. Telecommuters need dial-up systems that are easy to use. Client workstations need to call and connect to any of the other sites.

Ascend Communications, Inc. of Alameda, CA, focuses on remote access solutions supporting a number of digital transmission facilities, including DDS, SW56, T1, ISDN BRI, ISDN PRI, E1 and Frame Relay (Figure 3-33). Pipeline products connect branch offices and telecommuters to corporate LANs or the Internet. They provide 56 or 112 Kbps access to network resources, as if the users' computers were directly connected to the LAN.

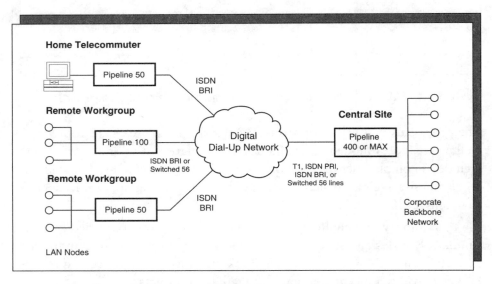

Figure 3-33. Dial-Up LAN access: remote site to central site *(Courtesy of Ascend Communications, Inc.)*

Ascend's Pipeline family of products is designed to support a number of remote access challenges. Members of the Pipeline family include the MAX series, the

400 series, and the 50 series. All members support both bridging and routing, with a significant array of security features.

The Ascend MAX is a system level, board and backplane unit that acts as a WAN hub at sites with large and growing connectivity and bandwidth requirements, such as at the corporate central site. It allows up to 95 simultaneous connections from telecommuters or remote sites over up to 4 T1 or ISDN PRI lines. One unique feature of the MAX is its use of "digital modems". Digital modems allow modem-based users to dial the MAX from analog lines at the user's site and yet terminate the call to the MAX over one of the channels in the ISDN PRI. This means that the MAX supports both analog and digital (ISDN or Switched 56) dial-in over a common set of T1 or ISDN PRI lines.

The Pipeline 400 series is a WAN hub for smaller central sites or remote sites with significant bandwidth and connectivity requirements. It supports one T1 or ISDN PRI access line, for up to 23 incoming analog or digital calls.

The Pipeline 50 series is a dial-up bridge and router for telecommuters, smaller remote offices, or locations with reduced connectivity requirements. It connects directly to an Ethernet on the LAN side, and to either one ISDN BRI or two Switched 56 lines on the WAN side. It incorporates inverse multiplexing, which means that under light or normal traffic conditions, the connection will consist of only one ISDN B channel or one Switched 56 call. However, if traffic increases significantly (for example, during a file transfer), the Pipeline 50 will automatically dial an additional connection using the other B channel or Switched 56 line, and combine the bandwidth together for 112 or 128 kbit/s (2 x 56 kbps or 2 x 64 kbps). When traffic subsides, the second call will be removed, reducing bandwidth and lowering usage costs.

Telecommuting is one key application for Ascend Pipeline systems. Through the Ascend MAX, the backbone LAN can be accessed by callers with home ISDN-based workstations. Remote offices, domestic and international, can connect to the central site LAN by using Ascend Pipelines. Traveling computer users with modems can dial into the central LAN thanks to digital modems within the MAX. In addition, a trend is to allow non-corporate users (such as customers) dial-up access to corporate databases. The Pipeline products support numerous security features to assure that such access is properly managed. Ascend also provides Frame Relay access for those users whose extended connection times justify a permanent virtual connection to the central site.

Internet access is another key application for Ascend Pipeline products. There are two primary ways this can be provided. First, a MAX at a central site can be connected to an Internet service provider's Point-of-Presence (POP) with a leased line or frame relay circuit. All callers to the central site MAX therefore have access to the Internet as well.

Second, users with Pipelines can dial to an Internet service provider's POP for direct digital Internet access. Such digital dial-up access is being offered by a growing number of Internet service providers. Since many of these providers are using Ascend MAXs as their central site WAN hubs, inverse multiplexing is often supported as well, allowing up to 128 kbps per call.

The past several years have seen dramatic moves forward in the remote access marketplace. Protocols have become standardized and more robust. Modems have increased in speed capability. ISDN and other digital services have become much more available. Remote LAN access equipment has come of age and continues to add functionality.

Future directions in remote LAN access include the availability and use of Frame Relay and ATM switched virtual circuits. Frame Relay and ATM switched virtual circuits will allow users to dial to a network service provider (such as AT&T, MCI, or Sprint) and establish one or more virtual circuits to the intended destination(s). This will keep usage costs down, because traffic will be transported within the carriers' backbone networks over packet-based Frame Relay or cell-based ATM links instead of over more expensive dedicated circuits.

To summarize, this chapter has covered a number of transmission facilities for LAN-to-WAN internetworking. Some of these, such as dial-up or analog leased lines, have been in service for years; LAN requirements have merely provided a new application for existing transmission technologies. Other WAN facilities, such as ISDN and frame relay (which employ digital transmission), are creating the all-digital enterprise network. Chapter 5 will investigate these broadband technologies in detail, and Chapter 6 will present case studies of LAN-to-WAN designs.

3.10 References

[3-1]   Bell Communication Research, Inc. *Telecommunications Transmission Engineering*, Volumes 1–3, 3rd ed., document number ST-TEC-000063, 1990.

[3-2]   Bell Telephone Laboratories, Inc. *Transmission Systems for Communications*. 5th ed. 1982.

[3-3]   Freeman, Roger L. *Telecommunication System Engineering—Analog and Digital Network Design*. New York: John Wiley & Sons, 1980.

[3-4]   AT&T. *Data Communications Using the Switched Telecommunications Network*. PUB 41005, May 1989.

[3-5]   AT&T. *Data Communications Using Voiceband Private Line Channels*. PUB 41004, October 1973.

[3-6]   AT&T. *Transmission Parameters Affecting Voiceband Data Transmission—Description of Parameters*. PUB 41008, July 1974.

[3-7]   AT&T. *Analog Voice—Total and Coordinated Services*. PUB 43202, May 1985, and addendum 1, August 1988.

[3-8]   Douglass, Jack L. *Applied Data Communications Handbook*. Motorola Information Systems Group, 1987.

[3-9]   Stallings, William. *Data and Computer Communications*. 4th ed. Macmillan, 1993.

[3-10]   McNamara, John E. *Technical Aspects of Data Communication*. 4th ed. Digital Press, 1993.

[3-11]   Douglass, Jack. "How to Find Phone-line Faults and What to Do About Them." *Data Communications* (September 1988): 179–197.

[3-12]   AT&T. *Digital Data System Channel Interface Specification*. TR 62310, August 1993.

[3-13]   Quiat, Barry. "V.FAST, ISDN or Switched 56." *Network Computing* (March 1, 1994): 70–87.

[3-14]   Langer, Mark. "A Straightforward Decision." *Network World* (October 3, 1994): 57–63.

[3-15]   AT&T. *Business Communications Services Guide*. Document 015-358-027, December 1994.

[3-16]   Quiat, Barry and Gary A. Bolles. "WAN Services —You'd Better Shop Around." *Network Computing* (January 1993): 68–76.

[3-17]   Bisson, Berry and Ed Loeswick. "WAN Services". *LAN Times* (September 5, 1994): 89–110.

[3-18]   AT&T. *Digital Multiplexes Requirements and Objectives*. PUB 43802, July 1982.

[3-19]   AT&T. *Access Specification for High Capacity (DS1/DS3) Dedicated Digital Services*. TR 62415, June 1989.

[3-20]   Flanagan, William A. *The Guide to T-1 Networking*. Telecom Books, 1990.

[3-21]   Bellamy, John C. *Digital Telephony*, 2nd ed. New York: John Wiley & Sons, 1991.

[3-22]   AT&T. *Digital Channel Bank Requirements and Objectives*. PUB 43801, November 1982.

[3-23]   AT&T. *Requirements for Interfacing Digital Terminal Equipment to Services Employing the Extended Superframe Format*. TR 54016, September 1989.

[3-24]   Rux , Peter T. and Clifford V. Ciles. "ESF Rx for Healthy T1 Nets." *Data Communications* (May 1990): 81–94.

[3-25]   Heckart, Christine and Christopher Finn. "Leased-line Subtleties Reign Supreme." *Network World* (May 16, 1994): 43–50.

[3-26]   Integrated Network Corp. "The Inside Guide to T1 and Fractional T1 Services." July 1994.

[3-27]   AT&T. *Accunet Spectrum of Digital Services*. TR 62421, December 1989.

[3-28]   Halsey, J. R, et. al. "Public Data Networks: Their Evolution, Interfaces and Status." *IBM System Journal* Vol. 18, no. 2 (1979): 223–243.

[3-29]   Schlar, Sharman K. *Inside X.25: A Manager's Guide*. New York: McGraw-Hill, Inc., 1990.

[3-30]   Dziatkiewicz, Mark. "ISDN's Making the Grade." *America's Network* (October 1, 1994): 40–46.

[3-31]   Khouri-Haddad, Najib. "ISDN and Data Networking" *3TECH, the 3Com Technical Journal* (January 1995): 11–18.

[3-32]   Bell Communications Research, Inc. *National ISDN-1*. Document SR-NWT-001937, February 1993.

[3-33]   Bell Communications Research, Inc. *National ISDN-2*. Document SR-NWT-002120, June 1993.

[3-34]   Ameritech Corp. *ISDN Sketchpad*. Document CS-8, January 1994.

[3-35]   Kessler, Gary C. *ISDN*, second edition. New York: McGraw-Hill, 1993.

[3-36]   Johnson, Johna Till. "Rebuilding the World's Public Networks." *Data Communications* (December 1992): 60–68.

[3-37]   Krivda, Cheryl D. "Calling All WAN Customers." *STACKS* (August 1994): 41–45.

[3-38]   Ellis, Robert L. *Designing Data Networks*. New York: Prentice-Hall, 1986.

[3-39]   Cope, Patricia. "Building a Better Network." *Network World* (January 4, 1993): 34–40.

[3-40]   Ascend Communications, Inc. *The Nuts and Bolts of Bandwidth on Demand and Inverse Multiplexing*, 1994.

4 X.25 Protocols

Research into the technologies currently known as packet switching began in the 1960s and was dictated by U.S. military requirements. Behind the research conducted in the United States at that time was a basic understanding that, in a wartime environment, it is essential to provide secure communications links between various command posts. The military always considered the possibility that the enemy could tap into a secure communications link and capture sensitive information. To reduce this risk, researchers proposed that a sensitive message could be divided into a number of small elements, called packets, and each of these elements could then be transmitted using a different communication path. Should the enemy tap any single channel, they would receive only a portion of the overall message. Major contributions to fundamental packet switching technology were also made in Europe thanks to the work of Englishmen Donald Davies and Derek Barber at the National Physical Laboratory at Teddington. From their packet-switching research came the development of packet switched public data networks (PSPDNs), which made the researched technology available for commercial use. (Throughout this chapter, we will use the term PSPDN to indicate that the public data network in question provides packet switching services. In some literature, this term is shortened to public data network, or PDN.)

Before long, it became clear that an interface standard was required to provide a common access method to these PSPDNs. The result was the ITU-T X.25 standard. Reference [4-1] provides some interesting historical and architectural information about these early projects. To begin our study of the X.25 protocols, we will first investigate the development of commercial PSPDNs.

4.1 Packet Switched Public Data Networks Development

In 1969, the Advanced Research Projects Agency Network (ARPANET)—sponsored by the U.S. Defense Department—became operational with four nodes and led to three significant internetworking developments [4-2].

First, a worldwide family of packet switched public data networks (PSPDNs) was made operational. Early PSPDNs included Telenet (U.S.A.), established in 1975; Datapac (Canada) and Tymnet (U.S.A.), created in 1977; and Transpac (France) and Accunet (U.S.A.), placed into operation in 1978. (Appendix E lists addresses and phone numbers for many North American carriers that offer PSPDN service using the X.25 interface.)

Second, the ITU-T, driven by the need to create an interface for these PSPDNs, adopted in 1976 the X.25 recommendation entitled "Interface Between Data Terminal Equipment (DTE) and Data Circuit-Terminating Equipment (DCE) For Terminals Operating In The Packet Mode and Connected To Public Data Networks By Dedicated Circuit" [4-3]. X.25 is a suite of protocols that provide an interface between a synchronous packet-mode host (or other device) and a PSPDN, over a dedicated (or leased-line) circuit.

Third, the interconnection between Telenet (U.S.A.) and Datapac (Canada), established in 1978, pointed to the need for PSPDN internetworking. Thus the X.25 recommendation "Packet-Switched Signalling System Between Public Networks Providing Data Transmission Services" was also drafted in 1978 [4-4].

ITU-T conventions in subsequent years have helped these protocols mature to the point where today the X.25 technology is well-understood and implemented by a large number of PC, minicomputer, mainframe, LAN, and WAN vendors. In addition, favorable results with X.25 have sparked interest among many vendors to migrate their products, and their customers for those products, to broadband WAN connections, such as frame relay or ATM [4-5].

Before we study the protocols and examples of LAN implementations, let's look at the architecture of a PSPDN.

4.2 PSPDN Architecture

First, let's define what the X.25 protocols do—and do not—provide. X.25 defines the interface to a PSPDN, or more specifically, it defines the Data Terminal Equipment/Data Circuit Terminating Equipment (DTE/DCE) interface between a synchronous (as opposed to an asynchronous) packet-mode host and the PSPDN. The X.25 protocol suite does not, however, define the internal architecture of the PSPDN, nor does it define the PSPDN's operation. That function is the responsibility of the PSPDN designers, who may, in fact, consider the internal PSPDN architecture to be proprietary.

This DTE/DCE interface and the internal structure of the PSPDN are shown in Figure 4-1. Three different types of DTEs are displayed here. The first is a host computer with an X.25 interface. The second is a PAD (Packet Assembler/Disassembler). The PAD accepts asynchronous characters input from low-speed terminals, and assembles these characters into packets to be transmitted to the network. Conversely, the PAD also disassembles packets from the network so the data can be delivered as characters to terminals. The third type of DTE, and perhaps the one of greatest interest for LAN applications, is the gateway between a PSPDN and the LAN. We will look at some applications of these gateways in Section 4.9.

Access between the DTE and DCE is typically maintained by means of a low-speed, synchronous leased line operating between 9.6 and 56 Kbps. Either analog or digital lines can be used, including ISDN, depending upon transmission requirements and local availability. In addition, a pair of synchronous modems, or Channel Service Units/Data Service Units (CSU/DSUs), or an ISDN Terminal Adapter (TA) is required to complete the connection. Most PSPDNs can be locally accessed in all major cities, making the leased lines a local communication facility rather than a long-distance connection.

A PSPDN can implement one of two methods for internal communications. One method is the datagram, where every packet is given a complete source and destination address, and "dropped" into the network (much like you would mail a letter by dropping it into the mailbox). With a datagram, every packet finds its own route through the network so that it ends up at the destination host, although delivery of that packet is not guaranteed. (One example of a network that provides datagram service is Ethernet. On an Ethernet LAN, collisions may occur that prevent a packet (actually a frame) from being delivered.) Datagram service was eliminated from the X.25 standard in 1980 and replaced with an optional facility known as Fast Select, although a number of other network architectures (such as Ethernet) continue to use the datagram technique very effectively.

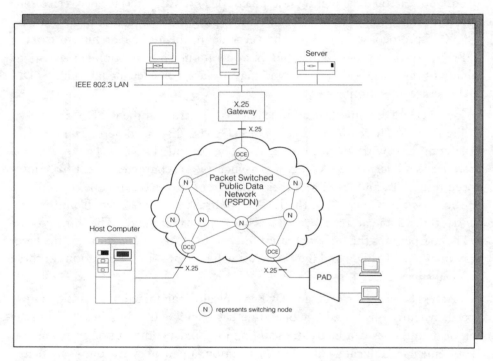

Figure 4-1. PSPDN architecture

The second method of internal communications is the virtual circuit, shown in Figure 4-2. The circuit is a DTE-to-DTE (end-to-end) connection, established by Call Request and Call Accept packets that function very similarly to the way in which a telephone call is placed. The circuit connection is established prior to the transfer of any data, and the connection provides a fixed route through the PSPDN for all packets associated with that virtual circuit. All packets experience a delay through the various networks' nodes, but they arrive in sequence, without duplication. The "virtual" part of the virtual circuit definition comes from the fact that the connection appears to be a circuit. In reality, it is a series of routing table entries within the various switching nodes. These table entries change on a dynamic basis as virtual calls are established or disconnected. We'll discuss the virtual call establishment process in Section 4.7.

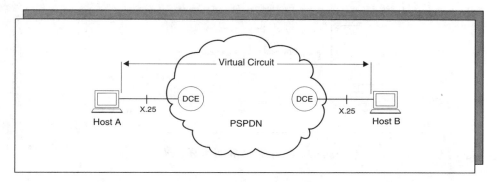

Figure 4-2. Virtual circuit connection *(Courtesy of Hewlett-Packard Company)*

To gain a better perspective on the PSPDN architecture, let's consider the three layers of protocols that make up the X.25 protocol suite. Recall from our discussion in Chapter 1 that a host (which is responsible for running application programs) interfaces with the communications subnetwork (or subnet), which in turn provides the WAN facilities and connection. The host implements all seven layers of the OSI model, but the subnet only implements the lower three. It is at these lower three layers that we find the X.25 protocol suite (see Figure 4-3)— the Physical Layer protocol transmits bits; the Data Link Layer protocol transmits frames; and the Network Layer protocol transmits packets. We'll look at the individual layers of X.25 in detail, beginning in Section 4.3.

In addition to the ITU-T standard, three references provide good background reading on X.25. References [4-6] through [4-8] explore the protocols in detail. Reference [4-9] discusses the DTE/DCE interface to PSPDNs. Reference [4-10] compares X.25 with OSI and TCP/IP-based networks. Reference [4-11] looks at the evolutionary advances in packet switching to include broadband and ATM technologies.

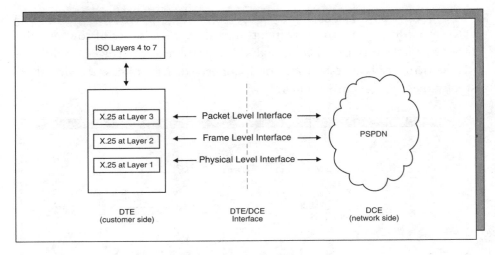

Figure 4-3. X.25 DTE/DCE protocols *(Courtesy of Hewlett-Packard Company)*

4.3 The X.25 Physical Layer

The X.25 Physical Layer offers several standards options, choices that are the result of the ITU-T's attempt to accommodate hardware options used on several different continents.

European networks use the X.21 interface, which is an electrically balanced interface similar to EIA-422. Interface X.21 is used in countries where the PSPDN can be accessed by digital (rather than analog) lines. The X.21 interface uses a DB-15 connector, supports a maximum DTE-DCE cable distance of 1,000 meters, and can operate in synchronous, half-, or full-duplex modes with transmission rates up to 10 Mbps.

The second standard is known as X.21 bis. ("Bis" is a French word meaning "alternate.") The X.21 bis standard specifies the use of V.24/V.28 interfaces, which are very similar to EIA-232-D. Most PSPDN applications in the United States do, in fact, use EIA-232-E (or the earlier EIA-232-D or RS-232-C) as the Physical Layer interface. (For further details on these interfaces, refer to Appendix E of the *LAN Troubleshooting Handbook, Second Edition,* a companion volume to this book.)

The third interface option, V.35, is used for transmissions with speeds of 48 Kbps in Europe, or 56 Kbps in the United States. The V.35 interface uses a rectangular 34-pin connector and is electrically balanced. V.35 is typically used with DSU/CSUs connected to 56 Kbps digital (or DDS) leased lines.

4.4   The X.25 Data Link Layer

The X.25 Link Access Procedure Balanced (LAPB) protocol is structured after the well-known ISO HDLC (High Level Data Link Control) format. LAPB was designed to be used in a point-to-point connection between the DTE (host) and the DCE (attaching network node). The transmission is serial, synchronous, and full-duplex. The "balanced" designation within LAPB indicates that the control of the link is balanced between the DTE and the DCE; either end can initiate a link-setup or link-disconnect command.

Flag characters (01111110) begin and end the frame. The frame header consists of Address and Control fields (one octet each), and the frame trailer contains a 14-bit Frame Check Sequence, specified as the CRC-CCITT (two octets). Within the frame Information field is the packet as prescribed by the X.25 Packet Layer Protocol. Note, in Figure 4-4, that one packet fits inside each frame.

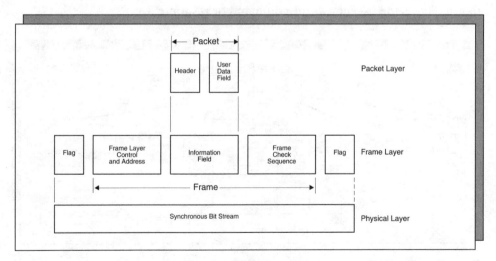

Figure 4-4. X.25 packet within a LAPB frame *(Courtesy of Hewlett-Packard Company)*

As shown in Figure 4-5, the Address field contains one of two possible addresses: A (03H) for the DTE, or B (01H) for the DCE. Command (C) frames contain the address of the opposite device; for example, if the DTE initiates the command, the Address field must contain a 01H (DCE). Response (R) frames contain the address of the responder; for instance, if the DCE issues a response, it would put a 01H in the Address field.

The Control field specifies which of three frame formats this frame contains. Information (I) frames are used for the sequenced transfer of data between DTE and DCE. The Least Significant Bit (LSB) of the Control field is set to zero (to indicate the I format). Two frame sequence counters—N(S) for sending and N(R) for receiving or acknowledgment—are also included within the Control field.

Supervisory (S) frames are used to supervise the exchange of I frames by acknowledging good frames and rejecting bad ones. The two LSBs of the S frame Control field are set to 01, and the remaining bits carry a code indicating the frame type and the acknowledgment number N(R).

Unnumbered (U) frames are used to establish and disconnect the DTE/DCE link. U frames are indicated when the two LSBs of the Control field are set to 11. The remaining bits are encoded to indicate the type of frame being sent (see the chart in Figure 4-5). Common to all three frame types is the Poll/Final bit (P/F) that indicates the urgency of the command or response.

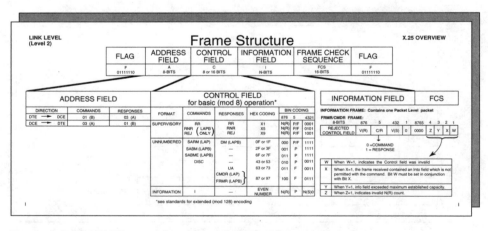

Figure 4-5. *X.25 LAPB protocol encoding (© 1994, Hill Associates, Inc.)*

The Information field of the LAPB I frames contains one X.25 packet. We'll look at the structure of this packet next.

4.5   The X.25 Network Layer

The Packet Layer Protocol (PLP) defines the format for the packet that is to be
sent into the PSPDN by the local DTE for delivery to the remote DTE. The protocol defines seventeen different packet types, which are designated by the third
octet (Packet Type field) of the packet itself. These seventeen packets can be divided
into six categories (see Figure 4-6).

Packet Type From DCE to DTE	From DTE to DCE	Service VC	PVC
Call set-up and clearing			
Incoming Call	Call request	X	
Call connected	Call accepted	X	
Clear indication	Clear request	X	
DCE clear confirmation	DTE clear confirmation	X	
Data and interrupt			
DCE data	DTE data	X	X
DCE interrupt	DTE interrupt	X	X
DCE interrupt confirmation	DTE interrupt confirmation	X	X
Flow control and reset			
DCE RR	DTE RR	X	X
DCE RNR	DTE RNR	X	X
	DTE REJ	X	X
Reset indication	Reset request	X	X
DCE reset confirmation	DTE reset confirmation	X	X
Restart			
Restart indication	Restart request	X	X
DCE restart confirmation	DTE restart confirmation	X	X
Diagnostic			
Diagnostic		X	X
Registration			
Registration Confirmation		X	X
	Registration Request	X	X

Figure 4-6. X.25 packet types (ITU-T Recommendation X.25)

Call Setup packets are used to establish the virtual circuits (end-to-end connections via the PSPDN) between DTEs. Data and Interrupt packets are used to transfer information. Expedited data, such as an urgent message from a higher layer protocol, uses the Interrupt packet format, and routine information is transferred in Data packets. The Flow Control and Reset packets provide control mechanisms for the virtual circuits. The Restart packet is used to re-initialize the DTE/DCE interface following the occurrence of an error condition. Diagnostic packets are generated by the network (DCE) in response to an erroneous packet received from a DTE, or if one of the PLP watchdog timers expires. Finally, Registration packets are used to request or obtain specific parameters of user facilities, such as a non-default packet size or window size. The service provided can either be a virtual circuit or a permanent virtual circuit (PVC). We'll look at these in detail in section 4.7.

The format of the first two octets of each packet type is identical (see Figure 4-7). The first four bits are known as the General Format Identifier (GFI) which determines data packet formats, acknowledgment parameters, and sequence counter sizes. The next twelve bits are the Logical Channel Identifier, which indicates which of the 4,096 possible logical channels is currently being used for this packet. This LCI includes the Logical Group Number (LGN), which is four bits, and the Logical Channel Number (LCN), which is 8 bits.

A detailed description of each packet type is available in references [4-6], [4-7], and [4-8], and interested readers are directed to those sources for more information. The Data packet, however, is of interest to internetwork designers, so we will spend some time investigating its characteristics.

The Data packet sets the LSB=0 of the third octet (Packet Type field) to distinguish it from other packets used for control purposes. (These control packets always have LSB=1.) The user data begins in octet four, which may be negotiated by the communicating parties to quantities from 64 to 4,096 octets, incremented in powers of two. The default is 128 octets, which is also the packet size supported by most PSPDNs in the United States. The user data is actually higher-layer information that has been downloaded from the host or LAN-attached workstation.

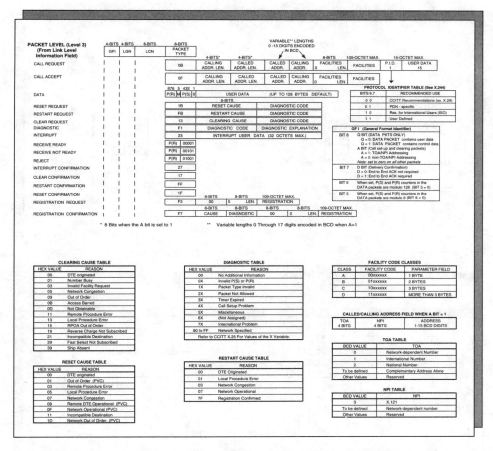

Figure 4-7. X.25 packet layer protocol encoding (© 1994, Hill Associates, Inc.)

Consider the Banyan VINES internetwork shown in Figure 4-8. The Banyan servers have a variety of LAN and WAN connectivity options (discussed in Section 9.2), including an X.25 interface for server-to-server communication at speeds of up to 64 Kbps. Each side of the internet is an IEEE 802.X LAN connected over an X.25 PSPDN to form a LAN-WAN-LAN connection. The VINES frame structure is shown in Figure 4-9. (A complete description of the frame is available in reference [4-12], or Chapter 6 of the *LAN Protocol Handbook*. We'll summarize it here.)

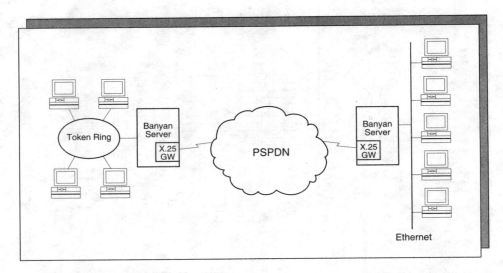

Figure 4-8. Banyan VINES X.25 interface

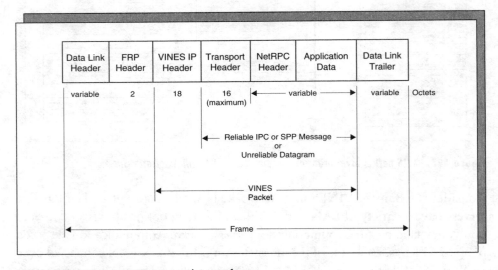

Figure 4-9. Banyan VINES Data Link Layer frame

The frame header and trailer are specific to the LAN hardware used (e.g. IEEE 802.3, 802.5, and ARCNET), and Banyan supports a variety of frame header and trailer options. The VINES Fragmentation Protocol (VFRP) header is next, and is used to segment or reassemble the VINES packets into multiple frames. The VINES Internet Protocol (VIP) and Transport Layer headers precede the NetRPC header, which provides Session and Presentation Layer services. The Application data (e.g. electronic mail and file transfer) completes the frame. Note that the VINES packet is defined beginning with the VINES IP header and ending with the Application data.

When a WAN facility is used to internetwork two Banyan servers, the VINES packet (shown in Figure 4-9) must be encapsulated within the X.25 LAPB frame (Figure 4-10). Also added will be the X.25 Packet Layer Protocol Header. When converted into an X.25 packet, a fragmentation is required to match the maximum packet size of the PSPDN (i.e. 128 octets). This function is performed by the VINES X.25 driver software, not VFRP. See reference [4-13] for more information on the VINES X.25 options.

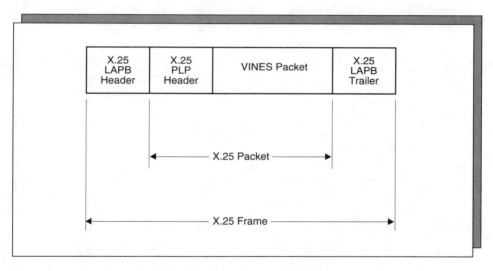

Figure 4-10. Banyan VINES protocol encapsulation

4.6 X.25 Related Protocols

Recall that the X.25 Recommendation specifies a synchronous connection between a DTE and DCE for PSPDN transport. DTE devices that do not have the X.25 protocols built into their software may transmit data to a PAD, which will then

157

convert that data to an X.25 packet. Many X.25 gateways function as a PAD by taking the LAN frame, stripping the LAN Data Link Layer header and trailer, and adding the X.25 LAPB header and trailer as well as the X.25 PLP header.

A number of additional protocols are required to support the PAD and its access to a PSPDN. We'll look at each of these briefly, but for a complete explanation refer to the respective ITU-T standards.

Recommendation X.3 [4-14] defines the operation of a PAD (see Figure 4-11). The PAD must handle the setup and clearing of the virtual call, assemble packets for transmission to the PSPDN, and disassemble packets for delivery to the attached terminal(s). Included in X.3 are twenty-two parameters that specify the PAD's profile. These parameters specify transmission speed and parity, flow control between terminal and PAD, and line-feed treatment.

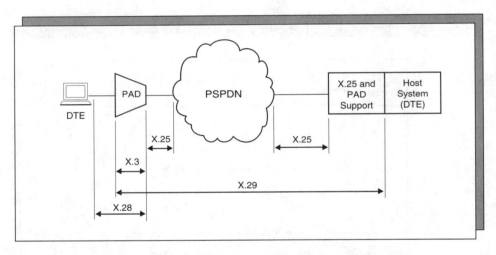

Figure 4-11. PAD protocols related to X.25 *(Courtesy of Hewlett-Packard Company)*

Recommendation X.28 [4-15] defines the interface between a start-stop (asynchronous) terminal and a PAD, and the manner in which the PAD will interact with that terminal. This interface requires a bi-directional control path. Commands are sent from the terminal to the PAD to read or modify the X.3 parameters, or to initiate or disconnect a virtual call. Messages from the PAD to the terminal are responses to the terminal commands, and are known as PAD Service signals. Figure 4-12 summarizes these X.28 commands.

PARAMETER NUMBER	PARAMETER FUNCTION	COMMON VALUES*	MEANING
1	PAD Recall Character	0 1	PAD recall not possible DLE (^P) character
2	Local Echo	0 1	No PAD echo PAD echo
3	Data Forwarding Characters	0 2 126	No data forwarding character Carriage Return (CR) All control characters & DEL
4	Idle Timer Delay	0 - 255	Value of idle timer in 1/20 sec
5	PAD to Terminal Flow Control	0 1	No use of XON/XOFF Use of XON/XOFF
6	Control of PAD Service Signals	0 1	No PAD service signals PAD service signals in std. format
7	PAD Action on Receipt of Break from Term	0 2	Nothing Reset
8	Discard Output	0 1	Normal data delivery Discard output
9	Padding after Carriage Return	0-255	Number of padding characters after Carriage Return
10	Line Folding	0 - 255	Number of characters/line
11	Async Speed (Read Only parameter)	3 11 12	1200 bps 75/1200 bps 2400 bps
12	Terminal to PAD Flow Control	0 1	No flow control by DTE XON/XOFF for flow control
13	Line Feed Insertion	0 1	No Line Feed (LF) insertion Insert LF after Carriage Return
14	Padding After Line Feed	0-255	Number of padding characters after Line Feed
15	Editing	0 1	No editing allowed Editing allowed
16	Character Delete	0 - 127	ASCII Character code from IA5
17	Line Delete	0 - 127	ASCII Character code from IA5
18	Line Display	0 - 127	ASCII Character code from IA5
19	Editing PAD Service Signals	0 1	No editing Editing for printing terminals
20	Echo Mask	0	All characters echoed
21	Parity Treatment	0 3	No parity checking or generation Parity checking and generation
22	Page Wait	0 - 255	Number of Line Feed characters for Page Wait function

* Refer to Recommendation X.3 in Blue Books for Less Common Values

X.28 COMMAND SUMMARY

FUNCTION	COMMAND
Establish Call	Call Selection

[optional_facilities] - address [user_data]

[optional_facilities] - .abbreviated_address [user_data]

Optional_facilities precede address:
 N(NUI), T(RPOA), G(CUG), R(Reverse
 Charging), C(Charging Information)

User_data follows address: Character P or D, <br> followed by up to 12 characters

These two fields are optional.

Clear call	CLR
Check user profile	PROF
Set user profile	PROF n
Set PAD parameter(s)	SET para_#:value
Set & read PAD parameter(s)	SET? para_#:value
Display PAD parameter(s)	PAR?
Display call status	STAT
Reset virtual call	RESET
Send INTERRUPT packet	INT

X.29 MESSAGES

4 BITS	4 BITS	8 BITS	8 BITS		X.29 MESSAGES
GF I	LGN	LCN	P(R)	M P(S) 0	

SET	02	PARM	VALUE
SET & READ	06	PARM	VALUE
PARAMETER INDICATION	00	PARM	VALUE
READ	04	PARM	00
INVITATION TO CLEAR	01		
ERROR	05	TYPE	CODE
INDICATION OF BREAK	03	08 *	01 *
RESELECTION	07	ADDRESS	FACILITIES

* optional

Figure 4-12. X.3, X.28 and X.29 protocol encoding *(© 1994, Hill Associates, Inc.)*

Recommendation X.29 [4-16] is used by a remote DTE to communicate with a PAD. For example, a remote host may need to communicate with a PAD in order to read and/or set various PAD parameters, such as the BREAK signal between the remote DTE and the local terminal. Protocol X.29 is a layer above the X.25 PLP, but it uses the X.25 packet (and the PSPDN) as the transmission path between host and PAD. Figure 4-12 also summarizes the X.29 messages.

4.7   Virtual Call Establishment

Reviewing Figure 4-6, we see that the X.25 Packet Layer Protocol defines seven-teen different packet types. We will look at three of these packets—the Call Request, Call Accept, and Data packets—in detail as we discuss how a virtual call or virtual circuit is established.

There are actually two different types of virtual circuits: permanent virtual circuits (PVCs), which are established by the network and are analogous to a leased telephone line; and switched virtual circuits (SVCs), which are analogous to a dial-up connection. Both PVCs and SVCs could be used in an internetwork environment, but the SVC is more common. An SVC connection is also referred to as a virtual call.

To establish the virtual call, we first assume that two DTEs need to communicate. These two DTEs are attached to their respective DCEs via the X.25 interface, as shown in Figure 4-13. Let's further assume that DTE 1440 wishes to contact DTE 5310. Establishing the call begins when DTE 1440 transmits a Call Request packet to its attached DCE. An unused logical channel, selected by DTE 1440, is used for that DTE/DCE communication. The network then processes the Call Request, and transmits it to the Destination DCE, which is attached to DTE 5310. That remote DCE also selects an unused logical channel for communication, and delivers an Incoming Call packet to DTE 5310.

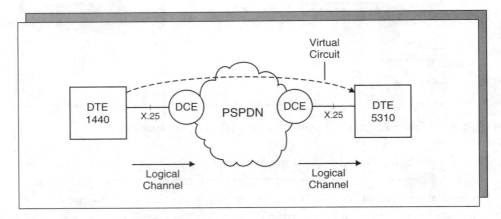

Figure 4-13. Virtual call establishment

Two points are noteworthy here. First, a logical channel is a DTE/DCE definition and is not likely to have the same number at each DTE/DCE pair. Second, the Call Request packet initiated by DTE 1440 undergoes a change when it is transmitted from the remote DCE to DTE 5310. Although transmitted as a Call Request packet, it is delivered as an Incoming Call packet. These packets are shown in Figure 4-14. The third octet (Packet Type field) of the Call Request/Incoming Call packet is set to 0BH. It is understood within the PLP that a Call Request is initiated by the DTE and an Incoming Call is initiated by a DCE, so no confusion occurs.

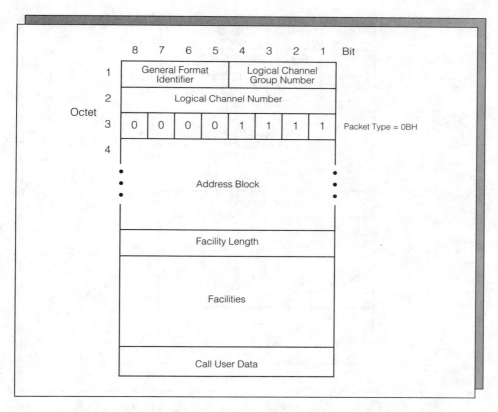

Figure 4-14. X.25 call request/incoming call packet (ITU-T Recommendation X.25)

If the remote DTE (5310) is willing to accept the call, it transmits a Call Accepted packet (see Figure 4-15) which is next delivered by the local DCE to DTE 1440 as a Call Connected packet. Both of these packets assign Packet Type equal to 0FH. A full-duplex data exchange can then occur using the Data packet format (Figure 4-16) that was established by the Call Request. At the end of the session, Clear Request/Clear Indication packets (see Figure 4-17) are used to signal termination.

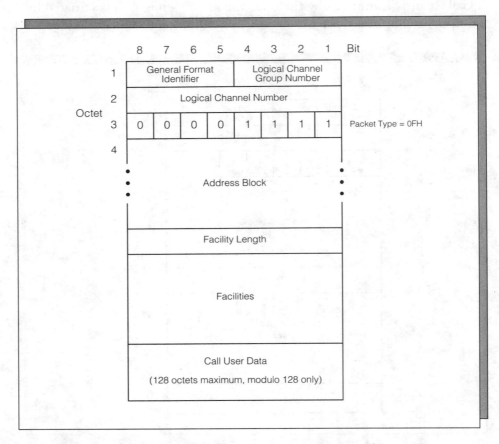

Figure 4-15. X.25 Call Accepted/Call Connected packet (ITU-T Recommendation X.25)

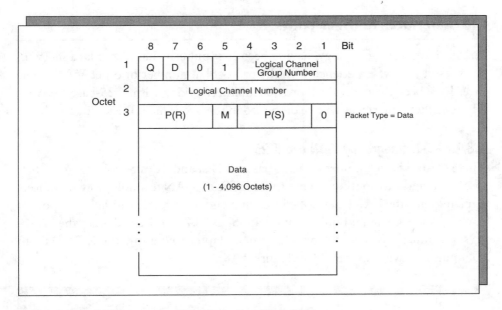

Figure 4-16. X.25 Data packet (ITU-T Recommendation X.25)

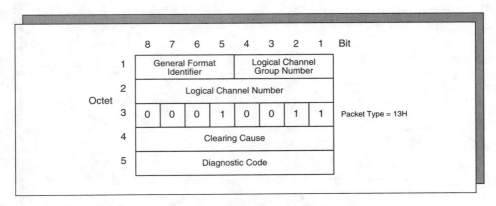

Figure 4-17. X.25 Clear Request/Clear Indication packet (ITU-T Recommendation X.25)

If DTE 5310 is initially unable to accept the Call Request, a Clear Request/Clear Indication packet will be returned. The Clearing Cause field elaborates on the reason—such as a remote DTE that was busy or out-of-order—that the call did not go through.

4.8 Interfaces to Other WANs

X.25 is a mature technology, having been first published as a standard in 1976. As a result of vast experience with the protocol, a number of other WAN interfaces have been defined, which provide internetworking with X.25-based WANs. Three of these interfaces will be discussed in this section: X.31, X.32 , and X.75.

4.8.1 X.31: Integrating ISDN and X.25

There exists a large number of X.25-based DTEs, and a desire on the part of network managers to continue to use those DTEs as WAN technology evolves. Recognizing this, the ITU-T developed Recommendation X.31, entitled "Support of Packet Mode Terminal Equipment by an ISDN" [4-17]. X.31 defines the protocols and functions required by a terminal adapter that allow the X.25 DTE to communicate with an ISDN (see Figure 4-18).

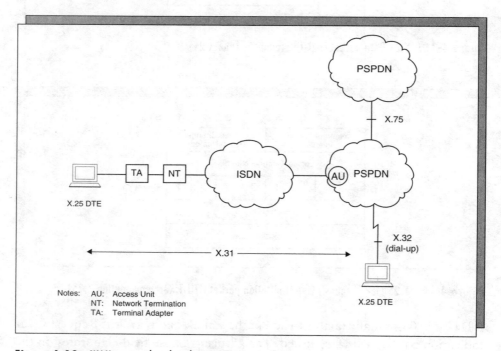

Figure 4-18. WAN protocols related to X.25

Two interconnection scenarios are defined by X.31, designated Case A and Case B. Case A defines a scenario for access to PSPDN services in which the ISDN transparently passes the X.25 packets from the DTE to the ISDN Access Unit (AU) port in the PSPDN. Case B is a more complex scenario, in which the ISDN includes a packet handler function which completes the X.25 call. When viewed from the perspective of the X.25 DTE, the ISDN looks like an X.25 DCE. Some other protocol, such as X.75, is then used to connect the ISDN to the PSPDN.

4.8.2 X.32: Dial-up Access to PSPDNs

Not all DTEs can justify the expense of a dedicated line to the PSPDN, which is required as part of X.25. For example, asynchronous users may dial into a PAD, which then formats the asynchronous data into synchronous X.25 packets. PADs require capital investment, and therefore lower cost alternatives are required in some cases. As a result of this need, the ITU-T published Recommendation X.32 in 1984, titled "Interface Between Data Terminal Equipment (DTE) and Data Circuit-Terminating Equipment (DCE) for Terminals Operating in the Packet Mode, and Accessing a Packet Switched Public Data Network Through a Public Switched Telephone Network or an Integrated Services Digital Network, or a Circuit Switched Public Data Network" [4-18]. X.32 defines a synchronous protocol that allows X.25 to operate over dial-up connections.

X.32 was originally defined to support low-volume DTEs, such as PCs or workstations that need occasional access to a PSPDN. Similar to X.25, X.32 defines three layers of protocol, designated Physical, Data Link, and Packet Layers. X.32 extends the X.25 capabilities, however, as it allows for V.-series Physical Layer implementations, such as V.32 modems. It also provides additional features supporting the authentication, or identification, of remote users. Dial-out capabilities by the PSPDN are also defined in X.32.

4.8.3 X.75: Interface Between Two PSPDNs

As PSPDNs became more popular, the need to interconnect these systems became apparent. The ITU-T published Recommendation X.75 in 1980, titled "Packet Switched Signalling System Between Public Networks Providing Data Transmission Services" [4-4]. X.75 is very similar to X.25. However, it defines an interface between two Signalling Terminal Equipment (STE) devices, not between a DTE and DCE. X.75 has three layers of protocol, again very similar to X.25. An enhancement to the Packet Layer Protocol provides for an extra field, called the Network Utilities field, which negotiates the various transmission parameters, such as packet size, reverse charging, and transit delay, between the two PSPDNs.

With this background on the X.25 and related protocols, let's next examine products that implement these protocols.

4.9 X.25 Internetworking Examples

The X.25 protocols lend themselves quite readily to remote LAN interconnections. The device that is typically used on the LAN is called an X.25 gateway—although from the OSI point of view, it is actually a router. The following sections will explore four different products that provide unique internetworking functions for X.25-based hosts.

4.9.1 Crystal Point, Inc. OutsideView

Crystal Point, Inc. of Bothell, Washington develops and markets terminal emulation software for DOS and Windows environments. Two of their products, PCTerm for DOS and OutsideView for Windows, support X.25 connectivity. These products allow a PC on a NetBIOS or Novell LAN to establish micro-to-mainframe and PC-to-PC connections via PSPDNs using the X.25 protocol (see Figure 4-19).

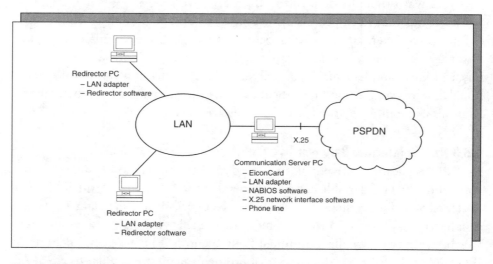

Figure 4-19. Outside View X.25 connectivity *(Courtesy of Crystal Point, Inc.)*

PCTerm or OutsideView terminal software works in conjunction with an add-in X.25 gateway PC card developed by Eicon Technology Corp. of Montreal, Quebec, Canada. The terminal software provides the Packet Assembler and Disassembler (PAD) functions, and implements the X.3, X.28, and X.29 protocols. The output of this software is an X.25 packet which is sent via the LAN to the EiconCard. The EiconCard takes that packet and sends it over a switched or dedicated connection to the PSPDN.

One of the workstations on the LAN functions as a communication server, and all other workstations function as redirectors. The redirector workstations contain a LAN adapter, plus software that connects to the communication server. The communication server contains a LAN adapter for LAN communication, the EiconCard for PSPDN communication, plus software that connects to both the LAN and the PSPDN.

Connection to the PSPDN involves several processes. First, the communication server and the EiconCard establish internal communication using Eicon's Network Adapter BIOS (NABIOS) software. Secondly, the X.25 Network Interface Software (NIS) establishes a connection to the PSPDN. Workstations that wish to access the PSPDN must also load the NABIOS software, which directs their communication to the LAN adapter in the communication server, from the LAN adapter to the EiconCard, and subsequently to the PSPDN.

To connect to a remote host via the PSPDN, the user accesses the communication menu in PCTerm or OutsideView. A number of call parameters are then entered, including the local and remote DTE addresses, plus the user data to be sent. The communication software establishes the connection to the communication server PC and hands off X.25 data packets, via the LAN, to the EiconCard, and subsequently to the PSPDN for transmission. Establishing the process to listen for an incoming X.25 call is performed in a similar manner.

4.9.2 Eicon Technology InterConnect Server

Eicon Technology Corporation of Montreal, Quebec, Canada has earned an international reputation for providing open platforms for X.25 communications. The backbone for these server-based connectivity solutions is the EiconCard, a family of intelligent co-processor communication cards for PCs, PS/2s, and compatibles. In addition to supporting the popular X.25 protocol,

EiconCards provide true multiprotocol support for SDLC, HDLC, Point-to-Point Protocol (PPP), frame relay, and ISDN WAN connections, at line speeds of up to 384 Kbps. Featuring a high speed connection for V.24 (EIA-232-E), V.35, and X.21 interfaces, EiconCards support DOS, Windows, OS/2, UNIX, Novell, Inc. NetWare, Windows NT, and other NetBIOS-compatible operating systems.

Eicon's most renowned solution for X.25 connectivity is the OSI Gateway, which supports a wide range of ISO/ITU-T and GOSIP-compliant network application software such as X.400 mail and File Transfer, Access and Management (FTAM). OSI Gateway's integrated X.3/X.28/X.29 PAD and COM port redirector, called X.PAD, supports a large base of third-party communications packages for terminal emulation, file transfer, and remote access. The OSI Gateway is currently certified for use on over 45 X.25 Public Data Networks all over the world, and can be installed along with Eicon's SNA Gateway to access IBM hosts concurrently over the same X.25 communications link.

Eicon Technology's InterConnect Server (ICS) consolidates all communications requirements, including those solved by Eicon's OSI and SNA Gateways, onto a single platform (see Figure 4-20). Currently available for a NetWare environment, ICS allows for simultaneous direct connectivity to SNA hosts, to Internet Protocol (IP), Novell IPX and AppleTalk LANs, and to X.25-attached hosts and servers. It offers manageable connectivity with both remote SNMP management and IBM NetView-based administration in a seamlessly-integrated platform. The ICS provides an excellent solution for corporations looking to connect a large number of remote office LANs directly to both mission-critical SNA hosts and LAN-based corporate information systems, while providing a platform for enterprise-wide messaging applications. The X.25 Switch and PAD functionality of ICS supports up to six X.25 or asynchronous devices, thus reducing communications costs.

In summary, the EiconCard provides an intelligent hardware platform for a number of X.25 connectivity options, including links to remote hosts, e-mail systems, and other LANs.

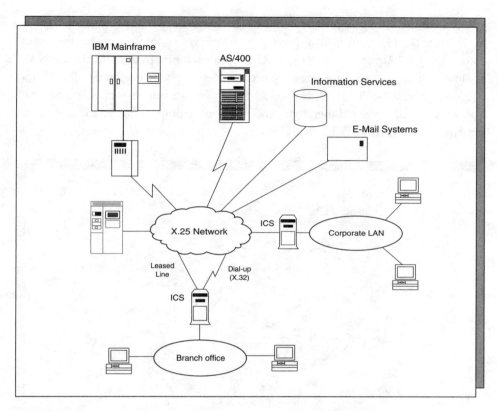

Figure 4-20. Eicon InterConnect Server *(Courtesy of Eicon Technology Corp.)*

4.9.3 Attachmate Remote LAN Node

Providing remote access to the corporate LAN is an area within the internet-working marketplace that has experienced dramatic growth in the last few years. Mobile workers, such as business travelers, sales and marketing professionals, and telecommuters can increase their productivity through seamless connectivity to the headquarters location. A second application is found in branch offices, which need connectivity to the headquarters location on an occasional basis, but cannot justify the expense of a full-time dedicated connection. Thus, remote access servers meet the needs of both client-to-LAN and LAN-to-LAN applications.

One of the strongest products in the remote server marketplace is the Remote LAN Node (RLN), from Attachmate Corp. (formerly Digital Communication Associates, Inc.), of Alpharetta, Georgia. RLN connects remote users to the LAN via analog or digital leased connections, switched 56 services, cellular radio, ISDN, and X.25 (see Figure 4-21). Since the product functions as a bridge, it is independent of upper layer protocols, and therefore supports Apple Computer's AppleTalk, Banyan Systems' VINES, Novell's NetWare, and many other operating systems.

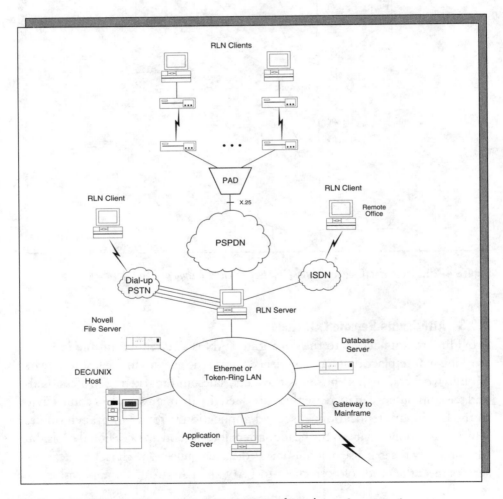

Figure 4-21. Remote LAN Access via X.25 *(Courtesy of Attachmate Corporation)*

The RLN architecture is PC-based, and comes in both a software-only version and a turnkey, plug and play, solution. Both configurations are available in Ethernet and token ring versions, for DOS, Windows, and OS/2-based clients. RLN supports up to 32 ports per server, and may be managed using SNMP. It comes with RLN Manager, a Windows application, which uses SNMP to configure and monitor the RLN server or servers. In addition RLN servers can be managed using third party network management platforms, such as Hewlett-Packard's Openview.

For X.25 applications, RLN is tightly integrated with X.25 adapters from Eicon Technology or OST, Inc., of Chantilly, VA. This allows the RLN server to support up to 4 synchronous X.25 adapters, which provide up to 32 Virtual Connections (VCs) per server. Each X.25 adapter has its own DTE address on the PSPDN, and can support speeds up to 256 Kbps. The client dials a local PAD and connects to the RLN server through the PSPDN, which then provides access to the destination LAN.

In addition to supporting PSPDNs, RLN can work with private, X.25-based data networks. This feature allows organizations with existing private data networks to utilize that network for remote LAN access. Remote access communication costs are therefore reduced, as the remote users call into local PADs instead of making a long distance call.

4.9.4 Microtronix ISDN-X.25 Transactor

Microtronix Datacom, Ltd. of London, Ontario, Canada, specializes in the development and manufacture of X.25 network access products. One of Microtronix' products, the ISDN-X.25 Transactor, provides a low-cost method of connecting to PSPDN-attached hosts via an ISDN Basic Rate Interface (BRI) D channel (see Figure 4-22).

In many areas, ISDN BRI services are more cost-effective than leased lines, and have the advantage of integrating voice, data and video traffic onto a single communication link. The BRI contains two B channels that operate at 64 Kbps and are typically used for voice, data and video traffic. The third channel, designated the D channel, operates at 16 Kbps, and is used for control signaling and data traffic, which may include X.25 if supported by the ISDN service provider.

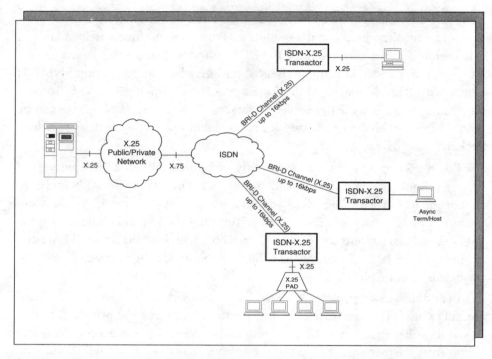

Figure 4-22. ISDN-X.25 Network Integration *(Courtesy of Microtronix Datacom Ltd)*

Microtronix' Transactor uses this D channel for X.25 communication, which eliminates the need of installing a leased line solely for X.25 traffic. Examples of applications that would benefit from this product include on-line transaction processing, such as travel reservations, credit and debit card transactions, and stock market data delivery.

The ISDN-X.25 Transactor is an ISDN terminal adapter that includes an integrated network termination, NT1. An EIA-232-C port on the unit provides the synchronous X.25 interface. That port may be configured for either X.25 DTE or DCE LAPB operation, with packet sizes ranging up to 256 octets in length. Up to 20 logical channels may be supported on the synchronous port. X.25 Packet layer parameters, such as packet and window size negotiation, reverse charging, and so on, may also be passed from the X.25 DTE to the ISDN switch via the Transactor. For asynchronous terminal or host connections, another port is available which includes an internal PAD function, supporting the X.3, X.28, and

X.29 protocols. For cases where two asynchronous devices need X.25 access, the synchronous port may be reconfigured to support an asynchronous connection, also utilizing the internal PAD.

By providing both ISDN and X.25 connectivity, users can migrate from current X.25-based communication services to ISDN, while still protecting their investment.

As we have seen, the X.25 protocols provide an extremely versatile option for LAN-to-host and LAN-to-remote LAN communications. The wide international acceptance of these protocols and their implementation techniques makes X.25 an excellent choice for both enterprise-wide and international internetworking. References [4-19] and [4-21] consider some of the international benefits of X.25, comparisons between this protocol and frame relay, and extending X.25 over ISDN, respectively.

In the next chapter, we will consider some of the newer technologies—frame relay, SMDS, and ATM—that can trace their origins to X.25.

4.10 References

[4-1]   Rosner, Roy D. *Packet Switching*. Belmont, CA.: Language Learning Press, 1982.

[4-2]   BBN Communications. *ARPANET, The First Decade*. NTIS Document no. ADA115440, April 1981.

[4-3]   International Telecommunications Union—Telecommunication Standardization Sector. Recommendation X.25, 1992.

[4-4]   International Telecommunications Union—Telecommunication Standardization Sector. Recommendation X.75, 1992.

[4-5]   Korostoff, Kathryn. "Can X.25 Vendors Make the Switch to ATM?" *Data Communications* (March 21, 1993): 17–18.

[4-6]   Deasington, R. J. *X.25 Explained: Protocols for Packet Switching Networks*. 2d ed., New York: John Wiley & Sons, 1984.

[4-7]   Schlar, Sherman K. *Inside X.25: A Manager's Guide*. New York: McGraw-Hill, 1990.

[4-8]   Black, Uyless. *X.25 and Related Protocols*. Los Alamitos, CA: IEEE Computer Society Press, 1991.

[4-9]   Dhas, C. R. and V. K. Konangi. "X.25: An Interface to Public Packet Networks." *IEEE Communications Magazine* (September 1986): 18–24.

[4-10] Piscitello, David M. and A. Lyman Chapin. *Open Systems Networking*. New York: Addison-Wesley, 1993.

[4-11] Smouts, Michel. *Packet Switching Evolution from Narrowband to Broadband ISDN*. Boston: Artech House, 1991.

[4-12] Banyan Systems, Inc. *VINES Protocol Definition*. Document no. 003673, May 1993.

[4-13] Banyan Systems, Inc. *VINES X.25 Guide*. Document no. DA184-04, January 1992.

[4-14] International Telecommunications Union—Telecommunication Standardization Sector. Recommendation X.3, 1993.

[4-15] International Telecommunications Union—Telecommunication Standardization Sector. Recommendation X.28, 1993.

[4-16] International Telecommunications Union—Telecommunication Standardization Sector. Recommendation X.29, 1993.

[4-17] International Telecommunications Union—Telecommunication Standardization Sector. Recommendation X.31, 1993.

[4-18] International Telecommunications Union—Telecommunication Standardization Sector. Recommendation X.32, 1993.

[4-19] Bondeville, Denys. "Over LAN, Over Sea." *LAN Magazine* (April 1992): 45–50.

[4-20] Henderson, Frank and Joseph McCoy. "Less is Faster." *LAN Magazine* (July 1991): 48–54.

[4-21] Tredinnick, Ian. "X.25: A New Lease on Life With ISDN." *Telecommunications* (March 1995): 74-77.

5 Broadband Networking

Communication systems, such as dial-up connections, leased lines, T1 and T3 service, and PSPDNs have supported data communication systems for well over a decade. With the maturity of these links has come a familiarity with their applications and knowledge of their operation. But for many network managers, the bandwidth that these systems provide is not adequate—especially for newer desktop applications such as video conferencing and multimedia.

The hunger for greater bandwidth has driven the development of broadband technologies, such as frame relay, Switched Multimegabit Data Service (SMDS), and Asynchronous Transfer Mode (ATM). (The term broadband as it is currently used within the data communication industry indicates large amounts of available bandwidth. Earlier interpretations of the term, which indicated an analog transmission system, as in "broadband Ethernet", are rarely used today.)

Frame relay is strictly a WAN technology, and SMDS may be used as either a MAN or a WAN. ATM is unique, however, as it may be used in any of these cases— LAN, MAN or WAN. And with that distinction comes greater interest in the technology from both users and vendors. In this chapter, we will provide an overview of the technologies and applications of these transmission systems. Readers needing an in-depth view of the technologies and their protocols are referred to another volume of the Network Troubleshooting Library, *Analyzing Broadband Networks*. Information on the broadband forums is given in Appendix B.

5.1 Broadband Transmission Technologies

In Chapter 1 we discussed the OSI Reference Model, and described its two major distinctions: the communications subnet that operates using OSI Layers 1 to 3, and the host processes that operate using OSI Layers 1 to 7. Broadband networks may also be described using the communication subnet portion of this model. Other technological factors to consider include the transmission rates, network topologies, and interface options available.

5.1.1 Comparing Broadband Networks with OSI

The functional definition of these broadband systems determines which of the OSI layers apply (see Figure 5-1). For example, the three layers of X.25 are aligned closely with the Physical, Data Link, and Network Layers of the OSI model. Frame relay, on the other hand, provides only some of the Data Link Layer functions, and none of the Network Layer operations. SMDS is derived from IEEE 802.6, part of the IEEE Project 802 LAN and MAN research. As such, the three levels of the SMDS Interface Protocol (SIP) provide the IEEE Physical (PHY) Layer and Medium Access Control (MAC) Layer functions only, which correspond with the OSI Physical Layer, and the lower portion of the OSI Data Link Layer, respectively.

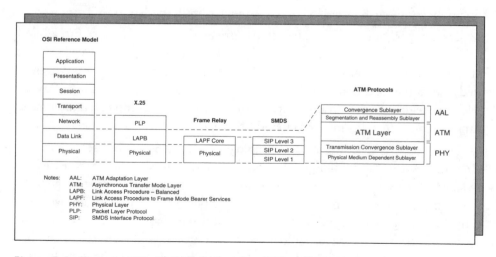

Figure 5-1. Comparing OSI with X.25, frame relay, SMDS, and ATM.

ATM is principally a three level architecture, defined by the Physical (PHY), ATM, and ATM Adaption Layer (AAL) functions. These capabilities map most closely into the OSI Physical and Data Link Layers. Other functions, however, such as circuit establishment (or signaling) and network management, are significant elements of the operation of an ATM network. And while these duties might be considered "background operations" (and therefore not shown on the right-hand side of Figure 5-1), their presence is nevertheless significant.

5.1.2 Broadband Transmission Rates

For many applications, the transmission rates available play a significant role in the selection of one technology over another (Figure 5-2). Frame relay service is defined at the DS0 (56/64 Kbps) and DS1 (1.544 Mbps) rates. SMDS is defined at the DS0, DS1, and DS3 (44.736 Mbps) rates. ATM is defined at a number of rates between DS1 and OC12 (622 Mbps). An equally (or possibly more) important issue is availability of a broadband service—not all services or rates are available from all carriers. Appendix E lists the carriers that offer broadband services. As these carrier offerings change from time to time, the reader is advised to consult the carriers in their area directly before investing significant effort into broadband network designs.

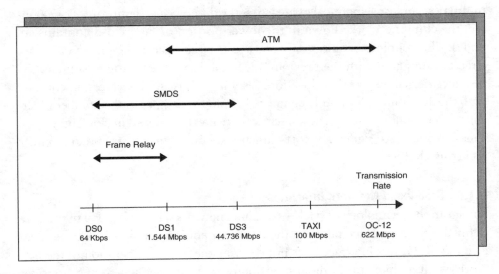

Figure 5-2. Broadband transmission rates

5.1.3 Broadband Network Economics

A significant element in the appeal of broadband technologies is the economies of scale that they bring to large organizations. To illustrate this point, consider the network topology at the top of Figure 5-3, which has six locations, or nodes. If each node is connected to every other node, a topology known as a fully-connected mesh network results. The number of connecting circuits for a mesh network is given by:

$$C = \frac{N * (N-1)}{2}$$

where N is the number of nodes, and C is the number of circuits required. For example, with N = 6, the number of circuits is 15 (6 * 5/2). The number of hardware interfaces (modems, CSU/DSUs, etc.) necessary to support a given number of circuits is twice that number, since one interface is required at each end of the connection. Thus, with 15 circuits, the number of interfaces required would be 30.

Broadband technologies are generally referred to as "cloud networks". The cloud network is so-named because the mesh topology resides inside the carrier's network, or inside the ATM switch, in the case of private ATM networks. While this may seem just symantical gymnastics, the difference is significant. For example, the cloud network shown in the lower portion of Figure 5-3 contains six nodes. This topology requires only one access circuit per node, for a total of six circuits, compared with the previous 15. In addition, the customer supplies the interface device only at their location, resulting in just six interfaces, in contrast with the 30 required for a fully connected mesh. In short, both the number of circuits and the number of network interfaces are greatly reduced in cloud networks. This can add up to significant cost reductions, both in first costs and in monthly recurring charges.

5.1.4 Broadband Network Interfaces

Similar to the technology of packet switching networks, broadband networks are defined by the interface between the customer equipment and the carrier. And also like X.25, this interface does not describe the internal operation of the network—that architecture is the responsibility of the carrier, which may consider the information to be highly proprietary.

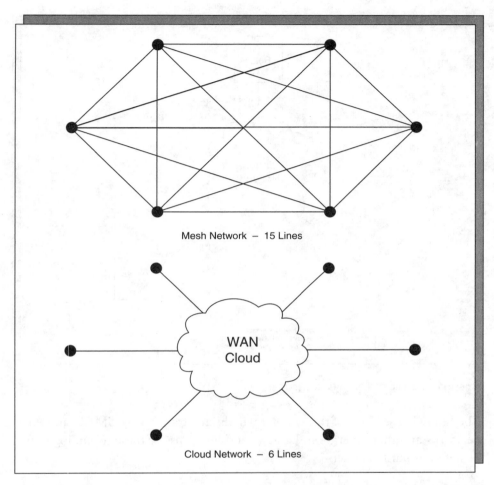

Mesh Network — 15 Lines

WAN Cloud

Cloud Network — 6 Lines

Figure 5-3. Mesh vs. cloud networks

These interfaces are called the User-Network Interface (FR_UNI) for frame relay service; the Subscriber Network Interface (SNI) for SMDS; and the User-Network Interface (ATM_UNI) for ATM network service (Figure 5-4). Note that the term "UNI" is used for both frame relay and ATM; the context of the discussion should reveal which architecture is under discussion.

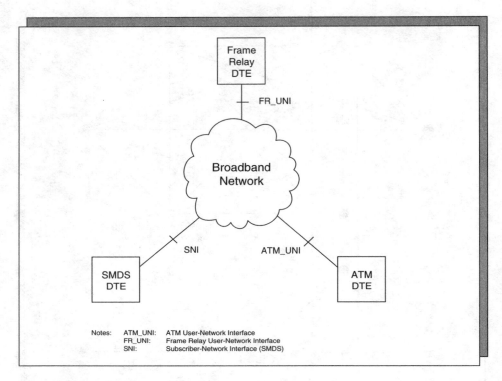

Figure 5-4. Broadband network interfaces

The following sections of this chapter will discuss frame relay, SMDS, and ATM networks and their operation. Design considerations for these technologies will be deferred until Chapter 6.

5.2   Frame Relay

Frame relay is a network interface standard derived from narrowband ISDN technology and developed by ANSI and the ITU-T (CCITT). Frame relay gets its name from its method of operation—the relaying of frames of information. Note that unlike X.25, which operates on both frames and packets of information, frame relay operates on frames only. As such, the frame relay protocol operates at the Data Link layer only, and does not include any Network or higher layer protocol functions. As a result, the protocol overhead is much less, and with that, the real time processing time is reduced as well.

Reducing the protocol overhead is dependent upon two key assumptions: that the underlying Physical layer transport is relatively error-free, and that any errors that do slip by will be recovered by the end-user devices and their upper layer protocols.

Frame relay is a connection-oriented service, with standards which implement both permanent virtual connections (PVCs) and switched virtual connections (SVCs). Access to frame relay service is available at rates up to DS1 (1.544 Mbps). At this writing, frame relay service is available from most of the regional Bell operating companies, including Ameritech, Bell Atlantic, BellSouth, NYNEX, Pacific Bell, Southwestern Bell, and US West. Interexchange carriers providing frame relay include AT&T, CompuServe, MCI, Sprint, and WilTel.

A consortium of vendors, carriers, and users initiated the Frame Relay Forum (FRF), which has international support. The FRF has forged a number of Implementation Agreements (IAs) that take the ANSI and ITU-T standards and derive specific details that are required for multi-vendor interoperability. The Internet community has also shown support for frame relay by developing standards for multiprotocol support over frame relay.

To summarize, frame relay is a connection-oriented, streamlined data transfer service that is positioned to replace conventional leased lines today, and to provide a transition to ATM in the future.

5.2.1 Frame Relay Standards

The documents that govern current frame relay implementations have been written by three different organizations: the International Telecommunications Union—Telecommunication Standards Sector (ITU-T), the American National Standards Institute (ANSI), and the Frame Relay Forum (FRF). The ITU-T frame relay standards are based upon Integrated Services Digital Network (ISDN) architecture. The ANSI standards are applicable to frame relay implementations in the United States, but are generally similar to the ITU-T work. The FRF documents address implementation issues, assuring that multivendor networks can interoperate [5-1].

The various documents address four general areas: architecture and service description, access signaling, data transfer, and circuit management. The architecture and service description documents define what functions the frame relay service is, or is not, intended to perform. The data transfer documents describe the formats used for the actual transfer of user information, or the core of the Data Link layer service that the frame relay interface is performing. The management documents deal with management of the interface between the end-user equipment and the network, and the control of congestion within the network. Finally, the access signaling documents define the messages used to establish and disconnect a frame relay connection.

Many of these standards are closely related, or perhaps derived from one of the other standards. For example, ITU-T Q.931 (ANSI T1.607) is an ISDN Layer 3 standard for basic call control. A subset of that standard, ITU-T Q.933 (ANSI T1.617), specifies frame mode basic call control. Derived from both of those standards is the Frame Relay Forum's implementation agreement, FRF.4, which details SVC service offerings at the user-to-network interface. Thus, in order to fully understand FRF.4, the reader must also have copies of Q.933 and Q.931 available. While this may seem somewhat circular, referring to previous standards prevents unnecessary repetition of the same information.

Key frame relay documents include:

Subject	ITU-T Standard	ANSI Standard
Architecture and Service Description	I.233	T1.606
Data Link Layer Core Aspects	Q.922 Annex A	T1.618
Permanent Virtual Circuit (PVC) Management	Q.933 Annex A	T1.617 Annex D
Congestion Management	I.370	T1.606a
Switched Virtual Connection (SVC) Signaling	Q.933	T1.617

Implementation Agreement documents developed by the Frame Relay Forum include:

Subject	FRF Document
User-Network Interface—UNI	FRF.1
Network-to-Network Interface—NNI	FRF.2
Multiprotocol Encapsulation	FRF.3
User-to-Network Switched Virtual Connection—SVC	FRF.4
Frame Relay/ATM Network Interworking	FRF.5
Frame Relay Service Customer Network Management	FRF.6
Frame Relay PVC Multicast Service and Protocol Description	FRF.7

5.2.2 The User-Network Interface

The UNI is the connection, or demarcation point, between the terminal equipment and the transport facility (see Figure 5-5). The term FRAD, which stands for frame relay access device, is often used to indicate the terminal equipment. The term FRND, which stands for frame relay network device (and not shown in Figure 5-5), is often used to designate the network's access equipment. Depending upon the design of the FRAD, other interfaces, such as the V.35, may provide a connection to an intermediate CSU/DSU.

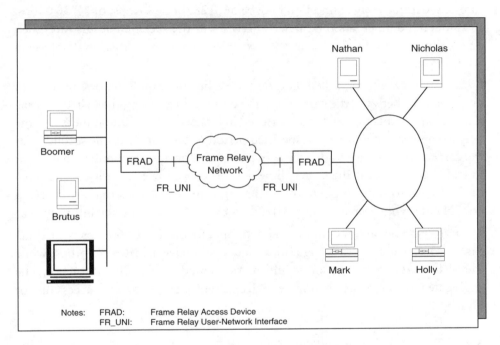

Figure 5-5. Frame relay network components

The functions that the network provides are clearly defined, so the design requirements for each side of the UNI are unambiguous. These functions include:

- Bidirectional frame transfer
- Preservation of the frame order
- Detection of transmission, format, and operational errors

⊗   Transparent transport of the user data

⊗   No frame acknowledgment

In addition to the UNI functions, the physical interface that is used to access the frame relay service must be considered. Frame relay network service is defined in the standards at DS0 and DS1 access rates. Some carriers, such as Pacific Bell, offer other access options, such as service at the fractional T1 rates of 128 Kbps and 384 Kbps. Thus, the carrier's specification might indicate that the access rate of the frame relay connection may be 56, 128, or 384 Kbps, or 1.536 Mbps. In summary, data enters the carrier's network at the specified access rate, such as 56 Kbps, and all data for all PVCs or SVCs flows over this single physical connection.

Another parameter, called the Committed Information Rate, or CIR, defines an agreement between the carrier and the customer regarding the delivery of the data on a particular VC. CIR is measured in bits per second, and it measures the average amount of data over a specified period of time, such as one second, that the carrier will attempt to deliver with a normal priority. Data bursts that result in traffic that exceeds the CIR will be delivered at a lower priority, or possibly discarded, according to the terms of that agreement. Circuits that are carrying critical data would have a higher CIR than those carrying routine information.

For example, assume that a line with an access rate of 56 Kbps is carrying three PVCs. The PVC carrying critical data could have a CIR of 32 Kbps, while the PVCs carrying more routine information could have a CIR of 8 Kbps. The aggregate CIR on the line would be 48 Kbps, which is less than the access rate of 56 Kbps.

5.2.3   Data Link Connection Identifiers

Frame relay connections, which are logical channels between the FRAD and network, are identified by an address called the Data Link Connection Identifier, or DLCI. Each PVC or SVC on a UNI is assigned a DLCI. Thus, a UNI in Denver with permanent connections to two other cities would have a DLCI assigned for each PVC (Figure 5-6). The combination of the UNI and the DLCI specifies the end point for a particular VC. Note that DLCI assignments have local, not end-to-end, significance. The two DLCIs are connected inside the frame relay network by carrier.

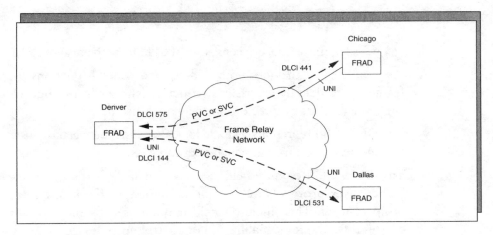

Figure 5-6. Frame relay connection

5.2.4 The T1.618 Frame

The frame relay frame format is defined by ANSI T1.618, and is derived from the earlier High Level Data Link Control (HDLC) standard, ISO 7809. The most significant difference between the HDLC and T1.618 frame formats is the absence of the Control field in the T1.618 frame (Figure 5-7). This function is included within the frame relay Address field, thus streamlining the protocol processing required.

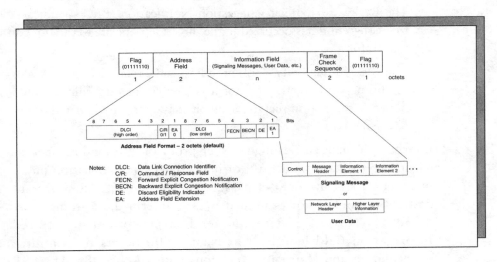

Figure 5-7. T1.618 frame format *(Reproduced with permission of ATIS)*

The fields of the T1.618 frame are:

- Flag: a one-octet, fixed sequence consisting of 01111110 (binary) or 7EH.

- Address: a field that includes both address and control functions for the frame. The default length is two octets (shown in the figure), although longer fields of three or four octets are also defined.

  - The DLCI field represents a single logical channel between the user and the network, through which data can pass.

  - The Command/Response field (C/R) is provided for the use of the higher layer protocols and is not examined by the frame relay protocol itself. This single bit field may be used by the end-user devices (FRADs) for signaling and/or control purposes.

  - The Address Field Extension (EA) bits are used to extend the addressing structure beyond the two-octet default, to either three or four octets: more address octets follow (EA = 0) or last address octet (EA = 1).

  - The Explicit Congestion Notification bits are set by the network to indicate the direction of congestion within the network. The Forward Explicit Congestion Notification (FECN) bit indicates that congestion has occurred in the same direction as the traffic flow. The Backward Explicit Congestion Notification (BECN) indicates that congestion has occurred in the direction opposite to the flow of that traffic.

  - The Discard Eligibility (DE) bit indicates the relative importance of the frame, and whether or not it is eligible for discarding, should network congestion dictate. This bit may be set by either the user or the network.

- Information field: carries higher-layer protocol information, such as client/server data from a LAN or inter-router communication on an internetwork. This field is passed transparently from source to destination and is not examined by any intermediate frame relay devices. ANSI T1.618 recommends a maximum negotiated Information field length of at least 1,600 octets to minimize segmentation and reassembly functions with LAN traffic. The FRF implementation agreement (FRF.1) requires that this field length of 1,600 octets be supported by the network and the user.

⊗ Frame Check Sequence: implements a two-octet Cyclic Redundancy Check (CRC) sequence using the CRC-16 polynomial. The use of this polynomial provides error detection for frames up to 4,096 octets in length.

5.2.5 The Local Management Interface

The operational support protocol for the UNI is called the Local Management Interface (LMI). This standard was originally developed by the Consortium and published in 1990. Derivatives of the Consortium LMI were formally adopted as T1.617 Annex D, and Q.933 Annex A. Differences exist in these three standards, such as the DLCI used and the message formats.

The LMI defines a polling protocol between the FRAD and the network to exchange information on the status of that interface and its defined PVCs (Figure 5-8). The T1.617 standard defines four purposes for this protocol:

⊗ Notification of the addition of a PVC.

⊗ Detection of the deletion of a PVC.

⊗ Notification of the availability or unavailability of a configured PVC.

⊗ Verification of the integrity of the link (UNI).

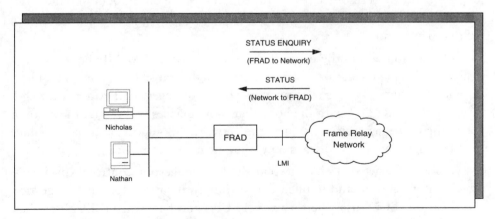

Figure 5-8. Status reporting via the LMI

The LMI procedures define an asymmetric protocol, with the FRAD periodically issuing a STATUS ENQUIRY message, and the network responding with a STATUS message. The polling period is a negotiable parameter, with a default of 10 seconds. The first poll requests a link integrity verification response to determine the status of the in-channel signaling link. After a few (typically six) of the link integrity verification polls have been issued, the user requests the status of all PVCs on the interface. This full status message is a more complex response, containing information on every PVC configured on that bearer channel. The information transmitted includes the recent history of that PVC (already present or new), and its availability (inactive or active).

Error conditions, such as reliability errors of the in-channel signaling link (DLCI 0), signaling link protocol errors, or internal network problems, are also detected by the periodic polling.

5.2.6 Congestion Control

Frame relay networks add a unique dimension to the challenges of LAN–WAN networking, as the universe of network subscribers shares a common resource—the available bandwidth of the carrier's network. Each VC is configured for a specific CIR, and the carrier contractually agrees to deliver that bandwidth. Should additional bandwidth be required for additional traffic or data bursts, the network will attempt to deliver that excess.

In more traditional network facilities, such as leased lines, the users do not share a bandwidth resource per se. Instead, they lease the amount of bandwidth required between the various network locations, and have full and complete use of that bandwidth.

Congestion within the network is thus handled in two different ways. If a leased line is congested, then you either increase the transmission rate of that line, or add more lines. If frame relay networks become congested, they notify the end-user devices (FRADs), with the hope that those devices will reduce the amount of traffic that they are sending into the network. Should the request to reduce traffic be ignored, frame discarding within the network may occur.

Frame relay networks have two methods of congestion control: explicit congestion notification, and implicit congestion notification. Explicit congestion notification (ECN) uses the forward (FECN) and backward (BECN) explicit congestion notification bits that are included in the T1.618 Address field. The use of these bits is determined by which end of the system is controlling the transmission of the data. If the transmitter of the data is controlled at the destination of the data, the FECN bit is sent in the same direction as the data flow (Figure 5-9). If the transmitter of the data is controlled at the source of the data, the BECN bit is sent in the opposite direction to the flow of the data.

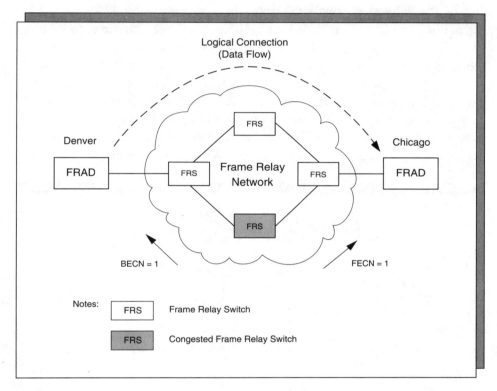

Figure 5-9. Congestion notification with frame relay networks

Implicit congestion notification relies upon the upper layer protocols in the FRADs or other terminal device, such as a host, to control the amount of data that is entering the network. This function is generally implemented by a Transport Layer flow control mechanism in both the transmitter and receiver. The transmitting device is allowed to send a certain amount of data, but is then constrained from further transmission until acknowledgments from the remote device have been received. Processes within these devices would monitor the network conditions, such as frame loss. The implicit congestion notification process would then control the offered traffic, which, in turn, would control the congestion.

An addendum to T1.606 addresses these principles of congestion management that affect the design of frame relay networks.

5.2.7 The Network–Network Interface

Up to this point, our discussions have centered on the relationship between a single user and a single network—the User-Network Interface (UNI). In order to extend the user's communication capabilities beyond a single frame relay network, a Network-to-Network Interface (NNI) specification has been developed by the FRF, and documented in FRF.2. This specification is built upon multinetwork PVC service, which is a concatenation of two or more PVC segments (Figure 5-10). Note that the NNIs are defined between adjacent networks; UNIs are used between access and egress networks, as in the single PVC case studied earlier.

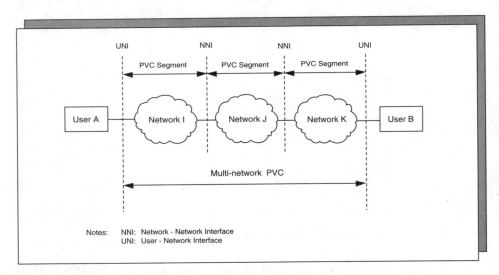

Figure 5-10. Multinetwork PVC *(Courtesy of the Frame Relay Forum)*

5.2.8 Frame Relay Internetworking

The encapsulation of X.25/X.75 traffic within a T1.618 frame is addressed in T1.617 Annex G. This standard defines an interworking function (IWF) which provides the encapsulation and decapsulation of the X.25/X.75 Link Access Procedure Balanced (LAPB) frames within the T1.618 frames. The IWF also contains provisions for congestion avoidance.

The interworking function is best illustrated using the protocol layers involved (Figure 5-11). An X.25 DTE contains its native protocols, LAPB and the Packet Layer Protocol (PLP). It connects to a network provider which supports both the X.25 and frame relay protocols, or in other words, an embedded IWF. From that point, the frame relay network may be accessed. The remote X.25 DTE must also contain the IWF in order to extract the LAPB frame from the T1.618 frame and pass it to the distant X.25 DTE. The encapsulation process places the LAPB Address, Control and Information fields inside a T1.618 frame. A new FCS is then calculated on the entire T1.618 frame, including the DLCI and other subfields within that frame. A reverse process (data extraction) is performed before delivery of the X.25 packet to the remote X.25 DTE.

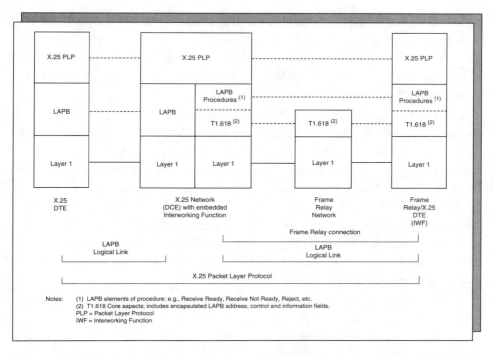

Figure 5-11. Frame Relay/X.25 Protocol Diagram with Embedded IWF *(Source: ANSI T1.617aDraft, subject to change. Reproduced with permission of ATIS)*

This section has studied the frame relay services that are currently available from a wide variety of Local Exchange Carriers (LECs) and Interexchange Carriers (IXCs) in the United States, plus other carriers around the world. Evidence of the widespread acceptance of this technology is found in references [5-2] through [5-5].

5.3 Switched Multimegabit Data Service

The second broadband networking technology that we will study is Switched Multimegabit Data Service (SMDS), which has been developed by Bell Communications Research, Inc. (Bellcore), the research and development organization that serves many of the Bell Operating Companies. SMDS is a connectionless data transport service, which is a subset of a metropolitan area networking (MAN) technology, the Distributed Queue Dual Bus (DQDB), defined by the IEEE 802.6 standard.

With access to SMDS currently available at rates up to DS3 (44.736 Mbps), and plans for the OC3 (155.520 Mbps), many applications for this high speed service have been identified. These include LAN interconnection, high-speed remote database access, packet audio and video, resource sharing by educational institutions, image transfer, and teleradiology.

At this writing, access to SMDS is available from most of the regional Bell operating companies, including Ameritech, Bell Atlantic, BellSouth Corp., Pacific Telesis Group, and US West, Inc. Southwestern Bell is planning to offer SMDS in the future. Nynex has announced that it will bypass an SMDS offering, and instead move directly to ATM. Among the independent (non-Bell) local exchange carriers (LECs), GTE Telephone Operations has SMDS in their portfolio. Interexchange carrier (IXC) MCI has also announced the availability of its SMDS service and an agreement with Bell Atlantic to provide local-to-long distance SMDS connections. Many European carriers have either field trialed or announced the availability of SMDS service as well.

Support for SMDS within the telecommunications industry is strong. The SMDS Interest Group (SIG) was chartered in 1991, and includes service providers, equipment vendors, and users who have united to further this technology [5-6].

To summarize, SMDS accepts high speed customer data in increments of up to 9,188 octets, then divides it into 53-octet cells for transmission through the service provider's network. At the receiving end, these cells are reassembled into customer data.

5.3.1 SMDS Standards

As mentioned previously, SMDS was developed by Bellcore, which is responsible for the majority of the documentation on that service. Among the key SMDS documents are:

Document	Subject
TR-TSV-000772	Generic System Requirements for SMDS
TR-TSV-000773	Local Access System Requirements, Objectives and Interfaces for SMDS
TR-TSV-000774	SMDS Operations Technology Network Element Requirements
TR-TSV-000775	Usage Measurement Requirements in Support of Billing for SMDS
TA-TSV-001059	SMDS Networking Requirements
TR-TSV-001060	SMDS Requirements for Exchange Access and Intercompany Serving Arrangements
TA-TSV-001061	Operations Technology Network Element Requirements for Inter-switch and Exchange Access
TR-TSV-001062	Phase 1 SMDS Customer Network Management Service Requirements
TR-TSV-001063	Operations Technology Generic Criteria in Support of Exchange Access SMDS and Intercompany Serving Arrangements
TR-TSV-001064	SMDS Generic Criteria on Operations Interfaces—Information Model and Usage
TR-TSV-001239	Generic Requirements for Low Speed SMDS Access
TA-TSV-001240	Generic Requirements for Frame Relay Access to SMDS

In addition, the SMDS Interest Group (SIG) has defined a number of technical specifications. These address specific implementation issues such as AppleTalk over SMDS and DECnet over SMDS. The European SIG has also developed SMDS requirements that are tailored for the European marketplace. Many of the SIG documents are available via anonymous FTP on host *ftp.acc.com*, in directory *pub/smds*.

5.3.2 The Subscriber Network Interface

For end users, the relevance of SMDS is at the interface into the network, not the internal operation of the network itself (Figure 5-12). The internal network operations are vital for the SMDS network provider, but of less interest to the end user. The demarcation point defined by Bellcore between the CPE and the network is called the Subscriber Network Interface, or SNI. At that point, the CPE connects to the network via a dedicated transmission link. By saying "dedicated", it is understood that a single customer's data, not shared data from several customers, is transported on that link. The physical connections that are currently defined for SMDS include DS0 (56/64 Kbps), DS1 (1.544 Mbps), and DS3 (44.736 Mbps).

Two connection alternatives between customer premises equipment (CPE) and an SMDS network have been defined: using the SMDS Interface Protocol (SIP) across the SNI, and using the Data Exchange Interface across the SNI (DXI-SNI), both shown in Figure 5-12.

SMDS-capable hosts or workstations (those that implement all three levels of the SIP) connect to the SMDS network using DS1 or DS3 circuits. Standard CSU/DSUs, operating at the appropriate rate (DS1 or DS3), provide the physical connection between this SMDS-capable customer equipment and the network.

It is also possible for the three levels of the SIP to be divided among two devices: an SMDS-capable CSU/DSU and a router. The interface between this SMDSU and router is called the Data Exchange Interface (DXI). The SMDS-capable CSU/DSU (generally referred to as an SMDSU) provides the SIP Level 1 and 2 protocol processing, while the router completes the protocol stack with SIP Level 3. By dividing the labor in this way, a router can be re-programmed to support SMDS by a simple software upgrade, with the SMDSU providing the more complex interfacing to the SMDS network. The DXI was a joint development between CSU/DSU vendors, such as ADC Kentrox (Portland, Oregon) and Digital Link Corp. (Sunnyvale, California), and router vendors such as Cisco Systems, Inc., (Mountain View, California). It is also possible for the SIP Level 1 and 2 protocol processing to be moved inside the network. In other words, the router would provide SIP Level 3, and the network supporting SMDS would provide SIP levels 1 and 2. A standard CSU/DSU is used in this case. The interface is thus referred to as the DXI-SNI (also shown in Figure 5-12), but is currently defined at only the DS0 rate of 64 Kbps.

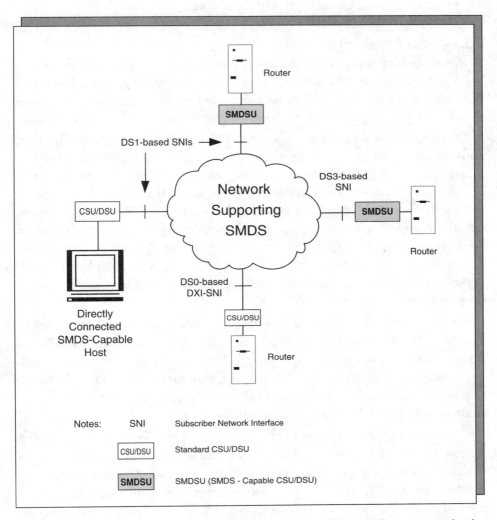

Figure 5-12. Role of SMDS in an enterprise network *(Copyright © 1994, Bellcore. Reprinted with permission.)*

Connection between two SMDS-based networks is achieved through an Interexchange Carrier Interface (ICI), as shown in the figure. When both intra- and inter-Local Area Transport Area (LATA) carriers are involved in providing SMDS service, the term Exchange Access SMDS (XA-SMDS) is used. Since our focus is on the use of, rather than the design of, an SMDS-based network, we will concentrate on the technical aspects of the SNI and SIP.

5.3.3 SMDS Addressing

SMDS is a public, packet-switched service that allows end users to exchange data units that are up to 9,188 octets in length. Two features impact the delivery of these data units: the SMDS addressing structure, and the various access classes assigned to that information flow, which will be considered in the next section.

Each of these data units is transmitted independently of any other data unit, and contains addresses that identify both the sender and the receiver of that data unit (Figure 5-13). SMDS addresses are assigned by the service provider, and identify the Subscriber Network Interface (SNI) from which a data unit was sent, or the SNI for which the data unit is intended. Two types of addresses have been defined: individual addresses and group addresses. An individual address is assigned uniquely to a single SNI. Each SNI can have a maximum of 16 addresses assigned. Group addresses allow an SMDS data unit to be delivered to multiple SNIs, analogous to a LAN multicast address. Multiple SNIs may thus be identified with a group address.

In the United States, SMDS addresses, both individual and group, consist of a prefix of "1", followed by a ten-digit number. In other countries, SMDS addresses begin with the country code of that country. These addresses are assigned according to the ITU-T E.164 standard, "Numbering Plan for the ISDN Era." The function of the address, identifying an individual or a group, is further defined by an Address Type field which precedes the address itself.

To create a logical private network, addressing restrictions, known as address screens, may be used. An Individual Address Screen scrutinizes destination addresses of data units that are sent by the CPE, and source addresses of data units to be delivered to the CPE. The Screen consists of either a set of allowed addresses, or a set of disallowed addresses, but not both. The Group Address Screen scrutinizes destination addresses of data units that are sent by the CPE. This screen also consists of a set of allowed addresses or disallowed addresses, but not both.

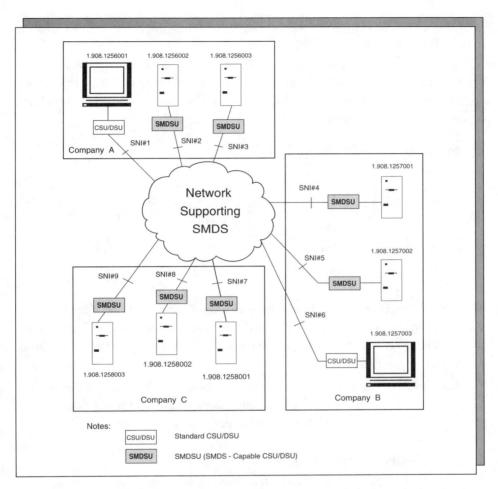

Figure 5-13. Inter-enterprise network using SMDS *(Copyright © 1994, Bellcore. Reprinted with permission.)*

5.3.4 Data Transfer via SMDS Networks

The physical path between the customer and the network is a leased line operating at the DS0, DS1, or DS3 rates. When data is transferred on those paths, it is sent at the maximum effective bandwidth: *56/65 Kbps, 1.17 Mbps, or 34 Mbps,* respectively, after any overhead is removed. Since each customer's traffic flow into the network varies, a prediction of the amount and duration of this traffic flow is required by the network. That measurement is called the Sustained Information Rate (SIR), given in Mbps.

The amount of data flowing on DS0- or DS1-based access lines is not measured by the network. For traffic flowing from CPE to the network on DS3-based access lines, traffic enforcement, using the SIR, applies. That enforcement is defined by one of five Access Classes:

Access Class	SIR (Mbps)
1	4
2	10
3	16
4	25
5	34

The Access Class constrains the duration of a data burst, and therefore the average rate of traffic flow. This parameter is determined at subscription time. It allows the customer to define their requirements, and the network to allocate its resources to meet these requirements.

Access Classes 1 and 3 are designed to support IEEE 802.5 LANs; Access Class 2 is meant for IEEE 802.3 LANs; and Access Class 5 is the maximum effective bandwidth across a DS3-based Subscriber Network Interface.

5.3.5   The SMDS Interface Protocol

The protocol operating at the Subscriber Network Interface, SMDS Interface Protocol, or SIP, is also based upon the 802.6 DQDB protocol. The operation of SIP across the SNI is defined as "access DQDB", to distinguish that function from other uses of the DQDB protocol. SIP is a three level protocol that is implemented in both the CPE and the SS (Figure 5-14). It uses the MAC Service to LLC (connectionless service) defined in 802.6. The three levels of SIP are grouped for design convenience and do not correspond to the lower three layers of the OSI Reference Model. SIP Level 3 handles addressing and error detection; SIP Level 2 handles framing and error detection; and SIP Level 1 handles the physical transport. Thus, the functions of these three levels are performing OSI Physical and Data Link layer operations.

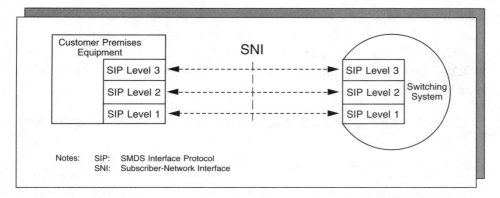

Figure 5-14. SIP protocol stack *(Source: TR-TSV-000772, © 1991, Bell Communications Research, Inc., reprinted with permission)*

Upper Layer Protocol (ULP) information, such as application data, comprises an SMDS Service Data Unit (SDU) (Figure 5-15). The SDU is transported within a Level 3 Protocol Data Unit (L3_PDU). The L3_PDU is then segmented into multiple SIP Level 2 PDUs (L2_PDUs). The SIP Level 1 process (not shown in the figure) handles the bit-level transmission functions across the physical interface. SIP Levels 3 and 2 are defined by Bellcore document TR-TSV-000772; while SIP Level 1 is defined in TR-TSV-00773.

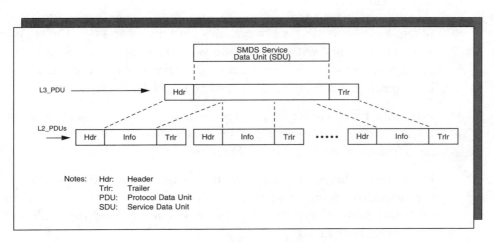

Figure 5-15. Encapsulation of user information by the layers of SIP *(Source: TR-TSV-000772, © 1991, Bell Communications Research, Inc., reprinted with permission)*

5.3.5.1 SIP Level 3

The L3_PDU Header is 36 octets in length, and contains twelve fields (Figure 5-16). Fields that are marked with the symbol X+ are used to align the SIP and DQDB protocol formats and are not processed by the network. The L3_PDU header fields are:

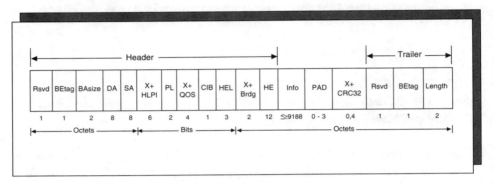

Figure 5-16. SIP Level 3 PDU format *(Source: TR-TSV-000772, © 1991, Bell Communications Research, Inc., reprinted with permission)*

- Reserved: a one-octet field that is filled with ZEROs by both the CPE and the SS.

- BEtag: a one-octet field which contains a beginning-end tag. The tag is a binary number with a value between 0–255, which forms an association between the first segment (containing the header) and the last segment (containing the trailer) of an L3_PDU.

- BAsize: a two-octet field containing the length, in octets, of the L3_PDU, from the beginning of the Destination Address field, up to and including the CRC32 field, if present.

- Destination Address: an eight-octet field which contains the address of the intended recipient of this L3_PDU. This field contains two subfields, Address_Type (the four most significant bits) and Address (the sixty remaining bits).

- ⊗ The Address_Type subfield value indicates an Individual address (1100) or a Group address (1110).

- ⊗ The Address subfield contains the SMDS address for which the L3_PDU is intended. For SMDS implementations in the United States, this subfield contains 0001 (indicating the country code for World Zone 1, North America); ten Binary Coded Decimal (BCD) digits (four bits each); and ends with sixteen ONE bits.

- ⊗ Source Address: an eight-octet field which contains the address of the sender of this L3_PDU. This field contains the Address_Type and Address subfields, as in the Destination Address. The value of the Address_Type field always indicates an Individual address (1100).

- ⊗ Higher Layer Protocol Identifier: a six-bit field that aligns the SIP and DQDB protocol formats.

- ⊗ PAD Length: a two-bit field which indicates the number of octets in the PAD field that are required to align the L3_PDU on a 32-bit boundary.

- ⊗ Quality of Service: a four-bit field which aligns the SIP and DQDB protocol formats.

- ⊗ CRC32 Indication Bit: a single-bit field which indicates the presence (value = 1) or absence (value = 0) of the CRC32 field.

- ⊗ Header Extension Length: a three-bit field which indicates the number of 32-bit words in the Header Extension field. Both CPE and SS populate this field with the value 011, indicating a three-word (or 12-octet) Header Extension field.

- ⊗ Bridging: a two-octet field which aligns the SIP and DQDB protocol formats.

- ⊗ Header Extension: a twelve-octet field, which contains version and carrier selection information, presented in a variable number of subfields:

  - ⊗ Element Length: a one-octet subfield which contains the combined length of the Element Length, Element Type, and Element Value fields, given in octets.

⊚ Element Type: a one-octet subfield that contains a binary value indicating the type of information found in the Element Value field:

Element Type	Meaning
0	Version - the version of SMDS access in use.
1	Carrier Selection—supports the per-L3_PDU carrier selection feature of exchange access service.
2–127	Reserved.
128–255	For use by other entities, such as Interexchange Carriers.

⊚ Element Value: a variable-length field, with a value dependent upon the Element Type and its function.

⊚ HE PAD: a variable length field, 0–9 octets in length, that assures that the length of the Header Extension field is twelve octets.

⊚ Information field: a variable-length field, up to 9,188 octets in length, which contains user information, known as a Level 3 Service Data Unit (SDU).

⊚ PAD: a variable-length field, from 0–3 octets in length, filled with ZEROs. This field aligns the entire L3_PDU on a 32-bit boundary, as indicated by the PAD Length field.

⊚ CRC32: a four-octet field, which may be absent, that performs error detection on the L3_PDU, beginning with the Destination Address field, through and including the CRC32 field.

The L3-PDU Trailer is four octets in length, and contains three fields:

⊚ Reserved: a one-octet field that is filled with ZEROS by both the CPE and the SS.

⊚ BEtag: a one-octet field that contains a beginning-end tag. The tag is a binary number with a value between 0–255, which forms an association between the first segment (containing the header) and the last segment (containing the trailer) of an L3_PDU.

⊗ Length: a two-octet field that contains the same value as the BAsize field.

5.3.5.2 SIP Level 2

The L2_PDU header contains five fields (Figure 5-17):

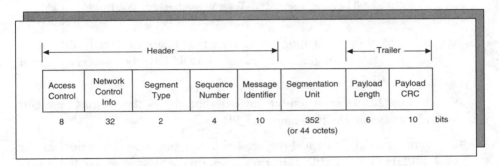

Figure 5-17. SIP Level 2 PDU format *(Source: TR-TSV-000772, © 1991, Bell Communications Research, Inc., reprinted with permission)*

⊗ Access Control: an eight-bit field that indicates whether the L2_PDU contains information (Busy = 1) or is empty (Busy = 0). It may also contain reservation priority information. There are two formats for this field: CPE to SS, and SS to CPE. For the CPE to SS case, the first bit is the Busy bit, and the next four bits are not processed by the network. The final three bits represent different DQDB priority levels in the distributed queue. For the SS to CPE case, the Busy bit is used, but the remaining seven bits are set to ZERO.

⊗ Network Control Information: a four-octet field that determines whether the L2_PDU contains information (value = FFFFF022H), or is empty (value = 0).

⊛ Segment Type: a two-bit field which indicates how non-empty L2_PDUs are to be processed by the receiver. The possible values are:

Segment Type Value	Meaning
00	Continuation of Message (COM)
01	End of Message (EOM)
10	Beginning of Message (BOM)
11	Single Segment Message (SSM)

⊛ Sequence Number: a four-bit number that is used to verify that all of the L2_PDUs belonging to a single L3_PDU have been received in the correct order.

⊛ Message Identifier: a ten-bit number that allows the various segments to be associated with a single L3_PDU.

⊛ Segmentation Unit: a 44-octet field that contains a portion of the L3_PDU. The LE_PDU, in turn, contains a header, upper layer protocol information, and a trailer, as discussed in the previous section.

The L2_PDU trailer contains two fields:

⊛ Payload Length: a six-bit field that indicates which of the 44 octets in the Segmentation Unit contain actual data. BOM and COM segments will always indicate 44 octets. EOM segments will indicate a number between 4 and 44 octets, in multiples of 4 octets. SSM segments will indicate a number between 28 and 44 octets, in multiples of 4 octets.

⊛ Payload CRC: a ten-bit CRC that performs error detection on the Segment Type, Sequence Number, Message Identifier, Segmentation Unit, Payload Length, and Payload CRC fields.

5.3.5.3 SIP Level 1

SIP Level 1 is responsible for the transmission of the L2_PDUs that are generated at SIP Level 2. These transmission functions are divided into two sublayers: an upper Physical Layer Convergence Procedure (PLCP) sublayer, and a lower Transmission System sublayer. The PLCP sublayer interfaces to the SIP Level 2 functions, and supports the transfer of both data (L2_PDUs) and control information. The Transmission System sublayer defines the format, speed, etc. for the data that is transmitted. The most common implementations for the Transmission System sublayer are based upon existing DS1 (1.544 Mbps) and DS3 (44.736 Mbps) technologies and standards. These two alternatives are point-to-point connections across the SNI. Bellcore document TR-TSV-000773 addresses both of these configurations.

5.3.6 The SMDS Data Exchange Interface

The Data Exchange Interface (DXI) protocol, defined by SIG-TS-001, allows LAN internetworking equipment, such as bridges and routers, to connect to the SMDS network facilities. This connection is made via a CSU/DSU, which provides the physical connection, using a DS1 or DS3 circuit to the network itself (Figure 5-18). The SIP Level 3 processing is done at the bridge/router, while the SIP Level 2 and 1 processing is done in the CSU/DSU. The bridge/router and CSU/DSU communicate using the DXI protocol. By splitting the functionality in this way, the internetworking equipment requires only a software upgrade, and existing Physical Layer interfaces, such as DS1 and DS3, may be used with the CSU/DSU. With the use of the DXI protocol, interoperability success between one vendor's CSU/DSU and another vendor's bridge/router is more likely.

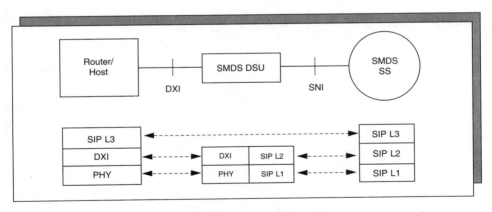

Figure 5-18. The DXI *(Source: TR-TSV-000772, © 1991, Bell Communications Research, Inc., reprinted with permission)*

5.3.7 SMDS Internetworking

SMDS has been designed for a great deal of internetworking capabilities, including bridging and routing. The next two sections will consider these configurations.

5.3.7.1 SMDS Bridging

Some LAN protocols, such as Digital Equipment Corp.'s Local Access Terminal (LAT) protocol, or the Network Basic Input/Output System (NetBIOS) protocol, do not contain Network Layer functions, and must therefore be bridged, not routed. In this case, the Data Link Layer is responsible for the internetworking functions (Figure 5-19). A bridge is used to connect to the LAN's MAC layer on one side, and the SMDS network on the other. The end system protocols, such as TCP, IP, and LLC, which are above SIP, are passed transparently through the SMDS network. Also illustrated in the figure are the similar functions provided by the MAC and SIP protocols—note that these two protocols are the only ones that operate in the bridge.

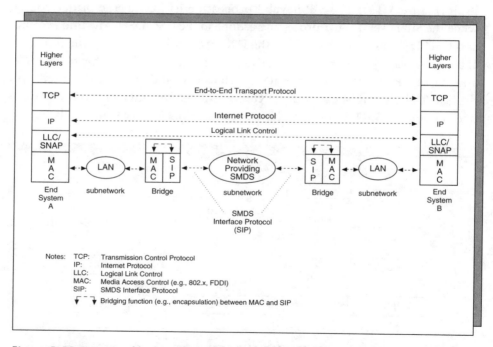

Figure 5-19. Scenario of bridging between an SMDS and a LAN *(Source: TR-TSV-000772, © 1991, Bell Communications Research, Inc., reprinted with permission)*

5.3.7.2 SMDS Routing

The Transmission Control Protocol/Internet Protocol (TCP/IP) suite developed by DARPA has become one of the most prominent internetworking solutions. Details on SMDS support for TCP/IP are detailed in RFC 1209 "The Transmission of IP Datagrams over the SMDS Service" [5-7], and also in Bellcore's TR-TSV-000772.

In this scenario, the logical connection between the LAN and the SMDS network is made at the Network Layer (Figure 5-20). End System A includes the higher layers, TCP, IP, LLC, and the MAC layer specific to the attached LAN. End System B also includes the higher layers, TCP, IP, and LLC, but the lower layer connects to the SMDS network using SIP. A router ties together the LAN and SMDS network, connecting to the LAN MAC layer on one side, and to the SMDS SIP layers on the other. Note that the higher protocols starting at LLC are passed transparently through the SMDS network.

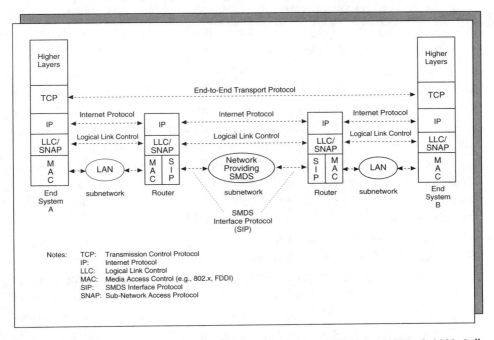

Figure 5-20. Scenario of using SMDS with DARPA protocols *(Source: TR-TSV-000772, © 1991, Bell Communications Research, Inc., reprinted with permission)*

At this writing, SMDS has emerged as a strong solution for organizations with geographically-dispersed locations, such as university campuses in several cities. References [5-8] through [5-10] are examples of carrier-provided information that demonstrates effective applications for this service.

5.4 Asynchronous Transfer Mode

Asynchronous Transfer Mode (ATM) technology is derived from standards developed by the International Telecommunications Union (ITU) that address the worldwide telecommunications infrastructure. Two significant developments have preceded ATM. In the early 1980s, the ITU developed standards for the Integrated Services Digital Network, ISDN. Narrowband ISDN (N-ISDN), as it is now called, defined two access interfaces: a Basic rate operating at 144 Kbps service, and a Primary rate operating at 1.544 Mbps. These interfaces were designed to carry a mixture of digital voice, data and control information. In the late 1980s, the N-ISDN work was further developed to include higher transmission rates, and was therefore called Broadband ISDN, or B-ISDN. The basis for B-ISDN is the ATM technology.

ATM is a connection-oriented service, in which the transmitted data from one user or source is organized into fixed-length cells. This datastream of cells, along with datastreams from other sources, are sent into the network. These various signal sources feed the ATM switch. These signals may include: constant bit rate service, such as a DS1 line operating at 1.544 Mbps; variable bit rate service, such as compressed video; or bursty data, such as LAN traffic. The signals are segmented into 48-octet payloads and prepended with a 5-octet header. The resulting 53-octet cells are input to the ATM switch and multiplexed together. They then contend for vacant slots in the outgoing ATM cellstream.

Information within the ATM header assures that each cell reaches the correct destination. Recall that ATM is a connection-oriented service, which requires the connection to be established prior to the transmission of data. Two addresses then identify the endpoint connections: a virtual channel identifier (VCI), and a virtual path identifier (VPI). The VCI and VPI formats will be studied in following sections.

The transmission delay of any one particular cell varies depending upon the traffic load presented by the other input datastreams. In other words, the arrival rate, or delay, of one particular datastream is not periodic. Therefore, the cell transfer is referred to as an asynchronous operation, or asynchronous transfer mode. This is in contrast with a synchronous transfer mode, which would have fixed periods for cell transmission and reception.

The B-ISDN protocol architecture model consists of three planes and four layers (Figure 5-21a). This model varies from the more familiar OSI Reference Model in that it uses three dimensions, instead of the two-dimensional model used with OSI. The planes could be thought of as protocol suites.

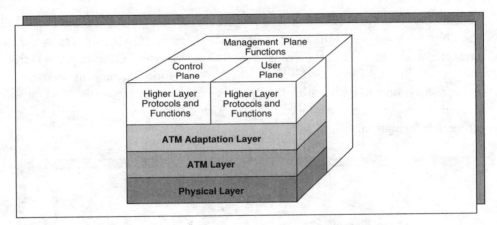

Figure 5-21a. B-ISDN Protocol Model *(Courtesy of* STACKS, The Network Journal*)*

The planes are designated User, Control, and Management. The User plane provides for the user-to-user information transfer, plus controls that are required for that information transfer, such as flow control and error recovery. The Control plane supports call control and connection control functions such as signaling. The signaling establishes, supervises, and releases calls and connections.

The Management plane controls the ATM device, such as a switch or a hub. Functions for this plane are divided into two subsets: Plane management and Layer management. Plane management deals with the system as a whole, management of the other planes, and coordination between the planes. Plane management does not have a layered structure. Layer management deals with the resources and parameters residing at each protocol layer. Operation and Maintenance (OAM) information flow, which is specific to a particular layer, is an example of a Layer management function.

The layers are designated Physical (PHY), ATM, ATM Adaptation (AAL), and Higher. The Physical layer is responsible for sending and receiving bits on the transmission medium, and for sending and receiving cells to and from the ATM layer. At the ATM layer, these cells are routed and switched to the appropriate circuit which connects with an end system and its specific application or process. The payload within that cell is generated at, or destined for, the AAL, a layer which interfaces the Higher layer functions and processes with the ATM layer.

Functions for the PHY and AAL layers are further subdivided (Figure 5-21b). The Physical layer is comprised of the Physical Medium (PM) sublayer, which interfaces to the cable, and the Transmission Convergence (TC) sublayer, which interfaces with the ATM layer. Likewise, the ATM Adaption Layer is divided into the Segmentation and Reassembly (SAR) sublayer, which generates the ATM payload, and the Convergence Sublayer (CS), which interfaces with the upper layer protocol information.

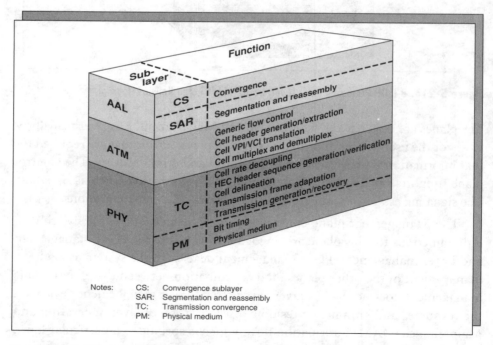

Figure 5-21b. ATM layers and sublayers *(Courtesy of STACKS, The Network Journal)*

5.4.1 ATM Standards

Standards for ATM networks have come from two key sources: the International Telecommunications Union—Telecommunication Standardization Sector (ITU-T), and the ATM Forum. The key ITU standards are:

I.113	B-ISDN Vocabulary of Terms
I.121	Broadband Aspects of ISDN
I.150	B-ISDN ATM Functional Characteristics
I.211	B-ISDN Service Aspects
I.311	B-ISDN General Network Aspects
I.321	B-ISDN Protocol Reference Model
I.327	B-ISDN Functional Architecture Aspects
I.361	B-ISDN ATM Layer Specification
I.362	B-ISDN ATM Adaptation Layer Functional Description
I.363	B-ISDN ATM Adaptation Layer Specification
I.413	B-ISDN User-Network Interface
I.432	B-ISDN User-Network Interface—Physical Layer Specification
I.555	Frame Relay and ATM Interworking
I.610	B-ISDN Operations and Maintenance Principles and Functions

Appendix D provides information on obtaining ITU-T documentation.

The ATM Forum does not develop its own standards, but instead seeks implementation consensus between users and vendors, thus assuring interoperability [5-11]. The key ATM Forum documents are:

ATM User-Network Interface (UNI) Specification, version 3.1 (1995).

ATM Broadband Inter Carrier Interface (B-ICI) Specification, version 1.1 (December 1994).

ATM Data Exchange Interface (DXI) Specification, version 1.0 (August 1993).

5.4.2 ATM Interfaces

A broadband network may include a number of distinct interfaces. The user-network interface (UNI) connects the ATM network and premises equipment, such as an ATM switch. Two types of UNIs may be present, public and private (Figure 5-22). A public UNI would connect a private ATM switch with a public ATM service provider's network. A private UNI would connect ATM users with the ATM switch.

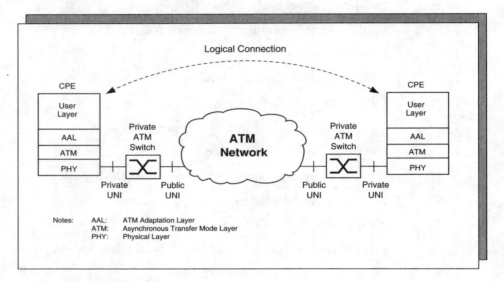

Figure 5-22. ATM network architecture

In some applications, the ATM protocol functions are divided between the Data Terminal Equipment (DTE), such as a router, and the hardware interface to the UNI, such as an ATM CSU/DSU. The ATM Data Exchange Interface (DXI) defines the protocol operations between these two devices (not shown in Figure 5-22).

The term network-node interface (NNI) is used to describe several network interconnection scenarios, either within a single carrier's network, or between two distinct carrier networks. The ATM Forum's designation for this is the Broadband Inter-Carrier Interface (B-ICI), which allows interconnection between public carriers that provide ATM service (also not shown in Figure 5-22).

When an ATM network connects to another network, such as frame relay or SMDS, conversions between the two network protocols are required. These conversions are performed by processes called interworking functions (IWFs), which are defined in the ATM Forum's B-ICI specification.

A number of Physical Layer interfaces have been designed in support of B-ISDN and ATM. The B-ISDN documents from ANSI's T1S1 committee specify Synchronous Optical Network (SONET)-based physical interfaces operating over single mode fiber (SMF), multimode fiber (MMF), and coax at 51.84 Mbps (the OC1 rate); interfaces operating over SMF, MMF, and coax at 155.52 Mbps (OC3); and a 622.08 Mbps (OC12) interface over SMF. In addition, a DS3 interface over coaxial cable (44.736 Mbps), plus a DS1 interface over twisted pair cable have been defined. The ATM Forum's UNI 3.0 specification includes a 100 Mbps interface over MMF, plus a 155.52 Mbps interface over either MMF or shielded twisted pair (STP) cable. The ATM Forum's UNI 3.1 specification adds a DS1 interface, plus two more SONET-based interfaces, 51.84 Mbps over unshielded twisted pair (UTP) cable and 155.52 Mbps over UTP. Other interfaces have been defined for use in Europe, operating at the E1 (2.048 Mbps), E3 (34.368 Mbps), and E4 (139.264 Mbps) rates. Quite a wide variety of choices for the network manager to ponder!

5.4.3 Virtual Connections

Each ATM cell, whether sent at the UNI or the NNI, contains information that identifies the virtual connection to which it belongs. There are two parts to that identification, a virtual channel identifier (VCI) and a virtual path identifier (VPI). Both the VCI and VPI are used at the ATM layer. The virtual channels, with their VCIs, and the virtual paths, with their VPIs, are contained within the physical transmission path, as shown in Figure 5-23.

The virtual channel is defined in I.311 as "a unidirectional communication capability for the transport of ATM cells." To originate or terminate a virtual channel link, a VCI is either assigned or removed. Virtual channel links are concatenated to form a virtual channel connection, or VCC, which is an end-to-end cell path at the ATM layer.

A virtual path is defined as "a bundle of virtual channel links", all of which have the same endpoint. In other words, the virtual path is analogous to a large telephone cable, where all of the circuits terminate in the same central office. To originate or terminate a virtual path link, the VPI is either assigned or removed. Virtual path links are concatenated to form a virtual path connection, or VPC.

Each end-user service is thus addressed by two VCI/VPI pairs: one for the transmit function, and one for the receive function.

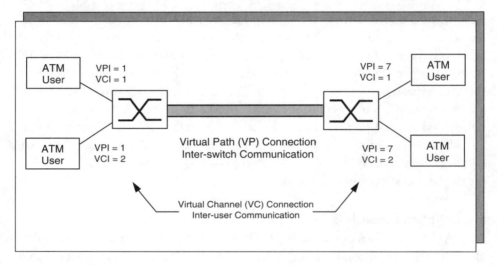

Figure 5-23. Virtual paths and channels

5.4.4 ATM Cells

An ATM cell is 53 octets in length, and consists of a 5-octet header and a 48-octet payload. Two formats for the header are defined: one at the User-Network Interface (UNI), and a second at the Network-Node Interface (NNI). The following sections will explore these formats separately.

5.4.4.1 ATM Cells at the UNI

The ATM header at the UNI consists of six fields (Figure 5-24):

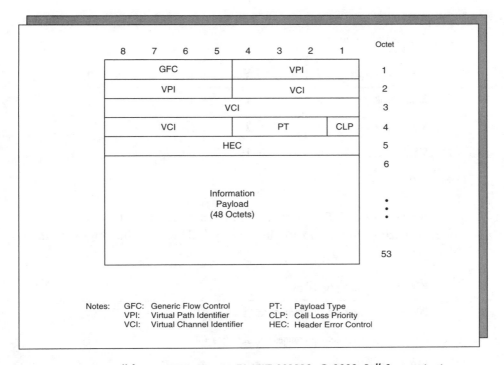

Figure 5-24. ATM cell format (UNI) *(Source: TA-NWT-001113, © 1993, Bell Communications Research, Inc., reprinted with permission)*

⊛ Generic Flow Control (GFC): a four-bit field that may be used to provide local functions, such as flow control. This field has local, not end-to-end, significance, and is overwritten by intermediate ATM switches. The UNI 3.1 specification states that this field should be filled with all ZEROs by the transmitting host.

⊛ Virtual Path Indicator (VPI): an eight-bit field which identifies the virtual path across the interface.

⊛ Virtual Channel Indicator (VCI): a sixteen-bit field which identifies the virtual channel across the interface. The UNI 3.1 specification defines some VPI/VCI values for specific functions, such as meta-signaling, used to establish the signaling channel; point-to-point signaling; and

Operations and Maintenance (OAM) cells. Examples of preassigned VPI/VCI values are:

Function	VPI	VCI
Meta-signaling	0	1
Signaling	0	2
SMDS	0	15
ILMI	0	16

⊛ Payload Type (PT): a three-bit field that identifies the type of information contained in the payload. The field has eight defined values:

PTI	Interpretation
000	User data, no congestion, SDU type = 0
001	User data, no congestion, SDU type = 1
010	User data, congestion, SDU type = 0
011	User data, congestion, SDU type = 1
100	OAM segment data, F5 flow related
110	Reserved, future traffic control and resource management
111	Reserved, future functions

⊛ Cell Loss Priority (CLP): a single bit field that is used by either the user or network to indicate the explicit loss priority of the cell.

⊛ Header Error Control (HEC): an eight-bit field that is used to detect and/or correct bit errors that occur in the header.

5.4.4.2 ATM Cells at the NNI

The ATM header at the NNI is also five octets in length, and is identical to the UNI format with the exception of the first octet (Figure 5-25). The NNI, which provides bundles of VCIs between switches, defines an additional four bits for the VPI. In other words, the NNI has twelve bits for the VPI and sixteen for the VCI. The UNI has eight bits for the VPI and sixteen bits for the VCI.

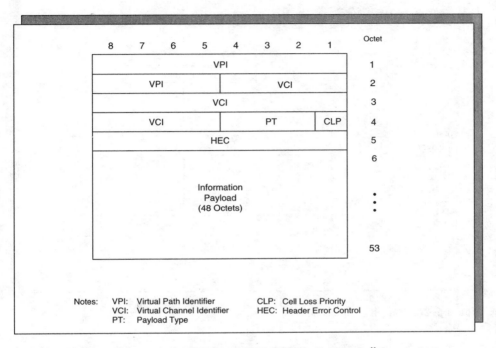

Figure 5-25. ATM cell format (UNI) *(Source: TA-NWT-001113, © 1993, Bell Communications Research, Inc., reprinted with permission)*

5.4.4.3 Generating the ATM Cell

User information, such as a voice, data, or image traffic, is passed from the User Layer to the Convergence Sublayer (CS) portion of the ATM Adaptation Layer being used (Figure 5-26). At the CS, header and trailer information is added, and subsequently passed to the Segmentation and Reassembly (SAR) Sublayer. The SAR Sublayer is responsible for generating the 48-octet payloads, which are then passed to the ATM Layer. The ATM Layer adds the appropriate header (UNI or NNI), resulting in a 53-octet cell. That cell is then transmitted over the physical media, such as a SONET connection, to an intermediate or destination switch, which is eventually delivered to the end-user process.

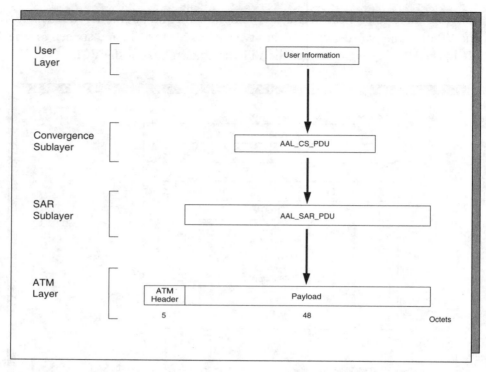

Figure 5-26. ATM cell encapsulation

5.4.5 ATM Management

One of the significant elements of the B-ISDN architecture is the management plane (review Figure 5-21a). The ATM Forum developed the Interim Local Management Interface (ILMI) to address those management requirements. The ILMI assumes that each ATM device, which is supporting at least one UNI, has a UNI Management Entity (UME) associated with each UNI. Network management information is then communicated between UMEs (Figure 5-27). The protocol chosen for the ILMI communication is the Simple Network Management Protocol (SNMP), which is designated as SNMP/AAL. At the ATM Layer, one VCC is provisioned for this ILMI communication, with a default VPI/VCI = 0/16.

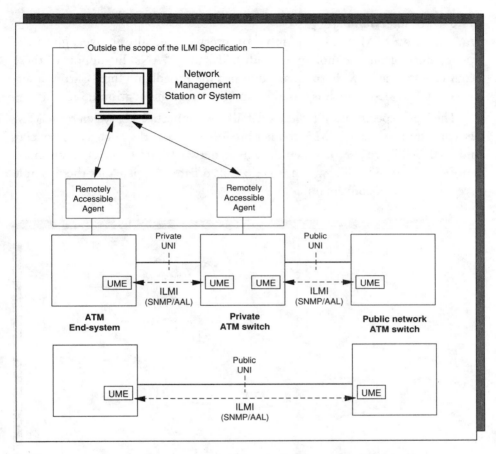

Figure 5-27. The ATM Interim Local Management Interface *(Courtesy of The ATM Forum)*

The management information defined by the ILMI provides status and configuration information from the UME regarding the UNI. This information is organized into a Management Information Base (MIB), which contains several groups of managed objects. Examples include Physical Layer details, such as the transmission media type (SONET, DS3, etc.); and ATM Layer statistics, such as the number of ATM cells transmitted or received. Further details on the ILMI are found in the ATM Forum's UNI 3.1 Specification [5-12].

5.4.6 ATM Interworking

Standards for ATM define a number of interworking alternatives, given the applicability of this technology to both LANs and WANs. In support of these requirements, the ATM Forum has published the Broadband Inter-Carrier Interface (B-ICI) [5-13], which is based upon ITU Recommendation I.555.

The B-ICI specification includes details for connections between both ATM networks and between ATM and other broadband networks, such as frame relay and SMDS (Figure 5-28). When dissimilar networks are connected, an interworking function (IWF), which functions as a gateway, provides the multiple layers of protocol conversion.

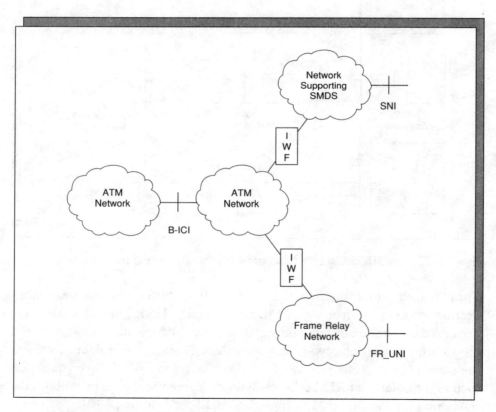

Figure 5-28. ATM interworking

Connections between frame relay and ATM are based upon PVCs between an ATM UNI and a frame relay UNI or NNI. Interoperability issues that must be addressed by such a system include: conversion between frame relay and ATM protocols; mapping between frame relay and ATM virtual circuits; alignment of frame relay and ATM traffic management parameters; and mapping of local management information, such as the frame relay LMI and the ATM ILMI.

For SMDS and ATM network connections, two scenarios have been proposed. The first scenario assumes that the CPE is using all three levels of SIP, with a subsequent conversion into the ATM protocols. The second scenario considers that an ATM User Layer protocol, defined by Bellcore as SIP Connectionless Service (SIP_CLS), is operating on top of the ATM protocol stack. Both of these alternatives are addressed in Bellcore's TA-NWT-001110 document [5-14].

5.5 Broadband Internetworking Examples

The following sections will profile three different IXC and LEC service offerings, supporting frame relay, SMDS, and ATM applications, respectively.

5.5.1 CompuServe Network Services FRAMENet FRAD

CompuServe, Inc. of Columbus, Ohio, provides FRAME-Net, a global public frame relay service supported by CompuServe's existing StrataCom-based network that also offers worldwide X.25 packet services. CompuServe offers frame relay service across the United States and in 13 other countries. Access rates include 56, 128, 256, 384, 512, 640, 768, and 896 Kbps, plus 1.024 and 1.544 Mbps in the U.S. and Canada. In other countries, the service is available with 64 Kbps access, with the exception of the United Kingdom, where FRAME-Net is available at 64 and 128 Kbps access rates. At the time of this writing, only PVC service is available.

In August 1994, CompuServe announced plans to offer ISDN-based SVC service via StrataCom's INS server. Access for the service will initially range from 64 to 128 Kbps. At the time of this writing, pricing and availability for this service have not been determined.

The Committed Information Rates (CIRs) available on these PVCs range up to 512 Kbps. As part of its service offering, CompuServe arranges for the digital access line from the customer's premises to the CompuServe frame relay service center. It also provides the CSU/DSUs as required for that access rate. In addition, CompuServe offers its FRAME-Net CPE Advantage program, which gives the customer the option of leasing, through CompuServe, routers, FRADs, and SDLC FRADs for a complete solution.

FRAME-Net's pricing structure is a flat rate per PVC. It varies by the CIR, with term and volume discounts available. FRAME-Net is configurable in 4 Kbps increments and is priced in 16 Kbps increments up to 512 Kbps.

One of CompuServe's FRAME-Net Services that has received industry accolades is their SDLC FRAD [5-5], shown in Figure 5-29. The FRAME-Net SDLC FRAD broadens the scope of connectivity options for IBM SNA host and midrange platforms. Customers with a current investment in SNA networks are able to benefit from high-speed frame relay service without additional capital investment. CompuServe provides an end-to-end solution including configuration, installation, maintenance, and support of the FRAD at the customer's premises for a single monthly rate. Pricing for this service is provided on a case-by-case basis.

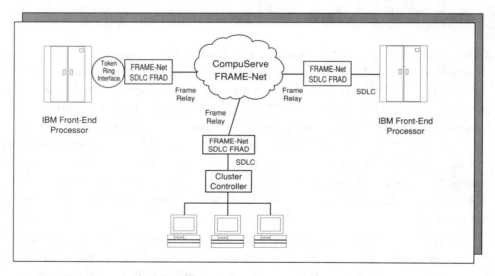

Figure 5-29. CompuServe FRAME-Net SDLC FRAD *(Courtesy of CompuServe Inc.)*

An SNA host or controller that does not currently support the frame relay interface is connected to the FRAME-Net SDLC FRAD (Figure 5-29). This FRAD accepts the host data in its preferred protocol, such as SDLC, IBM BSC 2780/3780,

IBM BSC 3270, token ring, or Ethernet. The FRAD encapsulates that data inside frame relay frames, and delivers it to the FRAME-Net network over the digital access line. At the other end of the connection, the SNA data is extracted from the frame relay frame and delivered to the user device.

In summary, CompuServe's FRAME-Net FRAD service delivers both the transport services and networking hardware to solve a commonly encountered challenge—a cost-effective, end-to-end connectivity solution for legacy systems.

5.5.2   Pacific Bell SMDS with TCP/IP

Pacific Bell, headquartered in San Francisco, California, is one of the most progressive LECs, serving subscribers in California and Nevada. Pacific Bell offers a full range of enhanced digital services, including frame relay, SMDS, and ATM.

Pacific Bell provides SMDS in eight out of California's ten Local Access Transport Areas (LATAs), resulting in SMDS availability to over 95% of all of its customers. SMDS is offered with throughput rates of 1.17, 4, 10, 16, 25, and 34 Mbps with a Subscriber Network Interface (SNI), as well as with a trunkside interface to compatible SMDS networks over the standard Inter Carrier Interface (ICI) with a 34 Mbps throughput rate. By the end of 1995, Pacific Bell plans to add a low speed (56/64 Kbps) option, which uses the SMDS Data eXchange Interface (DXI).

Pacific Bell pricing for all of its fast packet services is flat rated and mileage insensitive. Customers can receive LATA-wide connectivity with unlimited usage for one reasonable flat rate. This provides an economic alternative to private lines with three or more customer sites. At the time of this writing, SMDS charges for DS1 rate access are approximately $720 per month per site.

While SMDS is protocol independent, one of the more popular applications for the technology is providing connectivity for TCP/IP environments, as described in Bellcore's *SMDS User's Guide,* reference [5-9], and illustrated in Figure 5-30. For routers to communicate using SMDS, their SMDS interfaces need to be on the same logical Internet Protocol subnetwork (abbreviated LIS). In the example in Figure 5-30, this subnetwork has an IP address represented by 191.4.20.0. Three routers are connected to the network providing SMDS, using IP addresses 191.4.20.57, 191.4.20.58, and 191.4.20.59, respectively.

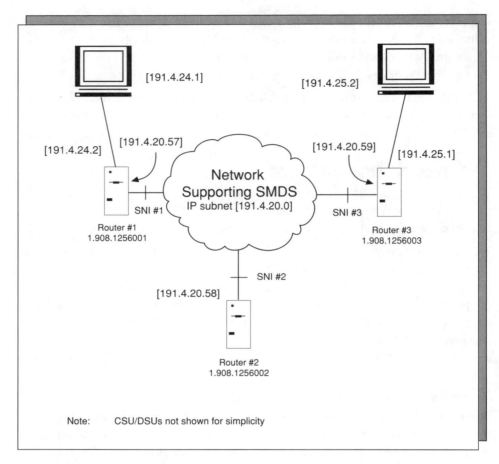

Figure 5-30. IP networking using SMDS *(Copyright © 1994, Bellcore. Reprinted with permission.)*

SMDS group addresses are used to carry Address Resolution Protocol (ARP) and routing protocol traffic, such as Routing Information Protocol (RIP) messages. An SMDS group address is selected as an ARP and/or IP multicasting address, and each router is configured to recognize that same multicast address.

For each of the three SNIs, an allowed SMDS individual address screen is established that contains the SMDS addresses for all of the SNIs within that LIS. Secondly, an allowed SMDS group address screen is established that contains the SMDS group address that is defined for the ARP and/or routing protocol messages. Finally, each router may be configured with a static table which maps the IP addresses to the SMDS addresses, as follows:

IP Address	SMDS Address
191.4.20.58	C19081256002
191.4.20.59	C19081256003

Alternatives to SMDS are private lines, frame relay, and ATM. SMDS is different from other fast packet services in its connectionless nature, which provides any-to-any connectivity without the need to provision permanent virtual circuits (PVCs) within either the customer's router or Pacific Bell's network. In addition, bandwidth scalability from 56 Kbps to 34 Mbps allows the network manager to select the optimum bandwidth needed at each site. SMDS is designed as a data-only service, but provides a good migration for a customer's data requirements into the similarly cell-based ATM network in the future.

In summary, SMDS is an economic and scalable alternative for customers with at least three locations requiring connectivity at data rates from 56 Kbps through 34 Mbps. SMDS extends the features and functionality of Local Area Networking over a metropolitan or wide area network.

5.5.3 AT&T InterSpan ATM Service

AT&T, headquartered in Basking Ridge, New Jersey, offers InterSpan ATM Service, which is designed to meet the needs of businesses with multiple locations that require high bandwidth services for data, video, and voice applications. InterSpan ATM is one of AT&T's Data Communications Services, which include the ACCUNET Digital Services, dedicated and switched analog and digital leased lines, packet and frame relay services.

InterSpan ATM Service is available in the United States at more than 300 locations. The service can be accessed at 45 Mbps. InterSpan Frame Relay Service is available at access rates from 56 Kbps to 1.5 Mbps at more than 500 locations across the United States and Canada, plus 16 European countries and the Pacific Rim. InterSpan Information Access Service provides customers with dial access to AT&T's packet and frame relay networks.

AT&T's frame relay and ATM services share a common architecture, with different interfaces (see Figure 5-31). This architecture is based upon AT&T Network Systems GlobeView-2000 Broadband Switching System, a 20-gigabit cell-net switching system; and the Stratacom, Inc. StrataCom Broadband Packet Exchange (BPX) 9.6 gigabit switching platform, which provides interworking between frame relay and ATM.

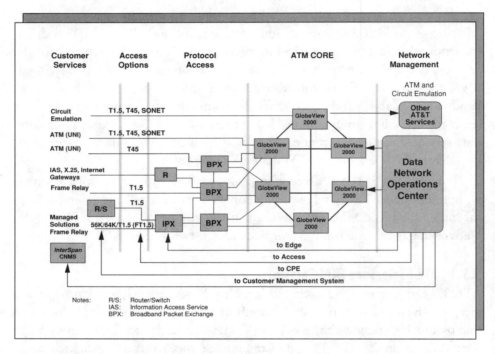

Figure 5-31. AT&T InterSpan High Speed Services architecture *(Courtesy of AT&T)*

InterSpan ATM Service is available from more than 300 locations (or Points of Presence—POPs) at 45 Mbps. The number of locations will increase to over 400 when 1.5 Mbps access is added during 1995. The GlobeView-2000 is equipped, today, to support SONET interfaces at 155 Mbps. The service will provide that interface as customers need it. In addition, ATM DXI is under consideration.

InterSpan ATM Service offers Class A capabilities (for voice, video, and circuit emulation) and Class C capabilities for frame relay and X.25 traffic. At the time of this writing, only PVC service is available, although SVC service is planned in the future.

AT&T's leased lines are priced according to published tariff rates, while the InterSpan services are offered under contract rates. The prices for InterSpan ATM Service are based upon port charges, PVC monthly recurring charges, plus one-time installation charges. Class A service PVCs are bandwidth and distance sensitive, while Class C PVCs are bandwidth sensitive only.

AT&T also offers its customers the ability to manage their ATM and frame relay networks through its Customer Network Management Services (CNMS), also shown in Figure 5-31. Customers have two interfaces, SNMP Access and Advanced Reports. The SNMP Access interface allows customers to view their network configuration and obtain real time performance information. The Advanced Reports interface provides customers with information about their network utilization, which can be used to optimize the network for highest performance and lowest cost.

This chapter has investigated what many believe to be the future of computer networking—broadband technologies. Readers needing additional technical details are referred to another volume of the Network Troubleshooting Library, *Analyzing Broadband Networks* [5-15]. In the next chapter, we will study applications for these technologies, and products that are used for LAN-to-WAN connections.

5.6   References

[5-1]   Information on the Frame Relay Forum may be obtained from:
Frame Relay Forum North American Office
303 Vintage Park Drive, Foster City, CA 94404
Telephone (415) 578-6980
Fax (415) 525-0182
Faxback Service (415) 688-4317

[5-2]   *A Guide to Frame Relay, Business Communications Review Supplement,* (October 1991): 1–39.

[5-3]   Bellcore. *Frame Relay User's Guide,* document PB2332-1, November 1994.

[5-4]   Pacific Bell. *Frame Relay Interface Specification*, document PUB L-780079-PB, October 1993.

[5-5]   Salamone, Salvatore. "One-Stop Shopping for SNA." *Data Communications*, (January 1994): 64.

[5-6]   Information on the SMDS Interest Group may be obtained from:
        SMDS Interest Group
        303 Vintage Park Drive
        Foster City, CA 94404
        Telephone (415) 578-6979
        Fax (415) 525-0182
        Faxback Service (415) 688-4314

[5-7]   Piscitello, D. and J. Lawrence. "The Transmission of IP Datagrams over the SMDS Service." RFC 1209, March 1991.

[5-8]   *SMDS Today—Networks in Action, Business Communications Review Supplement* (September 1993): 1-31.

[5-9]   Bellcore. *SMDS User's Guide*. May 1994.

[5-10] Pacific Bell. *SMDS Network Interface Specification*. PUB L-780090-PB/NB, August 1992.

[5-11] Information on the ATM Forum may be obtained from:
        ATM Forum Worldwide Headquarters
        303 Vintage Park Drive
        Foster City, CA 94404
        Telephone (415) 578-6860
        Fax (415) 525-0182
        Faxback Service (415) 688-4318

[5-12] The ATM Forum. ATM User-network Interface Specification version 3.1. New York: Prentice-Hall, 1995.

[5-13] The ATM Forum. BISDN Inter Carrier Interface (B-ICI) Specification Version 1.1. September 1994

[5-14] Bell Communications Research, Inc. "Broadband ISDN Switching System Generic Requirements." TA-NWT-001110, August 1993.

[5-15] Miller, Mark A. *Analyzing Broadband Networks*. New York, M&T Books, Inc., 1994.

6 LAN to WAN Internetworking

Enterprise-wide internetworks are rarely built from scratch. Instead, they evolve, perhaps from mainframe- or minicomputer-based networks, adding LAN, remote office and remote access capabilities as required. Central to this enterprise-wide network case, however, is the need to effectively use WAN transmission facilities. In this chapter, we'll look at applications that meet specific requirements for internetworking environments.

To begin, let's assume that we have a system in which the network resources are located at different sites. The network may not have started out that way, however. Since the initial installation, new network requirements may have evolved: expansion, access to new resources, and different platform connectivity. First, the network has invariably grown. A growth rate of 100–200 percent in the first year is not uncommon. Second, the network now needs to access other identified resources (at separate locations). These other resources may be another LAN, a host computer, or a remote workstation—such as that belonging to a traveling salesperson or to telecommuters. Third, the platforms requiring connectivity might not be the same; they may range from Macintosh to UNIX. All of these user requirements will invariably require the use of WAN facilities. (This subject has received much publicity lately—see references [6-1] through [6-5] for examples of LAN-WAN applications and current issues.)

The topic of LAN-WAN interconnection is a broad one. Many fine products are available. In order to put some structure into our study, Section 6.1 will first investigate the design issues of LAN-WAN interconnectivity, answering the question of how to determine the type of transmission facility that is required for a particular application. In our study of design issues, we will look at analog and digital leased lines, frame relay, SMDS, and ATM issues. Sections 6.2 through 6.8 will describe products that are used with the various transmission facilities. For these sections, we'll begin with the lower-speed, dial-up lines, and conclude with the high-speed SMDS and ATM products.

6.1 Designing the LAN-WAN Connection

Let's assume that the internetwork contains segments (or subnetworks) in dissimilar locations. The objective is to design the LAN/WAN transmission facilities required for this internetwork. Since this can be an involved process, let's break it down into a number of smaller steps.

Define the Goals. Determine the functional goals for the internetwork. Write these down as a statement of objective, so that all parties associated with the internet are aware of what is being attempted. Reference [6-6], Chapter 5, includes an excellent tutorial on design goals. The issues discussed include cost, performance, maintenance and support, reliability, redundancy, and robustness. The last issue, robustness, is especially critical for LAN/WAN integration, as it addresses the ability of the internetwork to handle periods of heavy usage or peak activity.

Identify the Components. Identify the hardware/software components at each location that must be incorporated into the internetwork. Specifically address two issues. First: Which LAN hardware architectures (e.g. Ethernet, token ring) must be connected? If a long-range plan exists to convert one architecture to another (e.g. replacing Ethernet with FDDI or ATM), make sure that these long-term objectives are considered as well. Second: Which LAN operating systems (e.g. Novell's NetWare, Banyan's VINES, etc.) are implemented at each location? Or, has the TCP/IP protocol suite been implemented at any location? It is considerably easier to connect dissimilar systems if they have some degree of commonality in either their hardware or software platforms.

Understand the Applications. Consider the applications that are to be internetworked—such as electronic messaging using the CCITT X.400 standard, or file transfer using the Sun Microsystems NFS (Network File System). As with the hardware/software platforms, if there are common denominators at the Application Layer, the design job is that much easier.

Project the Growth. Make a projection of the growth that is expected to occur between various locations in the internetwork in the next 1, 3, and 5 years. Consider three growth areas: at individual locations, in the number of locations, and as a result of mergers or acquisitions that may occur during the projected period.

Analyze the Traffic. Determine the amount of network traffic between various internetwork locations. This study will begin by measuring the network traffic on each segment, and will then calculate the amount of inter-segment traffic. (Reference [6-7] discusses link capacity requirements in general, reference [6-8] discusses the Ethernet design case, and [6-9] provides a Token Ring example.)

A flowchart often helps get the LAN-WAN design process off the ground. Figure 6-1, taken from reference [6-10], provides a good starting point.

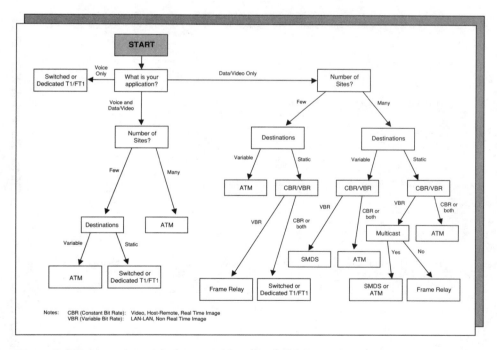

Figure 6-1. Service selection decision tree *(Courtesy of ADC Kentrox)*

6.1.1   Leased Line Network Configurations

Designs for leased line networks in particular, and broadband networks in general, begin with an analysis of the LAN-WAN-LAN traffic patterns. An excellent template for this traffic analysis is shown in Figures 6-2a through 6-2e, taken from Appendix A of reference [6-11]. While originally designed for Ethernet networks, many of the principles could be applied to other network designs. The analysis is broken down into five different worksheets:

Host Resource Worksheet #1

Host Type	Protocols	Applications Running	Max Users	Current Users	Resources Left
Host Type	Protocols	Applications Running	Max Users	Current Users	Resources Left
Host Type	Protocols	Applications Running	Max Users	Current Users	Resources Left
Host Type	Protocols	Applications Running	Max Users	Current Users	Resources Left
Host Type	Protocols	Applications Running	Max Users	Current Users	Resources Left

Figure 6-2a. Host Resource Worksheet #1 *(Courtesy of Vitalink Communications Corporation)*

Peripheral Resource Worksheet #2

Terminal Server	Protocol	Total Ports	Ports Used
_____	_____	_____	_____
_____	_____	_____	_____
_____	_____	_____	_____
_____	_____	_____	_____
_____	_____	_____	_____
_____	_____	_____	_____
_____	_____	_____	_____
_____	_____	_____	_____
_____	_____	_____	_____
_____	_____	_____	_____
_____	_____	_____	_____
_____	_____	_____	_____
_____	_____	_____	_____

Other Devices	Protocol
_____	_____
_____	_____
_____	_____
_____	_____
_____	_____

Figure 6-2b. Peripheral Resource Worksheet #2 *(Courtesy of Vitalink Communications Corporation)*

233

Traffic Worksheet #3

Site Name _____

Protocol _____

A. Number of Users _____
B. # of Packets per Sample _____
C. % of Total Ethernet Traffic _____

MULTICAST TRAFFIC

D. # of Multicast Packets per Sample _____
C. % of Total Ethernet Traffic _____
F. % of Protocol Traffic _____
G. Average Packet Size _____

USER TRAFFIC

H. # of Data Packets per Sample _____
I. % of Total Ethernet Traffic _____
J. Average Large Ethernet Packet Size _____
K. % of Large Packet Traffic _____
L. Average Medium Packet Size _____
M. % of Medium Packet Traffic _____
N. Average Small Packet Traffic _____
O. % of Small Packet Traffic _____

AVERAGE TRAFFIC PER USER PER PROTOCOL

B/A = *Total Number of Packets / Number of Protocol Users*
G∗F = *Average Multicast Packet Size ∗ % of Protocol Traffic*
J∗K = *Average Large Data Packet Size ∗ % of Large Packet Traffic*
L∗M = *Average Medium Data Packet Size ∗ % of Medium Packet Traffic*
N∗O = *Average Small Data Packet Size ∗ % of Small Packet Traffic*

P = *Average Number of Bytes per User for this Protocol*
P = *[(B/A)((G∗F) + (J∗K) + (L∗M) + (N∗O))]*

Average Number of Bytes per User for this Protocol _____

Figure 6-2c. Traffic Worksheet #3 *(Courtesy of Vitalink Communications Corporation)*

Remote Traffic Worksheet #4

Link Name _____

Site Name _____ to Site Name _____

In this section, the traffic per user for a specific protocol (taken from worksheet 3) is converted from the time unit of the sample to the time unit of one second (e.g. if the sample was 1 minute, then x would equal 60 for the conversion factor to seconds). This number is then multiplied by 8 to convert from bytes per second to bits per second. When multiplied by the number of remote users, this becomes the amount of bandwidth needed for this protocol in a remote environment.

Protocol	Traffic/User	Traffic/User /Sec	Bps/User	Remote Users	Bandwidth Needed
_____	_____ /x	_____ *8	_____ *	_____ =	_____
_____	_____ /x	_____ *8	_____ *	_____ =	_____
_____	_____ /x	_____ *8	_____ *	_____ =	_____
_____	_____ /x	_____ *8	_____ *	_____ =	_____
_____	_____ /x	_____ *8	_____ *	_____ =	_____
_____	_____ /x	_____ *8	_____ *	_____ =	_____
_____	_____ /x	_____ *8	_____ *	_____ =	_____
_____	_____ /x	_____ *8	_____ *	_____ =	_____
_____	_____ /x	_____ *8	_____ *	_____ =	_____

Bandwidth Needed = _____

It is advisable for reasons of throughput and ease of management to multiply the bandwidth needed by 1.30 to ensure that the link will have a 30% buffer to maximize throughput with bandwidth utilization at 70%.

Suggested Bandwidth = 1.30 * Bandwidth Needed

Figure 6-2d. Remote Traffic Worksheet #4 *(Courtesy of Vitalink Communications Corporation)*

Network Growth Worksheet #5

Link Name _____

Site Name _____ to Site Name _____

A = Peak Bandwidth Utilization of Link _____
B = # of Current Users _____
C = Peak Bandwidth per User _____

C = A/B

D = Additional Future Users _____
E = Future Bandwidth Requirements _____

E = C*(B+D)

Future Bandwidth Requirements = _____

Figure 6-2e. Network Growth Worksheet #5 *(Courtesy of Vitalink Communications Corporation)*

Worksheet number 1, the "Host Resource Worksheet," is designed to give a clear understanding of the host resources that are available to the remote user community. The parameters examined include:

⊛ Host Type: The manufacturer's designation for the host or workstation.

⊛ Protocols: The protocols that are actively implemented on the hosts.

⊛ Applications Running: These should be categorized as interactive, program compilation, file transfer, word processing, database, graphics oriented, etc.

⊛ Max Users: Either the maximum number of simultaneous users as stipulated by the manufacturer, or the number of users that will cause throughput to drop to an unacceptable level for your environment.

⊛ Current Users: The average number of people simultaneously logged into a host.

⊛ Resources Left: The difference between maximum users and current users. The amount of resource remaining for remote user load.

By completing Worksheet number 1, you detail the host resources that are available for sharing by any remote devices and users of the wide area network.

Worksheet number 2, the "Peripheral Resource Worksheet," provides a list of all nodes other than host nodes that exist on the network segments. This worksheet will indicate the growth permitted at this site by the existing hardware. Worksheet number 2 is also valuable if there are no tools to monitor the traffic, leaving traffic estimation to averages established by protocol and peripheral type.

Worksheet numbers 3 and 4 are for those who choose to closely monitor their Ethernet traffic with hardware and software. If you are not interested in doing this, skip to Worksheet number 5.

Worksheet number 3, the "Traffic Worksheet," will prove helpful to those who choose to monitor their Ethernet traffic at each site with Ethernet monitoring devices, such as LAN analyzers and network management hardware and software. Samples of traffic should be taken on the production network at a time of day that most accurately represents the typical amount of traffic on each segment. Multiple samples should be taken to establish trends in traffic flow, user activity, and traffic rates. When this has been accomplished, Worksheet number 3 should then be completed using the averages of these samples to derive numbers that are representative of the Ethernet environment. (The worksheet applies simple mathematics to arrive at the average number of bytes per user for the specific protocol.)

The information from Worksheet number 3 is used on Worksheet number 4, the "Remote Traffic Worksheet," which is a guide to estimating the bandwidth needed for effective throughput between two specific sites. By entering the information about each protocol operating at each site that will traverse the link between the two sites, the required bandwidth can be adequately estimated. Parameters on Worksheets 3 and 4 may vary depending upon the network architecture and LAN analysis tool that is used to gather the statistics. Here are some general guidelines to assist in completing the worksheet:

- Protocol: the operating standard that is being analyzed.

- Number of Users (A): the number of users who were using the above protocol at the time the sample was taken.

- % of Total Ethernet Traffic (C): the percentage of that protocol traffic.

- # of Multicast Packets (D): number of Multicast packets for this protocol.

- % of Protocol Traffic (F): the percentage of total protocol traffic for each type of packet.

- # of Data Packets (H): number of packets containing user information.

- Average Packet Size (J): mean packet size for this packet type. Suggested ranges: Large—1000 to 1518 bytes; Medium—400 to 999 bytes; Small—64 to 99 bytes.

Worksheet number 5, the "Network Growth Worksheet," takes information compiled on the preceding worksheets and allows the internetwork designer to use it to make a projection of the future requirements. The analysis is based upon the current Peak Bandwidth Required per user, and the future need is projected with a straightforward calculation that yields the Future Bandwidth Requirements. The designer can use this result to determine the transmission speed of the link between the two distant locations. The growth calculation is important to avoid obsolescence in the transmission facility hardware. (For further details, see reference [6-11].)

The 80/20 rule (given in reference [6-8]) estimates that 80 percent of a network's traffic remains local to that segment, while 20 percent of the traffic is directed to other segments. While this rule does not eliminate the need for an analysis of the traffic patterns, it may provide a starting point for a preliminary assessment of the transmission facility type and speed requirements. Also consider segments that will require redundant transmission paths for greater reliability.

Solicit Vendor Input. Solicit input from both WAN facility providers (e.g. AT&T and CompuServe) and internetworking equipment vendors. These services are usually available free-of-charge, and may identify alternatives that have not been considered.

Develop a Plan. Develop an internetwork implementation plan. This would include establishing specific milestones for network design, equipment procurement, installation, cutover, and documentation elements. We will discuss implementation issues in greater detail in Chapter 11.

Finally, remember that the internetwork design will, by its nature, be a multivendor network. We are all familiar with the finger-pointing that can occur between different vendors in these situations. Your best defense here is a strong offense: a thorough design, a well thought-out implementation plan, and reputable vendors. With these goals in mind, let's look at some representative products that can solve the LAN/WAN connectivity challenge.

6.1.2 Frame Relay Network Configurations

Frame relay, which has its roots in both ISDN and X.25 technologies, provides a high-speed and cost-effective alternative to leased lines. At the time of this writing, frame relay has a larger installed base of customers than either SMDS or ATM, and is supported by a large number of carriers worldwide. This technology also is quite popular in the press, as references [6-12] through [6-15] will attest.

Frame relay network designs can be simplified by following a straightforward process, complete with worksheets, developed by Bellcore [6-16].

The first step in the process is to gather traffic information about the network to be implemented. If the frame relay network is replacing an existing leased line network, the traffic patterns between the various locations should be estimated (Figure 6-3a). Note that the traffic should be recorded based upon the average peak hour traffic, which is the average data rate observed during the most active portion of the business day. If your network is typical of most, these peaks will occur sometime between 10:00 AM and 2:00 PM.

Source Location	Destination Location	Average Peak Hour Traffic (in Kbps)

Figure 6-3a. Leased Line Average Peak Rate Worksheet (Copyright © 1994, Bellcore. Reprinted with permission.)

For frame relay networks that are intended to carry LAN traffic, more extensive calculations are required. First, the average peak traffic on each LAN is measured, using a network management console or protocol analyzer. Secondly, an estimate of the percentage of traffic leaving one LAN and heading for another (i.e. LAN-to-LAN) can be made. When these two numbers are multiplied together, an estimate of the peak LAN-to-LAN is possible (Figure 6-3b). Note from the figure that a default estimate of off-LAN traffic is 20%, which corresponds with the 80/20 rule that was discussed above.

Source LAN	Average Peak Traffic (in Kbps) (Source LAN)	Estimated percent going to Frame Relay (Default = 20%)	Peak Rate times Percent

Figure 6-3b. LAN Average Peak Rate Worksheet *(Copyright © 1994, Bellcore. Reprinted with permission.)*

A third step is to document the protocols and applications that will be using the frame relay network (Figure 6-3c). Listing the protocols will identify any overhead or timing constraints that require special attention. Noting the applications will identify any critical functions that warrant alternate paths for redundancy, or any time-sensitive applications that justify faster circuits, with the associated higher cost.

Application Description	Does this Application Require Alternate Path?	Estimated Maximum Packet Round Trip Delay

Figure 6-3c. Applications Information Worksheet *(Copyright © 1994, Bellcore. Reprinted with permission.)*

With the data from the first three worksheets available, various network configurations, such as star, mesh, or hybrid topologies, may be proposed to carriers for their evaluation and price estimation.

The fourth step is to determine which UNI pairs require connectivity, and then to estimate the data rates required for the access circuits for each UNI (Figure 6-3d). To begin, note the UNIs (or locations) that are proposed for this network, along both the top and left hand side of the worksheet. Shade, or cross out, the boxes for which connectivity is not required. Note that the shaded portion of the worksheet follows a diagonal line, because it does not make sense to connect a UNI to itself, or to have redundant connections (i.e. UNI #1 connecting to UNI #2, and UNI #2 connecting to UNI #1).

	UNI #	UNI #	UNI #	UNI #	UNI #	UNI #	UNI Kbps
UNI #							
UNI #							
UNI #							
UNI #							
UNI #							
UNI #							

Figure 6-3d. PVC/Access Circuit Worksheet *(Copyright © 1994, Bellcore. Reprinted with permission.)*

Once the connectivity matrix is determined, the average peak rates for each UNI may be added to the worksheet (Figure 6-3d). Note that the required UNI access circuit data rate (noted in the far right hand corner of the worksheet) is the sum of all average peak rates for connectivity into that UNI. It is also wise to add a factor for future traffic growth, and any other unforeseen circumstances, by multiplying the aggregate traffic by a factor of 2 or 3.

The CIR of each frame relay PVC may also factor into the cost for that PVC. Recall from Section 5.2 that the CIR assigned to a PVC represents the average traffic volume between the two UNI locations connected by that PVC. In other words, the CIR is the guaranteed bandwidth that must be provided to the end-user application.

Data connections are rarely needed at maximum capacity (100%) all of the time. When multiple PVCs share one access line, it is therefore likely that the data bursts from one PVC may use the idle capacity from another. This property, which is similar to statistical multiplexing, allows the aggregate CIR on an access line to exceed the access rate. In most cases, the selected carrier will help with these traffic measurements and will assist their customer in determining optimum access rates and CIRs. After the network has been installed, periodic checks of the traffic levels should be made to validate the original assumptions and to see if any adjustments to the access rates or CIRs are warranted.

The final step in the process is to document the parameters of each UNI, such as access circuit speed, number of PVCs on that UNI, the DLCI for each of the PVCs, and the remote UNI that each connects to, as shown in Figure 6-3e. Much of the information from this worksheet may be provided by the carrier after the network has been provisioned and cutover.

Frame Relay UNI Data Sheet

UNI Number: _____

UNI Location*: _____/_____

Connected Equipment/Interface: _____

Access Circuit Speed*: _____

Notes: _____

Number of PVCs*: _____

* indicates this information needed to order service.

PVC Record Table

Local UNI (this sheet)			Remote UNI (another sheet)		
DLCI	CIR*	Higher Layer Address	UNI #	DLCI	Higher Layer Address

Figure 6-3e. Frame Relay UNI Data Sheet *(Copyright © 1994, Bellcore. Reprinted with permission.)*

6.1.3 SMDS Network Configurations

As we studied in Section 5.3, SMDS networks are LEC or IXC central office-based services. The popularity of this service has grown, as indicated by references [6-17] through [6-18].

For a successful network implementation, collaboration between the customer's and the carrier's engineering staffs is required. In support of these efforts, Bellcore developed a series of network configuration worksheets to aid the network manager with SMDS implementation. These worksheets are shown in Figures 6-4a through 6-4f, taken from reference [6-19] and are described below.

The first step in SMDS network planning is to identify all of the locations that will be using SMDS for communication. The Network Diagram Worksheet (Figure 6-4a) is designed for this documentation. On this worksheet, identify each location, the type of DTE that will connect to the SMDS network, and a brief description of the type of data that will be sent across that SNI. Since not all LECs and IXCs currently offer SMDS, it is also advisable to verify that SMDS access is available in each of these geographic locations. It is also helpful to make a preliminary estimate of the interface type and speed that each location requires, such as DS1 across SNI #1, DS3 with Access Class 2 (10 Mbps) across SNI #2, and so on. Traffic estimates, such as those discussed in Section 6.1.1, plus the network manager's experience, should be sufficient at this stage of the design.

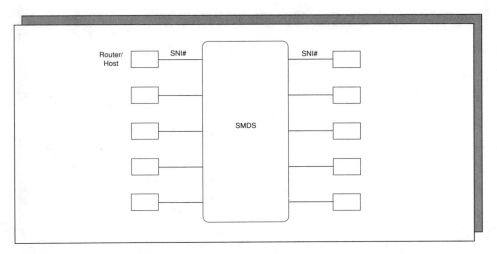

Figure 6-4a. Network Diagram Worksheet *(Copyright © 1994, Bellcore. Reprinted with permission.)*

The SMDS service provider will assign an individual address for each SNI. The SNI Summary Table (Figure 6-4b) is used to record this information.

The third step involves making a connectivity matrix, showing the details of inter-location communication (Figure 6-4c). All locations may not have a need to communicate with all other locations; therefore, this step in the design process further refines the traffic patterns and assumptions.

Location	SNI#	SMDS Individual Address

Figure 6-4b. SNI Summary Table *(Copyright © 1994, Bellcore. Reprinted with permission.)*

	SNI #	SNI #	SNI #	SNI #	SNI #	SNI #	SNI #	SNI #	SNI #	SNI #
SNI #										
SNI #										
SNI #										
SNI #										
SNI #										
SNI #										
SNI #										
SNI #										
SNI #										
SNI #										

Figure 6-4c. SNI connectivity matrix *(Copyright © 1994, Bellcore. Reprinted with permission.)*

SMDS creates virtual private networks. One of the service's attributes, known as address screening, allows a network manager to control the parties with which that network will communicate. Two types of address screening are defined, with both functions performed by the network. A Destination Address Screen checks each packet that your DTE sends across the SNI, and verifies that the destination specified is authorized. Likewise, a Source Address Screen is a verification by the network, prior to sending a packet across your SNI, that the packet's source is authorized to send packets to your SNI. There are two types of address screens: Individual Address Screens and Group Address Screens, and both of these are specific to an SNI. Individual Address Screens list individual addresses that are either allowed or disallowed across your SNI. Group Address Screens are only used for Destination Address screening, since the concept of a group source address has little, if any, practical application. Figure 6-4d, the SNI Worksheet, is used to document the address screens for each SNI.

SNI #

SMDS Individual Address[1]
(assigned by SMDS Service Provider) for the SNI: _____

Individual Address Screen[1]:   Group Address Screen[1]:

_____   _____

_____   _____

_____   _____

_____   _____

_____   _____

_____   _____

_____   _____

_____   _____

_____   _____

Address Screening for this SNI [1]:   ON _____   OFF _____

Type of Screens[1]:   Allowed _____   Disallowed _____

Notes: (1)   This information will be configured in the SMDS network
              by your service provider.

         (2)   Don't forget to notify other affected sites or companies when
              you change your SMDS configuration.

Figure 6-4d. SNI Worksheet *(Copyright © 1994, Bellcore. Reprinted with permission.)*

The next step involves identifying the upper layer protocols that are running across an SNI, and documenting those protocols on Figure 6-4e. For example, assume that all locations use Novell Inc.'s NetWare network operating system. A group address could be assigned to handle the NetWare broadcasts between all locations. Mapping between the Protocol Address and the SMDS Address is documented on the lower portion of Figure 6-4e.

SNI: _____

SMDS Individual Address _____
(assigned by your Service Provider)

Router Port ID _____
(for configuring the interface to the CSU/DSU)

Protocol Summary:

Protocols Running over this SNI	SMDS Group (Multicast) Address	New/Existing Group Address?
IP		
ARP		
Novell IPX		
SNA		
DECnet		
AppleTalk		

Static Mapping Summary:

Protocol	Protocol Address	SMDS Address	Note

Figure 6-4e. SNI Router Configuration Worksheet *(Copyright © 1994, Bellcore. Reprinted with permission.)*

Finally, Group Addresses, including all addresses that are members of that group, are documented on Figure 6-4f. For example, three auto parts suppliers and a major auto manufacturer may establish an SMDS-based intercompany network. Let's further assume that each individual company has five locations. Each of these firms could establish a group address for their internal communication, which would be screened from the other firms. Four Group Address Worksheets (Figure 6-4f) would be required for this example, with five member addresses on each worksheet.

Group Address: _____

Member Addresses[1]:

_____   _____

_____   _____

_____   _____

_____   _____

_____   _____

_____   _____

_____   _____

_____   _____

_____   _____

_____   _____

Note: (1) Remember that Group Address membership is NOT per SNI; e.g., 1.908.1256000 will have the same membership regardless of which SNI sends traffic to that group address.

Figure 6-4f. Group Address Worksheet *(Copyright © 1994, Bellcore. Reprinted with permission.)*

Excellent surveys of the various carriers' SMDS offerings, including address screening, protocol, and other support characteristics, are found in references [6-17] and [6-18]. Reference [6-19] provides further details and examples of SMDS network configurations.

6.1.4 ATM Network Configurations

ATM networks, having captured the interest of the majority of the computer and communications industries, are being planned and implemented by many organizations. To assist with those efforts, the ATM Forum sponsored a two-day tutorial at the 1995 ComNet Conference, entitled "How to Construct and Evaluate an ATM Request for Information (RFI)" [6-20].

The RFI is based upon the requirements of a fictional "GlobalCorp." It presents the firm's objectives and requests input from vendors regarding their products and services. The first day of the tutorial provided attendees with an outline to clarify network strategies, migration alternatives, and objectives for enterprise-wide ATM implementations. The second day of the tutorial presented the responses to the RFI provided by various ATM product and service vendors. The RFI is given below, as a model for ATM network design and implementation.

ATM Forum / Enterprise Network Roundtable
ATM RFI Ad Hoc Task Team
Mock ATM RFI White Paper

Notice, Disclaimers, and Copyright:

This document is offered to the ATM Forum and to the public-at-large as a basis for discussion. This mock ATM RFI document is not a binding proposal on the part of the ATM Forum or any member companies of the ATM Forum. This mock ATM RFI does not reflect the specific interest or requirements of any ATM Forum member company(s). This ATM RFI is a template or discussion item only, and is not expected to be responded to by vendors or service providers in order to sell services to the ATM Forum or member companies.

Table of Contents:

Section 1: General Instructions to Respondents

This section is intended to lay out ground rules for vendor responses specifically for the ATM RFI response.

1.1   Deadline for receipt of responses: _____
Sorry, no extensions will be allowed.

1.2   Total number of copies required to be submitted: Five hard copies of all documents.

1.3   Total number of machine readable copies required to be submitted: (Optional) one 3.5" disk containing file in MS/WORD (either DOS or Windows) format.

1.4   Point of contact for questions and where to deliver all documentation: _____

1.5   Length of responses: Unnecessary length and verbosity will adversely affect consideration of the entire response.

1.6   Please note that all submitted materials should be reproducible in 8.5" x 11" format to be considered.

Section 2: GlobalCorp Overview and RFI Background

The purpose and intent of this section is to place the network diagram and questions into the context of the real world.

GlobalCorp Overview

GlobalCorp is a multinational conglomerate with operations in several countries. GlobalCorp has diverse holdings in medical research, health care, telecommunications, energy, and high technology industrial research. GlobalCorp facilities are usually situated in large metropolitan areas near major universities or other institutions of higher learning and research. Each subsidiary operation operates private metropolitan area networks which provide access to a global private corporate network. GlobalCorp's current WAN/MAN topology is comprised of point-to-point leased T1, fractional T1, and DS3 service between site routers.

Typical LAN/MAN Topologies

Attached is a diagram of a typical site LAN/MAN topology (Figure 6-5). Each subsidiary group has separate facilities within its metropolitan area. Bandwidth requirements vary, however each site must gateway into local corporate operations groups and the two worldwide corporate headquarters facilities located in Los Angeles and London. Research and development sites are closely tied to the university and require high bandwidth in a private MAN topology.

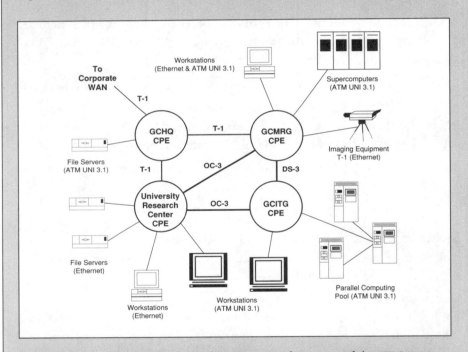

Figure 6-5. Typical GlobalCorp metropolitan area network (Courtesy of the ATM Forum)

GlobalCorp Medical Research Group (GCMRG)

GlobalCorp Medical Research Group is primarily an advanced cancer research facility which has an affiliate medical care facility for experimental patient test group evaluations. Equipment includes MRI and other medical imaging equipment. The computer center is located within the research laboratory and is shared by the treatment center across town. Each physician is on call 24 hours a day and needs remote access to medical imaging and computing facilities from home. GCMRG computer/medical imaging resources are also used by other locations including the local university. One goal of GCMRG is to provide the necessary bandwidth requirements at a reduced cost compared to the current dedicated DS3 service and thus make "physician home access" viable.

GlobalCorp Energy Group (GCEG)

GlobalCorp Energy Group is primarily involved in oil and gas exploration. One of its primary applications is geophysical mapping. The process requires enormous amounts of data to be exchanged between the supercomputer laboratories and remote workstations. Data are obtained from satellite ground tracking stations and transferred via a private corporate network to various research centers within the corporation.

GlobalCorp Industrial Technology Group (GCITG)

GlobalCorp Industrial Technology Group develops and tests new technologies for use in product development and manufacturing processes. GCITG has extensive bandwidth requirements to support transfer of enormous amounts of data between its supercomputers, workstations, and robotics equipment. Applications range from real time manufacturing to CAD/CASE modeling tools.

GlobalCorp Telecommunications Group (GCTG)

Globalcorp Telecommunications Group conducts large telecommunications research and development activities as well as production operations in virtually every major world market place. The primary business goal of GCTG is cellular communications equipment PCS, GSM, etc.

GlobalCorp Headquarters (GCHQ)

GlobalCorp Headquarters is the business side of GlobalCorp and has responsibility for international accounting and financial applications, human resources and executive offices. All sites must interact with GCHQ. In addition GCHQ wants to have daily video conferences with its various sites worldwide at reasonable costs.

GlobalCorp Enterprise Integration Strategy

The GlobalCorp enterprise transitional strategy is moving to a complete standardization of an ATM-based infrastructure by the year 2000. Each major metropolitan area will have a complete ATM deployment prior to that date due to the current bandwidth costs and requirements.

Why ATM is the Technology-of-Choice

The Board of Directors of GlobalCorp selected ATM technology as the basis for a global network solution. The decision was based on the need for a permanent infrastructure investment that could expand to satisfy long term requirements. Some of the business case issues are listed below.

To combine existing voice and data network infrastructure into a global enterprise network, with the objective of reducing operating costs and providing uniform service offerings based on international standards.

The ability to share research resources and equipment with major universities and other business units worldwide, and to do so at significantly reduced costs and with increased productivity ("telescience").

To provide critical medical information (e.g., CPR) to locations and hospitals worldwide, including on-line access from a physician's home ("telemedicine").

Section 3: General Questions of Respondents

3.1 Prospective Vendor Company Profile

    3.1.1 Total 1993 revenue

    3.1.2 Total employees (1993)

    3.1.3 Year founded

    3.1.4 Total 1993 R&D Investment (US dollars or percentage of sales)

    3.1.5 Total 1993 R&D staff

    3.1.6 Is the company public or privately held?

3.2 Prospective Vendor Company Partnerships and Alliances

   3.2.1 Please list all current partnerships and alliances involving your company related to the sale, distribution, or development of ATM products or services, including the purpose for and duration of the collaboration.

3.3 Prospective Vendor Company Affiliation with ATM-related Consortia

   3.3.1 Is the company a member of the ATM Forum? Which membership category?

   3.3.2 Is the company a member of the ITU?

   3.3.3 Please list all other pertinent consortia that the company is involved with.

3.4 Prospective Vendor Company Scope of Capability

   3.4.1 How many pieces of the network solution can the prospective vendor company provide and be responsible for supporting?

Section 4: Hardware Considerations

4.1 Switching

   4.1.1 What is the rated capacity of the switches? How was the capacity determined?

   4.1.2 What is the type of switch architecture?

   4.1.3 What is the number of switching stages?

   4.1.4 What is the switch transit delay?

   4.1.5 What is the number of cell buffers?

   4.1.6 Where are the cell buffers located?

   4.1.7 What is the maximum and minimum number of ports

per switch, if fully equipped?

4.1.8   What is the lowest port speed?

4.1.9   What is the highest port speed?

4.1.10   What is the number of ports operating (concurrently) at high speed?

4.1.11   Are RISC processors or ASICs used?

4.1.12   Are hot swappable interfaces provided?

4.1.13   Is the switching fabric redundant?

4.1.14   List the types of LAN interfaces.

4.1.15   Regarding power supplies and chassis:

   4.1.15.1   What are the power supplies for LAN interfaces?

   4.1.15.2   How many supplies?

   4.1.15.3   Are they loadsharing?

   4.1.15.4   Are chassis "UL" approved or provided with equivalent certification?

   4.1.15.5   Are systems/components FCC certified?

4.1.16   Is environmental monitoring provided? Describe.

4.1.17   Is there a limit to the number of switches that can be configured in a single network? If so, please describe.

4.2   Desktop

4.2.1   Are ATM adapters available for EISA, PCI bus, Microchannel, and S-bus?

4.2.2   What is the cost of the adapters?

4.2.3   With which vendors' switches has interoperability testing been done?

4.2.4   Are OC3c and/or 100 Mbps interfaces supported?

4.2.5   Is Category 5 at 155 Mbps and/or Category 3 at 51 Mbps available?

4.2.6   What type connector is used on the fiber interface?

4.2.7   Are LED indicators included? Are they software programmable?

4.2.8   How many slots are needed for the ATM adapters?

4.2.9   Are RISC processors or ASICs used?

4.2.10   Are microcode updates flash downloadable onto the adapter card?

4.2.11   Are configuration data/parameters stored in volatile or nonvolatile memory?

4.2.12   What is the maximum memory size?

4.2.13   Which type of memory is used (SRAM or CAM)?

4.2.14   What is the size of the ATM "ARP" cache?

4.2.15   What is the size of the transmit and receive buffers?

4.2.16   Are both PVCs and SVCs supported?

4.2.17   What is the number of supported VPs and VCs?

4.2.18   Is AAL5 supported? List the types of adaptations supported.

4.2.19   Is RFC-1483 implemented?

4.2.20   Which operating system drivers are available? Any support for OS/2 and NT?

4.2.21   Are data transferred to the application based on cells or delayed until arrival of entire PDU?

4.2.22   What is the estimated adapter throughput based on workstation/protocol/PMD used?

4.2.23   Will OAM loopbacks be responded to?

4.2.24   Is there an SNMP agent present on the adapter?

4.2.25 Where is the SAR function performed (onboard? in software?)

Section 5: Software Considerations

5.1 Network Management

5.1.1 Is billing and accounting included as part of the network management software?

5.1.2 If included, is there a performance penalty for enabling billing and accounting?

5.1.3 Under which enterprise network management package does the switch network management package work? (e.g., HP's OpenView, IBM's NetView, SunSoft's SunNet Manager)?

5.1.4 Does the network management package:

5.1.4.1 Allow the user to set allowed thresholds (by MAC address, by protocol)?

5.1.4.2 Provide a graphic representation of the virtual circuits set up?

5.1.4.3 Provide historical and real-time network performance statistics including peak traffic, average traffic, errors, etc.?

5.1.4.4 Allow user configuration of circuit characteristics?

5.1.5 Does the network management software allow the user to define quality of service contracts?

5.1.6 Does the network management software indicate when a user is violating a predefined contract?

5.1.7 How are the user defined parameters backed up?

5.1.8 Is special hardware or software required to run the network management software?

5.1.9　What are the hardware and operating systems required to support the network management system? List all supported (e.g., Sun workstation with Solaris, SunOS, PC with Windows, etc.).

5.2　Signaling

5.2.1　What classes of service are supported? What AALs?

5.2.2　How many quality of service parameters are supported? What are they?

5.3　Connection Management

5.3.1　As new network areas, capabilities and features become defined (e.g., LAN emulation, virtual work groups, switch-to-switch communications), how are these changes incorporated into the proposed system?

5.3.2　Are SVCs (Switched Virtual Circuits) supported?

5.3.3　Are SVPs (Switched Virtual Paths) supported?

5.3.4　Have SVCs been tested with other vendors' equipment? Which vendors? Results?

5.3.5　How many VCs (Virtual Circuits) are supported per switch?

5.3.6　How many VPs (Virtual Paths) are supported per switch?

5.3.7　Is connection management accomplished out-of-band? If yes, through what type of interface?

5.3.8　How many:

5.3.8.1　Switches can a single copy of the connection management support?

5.3.8.2　Copies of the connection management software can operate per network? Assume multiple switches?

5.3.9   What redundancy and fault tolerance features are supported in the connection management?

5.3.10   Can copies of the connection management software back each other up?

Section 6: Routing and Traffic Handling Considerations

6.1   Are PVCs/SVCs automatically re-established in case of link failures?

6.2   How is load sharing amongst parallel paths handled?

6.3   How are call building and preempt priorities handled?

6.4   Is there an ability to route over certain trunk attributes?

6.5   What is the path routing scheme/algorithm and metrics used between switches?

6.6   What is the range of VPIs and VCIs available?

6.7   What is the switch and call set up time for SVCs?

6.8   What is the signaling protocol used?

6.9   What is the maximum rate (per second) of call re-establishment during failure recovery?

6.10   Are PVCs manually mapped between multiple switches or is it performed automatically by the network management station?

6.11   How is multicast supported?

6.12   How is broadcast supported?

6.13   Is point to multiple-point support available?

6.14   Is traffic smoothed into the network and how?

6.15   What is the congestion control algorithm and how is it implemented?

6.16   What are the congestion control variables that can be set?

6.17 Is the "CLP" bit set?

6.18 How is traffic control between switches accomplished?

6.19 Is it possible to over-allocate a circuit?

6.20 Regarding clocking:

    6.20.1 Does the switch accept clocking from one interface and can it distribute clocking to other interfaces?

    6.20.2 Does the switch support both internal and external clocking?

    6.21 What standards conformance and multivendor interoperability tests have been completed?

Section 7: Support and Training Considerations

7.1 Regarding regular preventive maintenance:

    7.1.1 What is recommended?

    7.1.2 Who can/must/should perform it?

    7.1.3 If vendor/service provider maintenance, can customer control scheduling?

7.2 Can vendor provide support coverage for an entire customer network (perhaps including more than just ATM technology)?

7.3 What is the size and expertise level of your staff that is available to support a customer network?

7.4 What are the normal hours for response and is "7 x 24" available?

7.5 What help/training will vendor provide prior to, during and after installation?

7.6 Regarding Training:

    7.6.1 What is recommended for customer personnel?

7.6.2   Where is it available?

7.6.3   When is it available?

7.7   What support and training is included in the cost of the equipment and/or the maintenance contract?

Section 8:   Pricing and Distribution Considerations

8.1   For Product Vendors:

8.1.1   Through what channel(s) do you provide your products (distribution, resellers, direct, etc.)?

8.1.2   How do you price your solution with regard to product, support, installation services, extended warranties, other?

8.1.3   Are site licenses available (if applicable)?

8.1.4   Please include pricing for the campus portion of the network, including third party products. Pricing should be accurate to within twenty percent (20%).

8.2   For Service Providers:

8.2.1   How do you price your services?

8.2.2   Are ATM services discount agreements available?

8.2.3   Please include pricing for the WAN and/or MAN portion of the network, including third party products (e.g., required CPE) or services (e.g., access lines). Pricing should be accurate to within twenty percent (20%).

Section 9:   Differentiating Features

9.1   What differentiates your products/services from your competition?

> 9.2 Please explain how your solution might either:
>
> (a) help reduce customer costs.
>
> (b) provide greater value to the customer, or
>
> (c) both a and b above—when compared to other networking solutions, whether those alternative solutions be ATM-based or based on other technologies such as frame switching, routing, etc.

With that background into network configurations and designs, the balance of this chapter will look at various product solutions that solve specific LAN-WAN networking challenges. We will begin with low-speed, asynchronous solutions, and progress to high-speed, broadband solutions.

6.2 Communication Servers

Asynchronous Communication Servers (ACSs) go by a variety of other names, including "communications servers" and "asynchronous gateways." The ACSs are used to access the LAN via the dial-up telephone network, or to share a modem on the LAN for outgoing data calls among various workstations. An ACS can be either dedicated (with multiple ports) or non-dedicated (typically with one modem in a workstation). The practicality of the ACS lies in its ability to reduce the recurring monthly phone line charges. With network hardware costs dropping dramatically, a strong business case cannot be made for simply reducing the number of modems on the LAN. Eliminating extra phone lines to the network is another matter, however.

6.2.1 Communication Server Operation

Since we are all intimately familiar with using communication software to access a bulletin board system or remote asynchronous host, the operation of an ACS would appear to be equally straightforward. References [6-21] and [6-22] shed some light on why this function is more difficult than it may initially appear. A serial port is driven by an LSI device known as a UART (Universal Asynchronous Receiver/Transmitter), such as the Western Digital 8250. The PC controls this

8250 with ROM BIOS routines that are addressed through Interrupt 14 (INT 14H). For speed, however, most communication programs are written to address the 8250 directly, thus bypassing INT 14H. With a networked communication requirement, the data that was intended to go to/from the serial port must be placed on the LAN instead. According to reference [6-22], several such Application Program Interfaces (APIs) can be used for this purpose.

The first API is the NCSI/NASI (Network Communications Services Interface/Network Asynchronous Services Interface) developed by Network Products Corporation. Novell uses this interface in their NASC (NetWare Asynchronous Communication Server) product. This interface utilizes DOS interrupt vector 6BH to send and receive its information to and from the communication application in each workstation. A number of communication software packages—such as Crosstalk Mk.4 (Attachmate Corp., formerly Digital Communication Associates of Roswell, Georgia), Procomm Plus Network (Datastorm Technologies, Inc. of Columbia, Missouri), and Reflection (Walker, Richer, and Quinn, Inc. of Seattle, Washington)—support NCSI (reference [6-22]). The second type of API are interfaces that send and receive their information via INT 14H calls that conform to IBM's standard INT 14H (a specification has been published in every IBM PC communications book since the early 80s), as well as IBM's Extended 14H BIOS (EBIOS). These interfaces redirect the calls away from the PC's BIOS to themselves. In addition to being slow, another reason many developers don't call the PC's INT 14H to send/receive characters is that the standard specification does not give them a way to control the line signals. The application must be able to raise and lower Data Terminal Ready (DTR) as well as Request To Send (RTS), or to send a break function to the Host. IBM's EBIOS provides a mechanism to do these much-needed functions. The third type of API is the NetBIOS API (INT 5CH) used by IBM as well as others.

The fourth API alternative is a hardware redirector card installed in each workstation needing to run non-network modified software (i.e. the application reads and writes information directly to a COM hardware address). This card intercepts the write, sends the information down the network to the communication server, and then makes the received data available to the application to read as if it just came in from the local COM port (which, of course, does not have to be present in this workstation).

With this overview of the ACS architectural challenge, let's begin to look at some solutions. A number of these ACS devices are available from third-party vendors and Network Operating System (NOS) designers. In this section we'll look at one integrated hardware/software solution, the ChatterBox from J&L Information Systems. In Chapter 9, we will study the communications capabilities of the major LAN NOSs, such as Banyan, Microsoft, and Novell.

6.2.2 J & L Information Systems Network Communications Server

J&L Information Systems of Chatsworth, California markets a variety of hardware and software products for a dedicated ACS. The Network Communication Server (NCS/AX) supports both async and X.25 in one dedicated communication server. The communication server software supports COM ports, communication interface boards from DigiBoard, Inc., Eden Prairie, Minnesota, and WNIC X.25 boards from Newport Systems Solutions, Inc. (Cisco Systems, Inc. PC Access Business Unit), Irvine, California (Figure 6-6). Additionally, the latest version of NCS/AX provides Windows communications software support that is transparent to the end user.

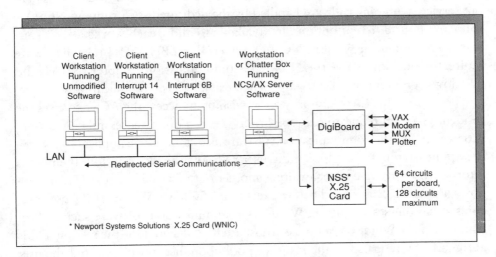

Figure 6-6. J&L Information Systems NCS/AX outgoing operation *(Courtesy of J&L Information Systems)*

The gateway software uses one of two techniques to communicate with the network operating system as it sends and receives information between each workstation and the Network Communication Server. The first technique uses Novell's Internet Packet Exchange (IPX) protocol, which is specific to Novell LANs. The second technique is NetBIOS, which is used to communicate with most other LANs, such as Banyan, Microsoft, IBM, etc.

J&L's flagship product is known as the ChatterBox. The ChatterBox line consists of the ChatterBox/Plus, the original product, based on a segmented passive back plane technology, and the ChatterBox/NRS, based on a hot-swappable modular technology. Each platform supports multiple PC-compatible Processing Units which are functionally equivalent to multiple network workstations in a single enclosure, either tower or rack-mount.

These Processing Units perform a combination of services like a 3270 or X.25 gateway, fax server, file server, or J&L's Network Communication Server. These types of applications fall into the category of Resource Servers, hence the name Network Resource Server (NRS).

The J&L ChatterBox is a communications platform for dial-in as well as dial-out service. Outgoing calls are handled by the dedicated ACS running NCS/AX software. Four different options are available to allow each workstation's software to communicate with the NCS/AX server: INT 6BH, INT 14H, a hardware redirector card known as the Network Communication Adapter (NCA), and Windows communication software. When using DOS communication software, like Procomm Plus LAN, a workstation wishing to access the ACS exercises the resident program requesting a type of service, and upon successful connection, proceeds to use the communication software as a stand-alone application. When the application is finished, or if the user re-boots the workstation, the port is returned to an inactive state, awaiting another outgoing call request. Under Windows, a small TSR is loaded before executing Windows. Whenever the user executes a dial-out session, using Windows communication software such as Procomm Plus for Windows, a port is transparently allocated for the session and is automatically returned to the resource pool upon disconnect, without the user exiting Windows.

J&L's NCS/AX, using Newport Systems Solutions, Inc.'s WNIC X.25 boards, allows up to 128 users to simultaneously connect to an X.25 service. Each WNIC board allows for 64 simultaneous circuits, with a maximum of 128 circuits per NCS/AX communications server. Additionally, both asynchronous and X.25 sessions can be supported simultaneously by the same NCS/AX server. Therefore, with two DigiBoards and one Newport WNIC board, a single communications server can support 48 asynchronous and 64 X.25 sessions simultaneously.

Incoming calls are handled exclusively with the ChatterBox hardware by connecting each incoming line to the COM port of the individual Processing Units. A remote-control software package such as Symantec's pcANYWHERE, Ocean Isle's ReachOut, Triton Technologies' CoSession, or Norton Lambert's Close-Up runs on the ChatterBox Processing Unit, waiting for an incoming call. When the remote user dials in, the program takes control of the ChatterBox processor attached to that incoming line. Since the Processing Unit is also connected to the LAN via the NIC, the remote user can assume control of a network-attached workstation. File access, printing, etc. can then proceed as if the remote user's workstation was physically attached to the LAN.

There are three main advantages to having a dedicated communication processor for remote access to the LAN. First, all of the screen and keyboard traffic generated by the remote program, such as updates to the remote user's screen, does not travel over the LAN cable, and therefore does not needlessly add to the network traffic. Second, since the fast hardware is at the host site, the remote user does not have to have the latest and fastest hardware to run the application software. For example, a user with an 8088 laptop can run Windows applications, since that application is actually running on a 90 Mhz Pentium process on the ChatterBox. Third, all application software and the necessary hardware to run it are at the host site, making the overall system easier to administer.

Management has become a critical issue for most system administrators. Visibility and control of the Processing Units is crucially important. J&L has developed ChatView to address these issues. ChatView allows the system administrator to view the status of each processor (via IPX or SNMP). It collects statistics for all remote sessions, and it allows a management reset (via IPX or SNMP) of a board that has stopped responding due to a lock-up. These management resets can be sent from anywhere on the LAN or WAN, whether it is on another floor or 8,000 miles away.

6.3 Analog Leased Line Connections

As we studied in Section 3.2, analog leased line facilities provide an optimized transmission path (via conditioning), thus permitting higher transmission rates and lower errors. For LAN-to-LAN traffic that requires higher throughput and longer connect times, leased lines may be preferred over dial-up PSTN connections. We'll look at two products, the Microcom Bridge/Router and the Rockwell Network Systems NetHopper dial-up routers, as examples of products using leased lines to connect LANs.

6.3.1 Microcom Bridge/Router

Microcom Inc. of Norwood, Massachusetts has long been known for its expertise in dial-up and leased-line modems, and is also known as the inventor of the Microcom Networking Protocol (MNP) used for data compression and error correction. The Microcom Bridge/Router (MBR) is a MAC-layer bridge for connecting geographically separate Ethernet or Token Ring LANs. What makes the MRB unique is its numerous options for the WAN facility interface. Four different models are available. The MBR/6000 and MBR/6003 bridge/routers are designed for dedicated leased line, and circuit switched services such as analog modems, ISDN, and Switched 56. THE MBR/6500 and MBR/6503 series are designed for packet switched services such as X.25 and frame relay. The MBR/6000 and MBR/6500 are designed for installations requiring maximum WAN port configurations, while the MBR/6003 and MBR/6503 have fewer WAN ports available.

Every conceivable WAN facility for either dial-up (see Figure 6-7a) or leased lines (see Figure 6-7b) is available. The dial-up WAN interface transmits at 9.6 Kbps using a V.32 modem, and incorporates MNP data compression. The synchronous interface for analog or digital leased lines uses the HDLC protocol for enhanced reliability. The X.25 WAN interface transmits over links at up to 500 Kbps with the recent addition of 2:1 compression, and supports a maximum of 15 virtual circuits. The ISDN WAN module provides a single BRI, for both circuit switched and X.25 connections at 64 Kbps. The modular design allows an easy upgrade path as the network transmission requirements increase. Additional links can be added by incorporating additional WAN interface modules into the bridge/router platform.

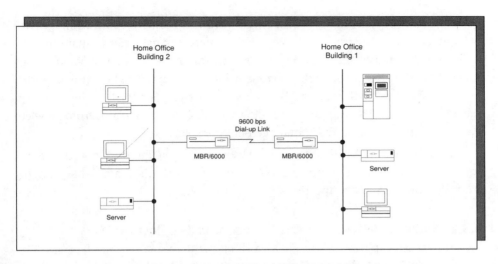

Figure 6-7a. Microcom LAN Bridge Dial-up Bridging Application *(Courtesy of Microcom, Inc.)*

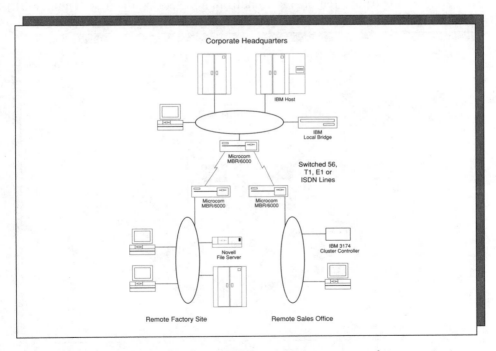

Figure 6-7b. Microcom LAN Bridge Remote Bridging Application *(Courtesy of Microcom, Inc.)*

A third component of the MBR architecture is the Microcom Management Station (MMS) software. The MMS allows a network manager to maintain statistics and alarm information on all MBRs within the network. The MMS implements SNMP for control of the various bridge parameters. The MBR supports industry-standard MIB I and MIB II, plus MIB extensions for building management applications. These applications allow the MBR to be managed from Hewlett-Packard's OpenView network management console.

In summary, the MBR series is an extremely flexible remote bridge platform. Its uniqueness is in the number of WAN interfaces that are available, ranging from dial-up to ISDN connections.

6.3.2 Rockwell Network Systems NetHopper Dial-up Routers

NetHopper dial-up routers from Rockwell Network Systems (Santa Barbara, California) use low-cost, dial-up connections to provide IP and IPX users with a transparent means of accessing remote files, servers, printers, and other resources, whether they are working from a remote location, from home, or on the road (Figure 6-8).

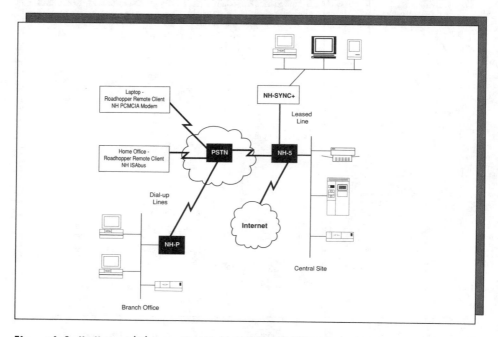

Figure 6-8. NetHopper dial-up routing *(Courtesy of Rockwell Network Systems)*

Dial-up routing is a simple, cost-effective way to connect users to backbones to run client/server applications, to access a remote file server, or to send email over low-cost dial-up links, such as the Public Switched Telephone Network (PSTN), Switched 56, and ISDN. Another key application is providing cost-effective links from remote offices to regional Internet access providers.

Since usage rates for dial-up links are typically based on per-call charges, these links offer economic advantages over more traditional leased lines which can cost thousands of dollars per month. Many small branch offices and remote sites simply don't have the budget—or traffic requirements—to justify those costs.

Rockwell currently offers three NetHopper products, each with a single Ethernet interface and varying numbers of modem interfaces. The NetHopper NH-P has one internal V.34 (28.8 Kbps) modem, while the NH-5 provides five internal modems. The NH-SYNC+ offers both an internal modem and a synchronous port for connecting to ISDN, SW56, or a DDS network.

In its design of the NetHopper, Rockwell has recognized that users at small sites and branch offices need not only a low-cost solution, but one that is easy to implement as well. An intuitive menu-driven configuration and integrated modems provide quick and trouble-free installation.

Another key feature—which further reduces connect time charges—is Rockwell's link optimizing techniques. For example, Novell's IPX is a very chatty protocol—in other words the clients and servers exchange network configuration information on a frequent basis. To reserve the WAN link for end-user traffic, the NetHopper products include spoofing and filtering into the client side of the connection to optimize the use of that transmission facility. Built-in data compression technology further reduces WAN link usage.

6.4 Digital Leased Line Connections: MICOM's Marathon Multiplexers

Digital (or DDS) lines further improve on their analog counterparts in two ways, as we studied in Section 3.3. First, the digital nature of the transmission is less susceptible to noise and is therefore more error-free. Secondly, digital lines are available at speeds of up to 56 Kbps, more than doubling the practical upper limit (19.2 Kbps) of the analog lines. Let's look at the MICOM Marathon product family as an example.

MICOM Communications Corporation of Simi Valley, California has a series of products that permit customers to integrate all interoffice communications (LAN, data, voice, and facsimile traffic) on leased lines operating from 9.6 to 128 Kbps. MICOM's integration products offer a low-cost internetworking solution in both product price and leased line services. The fact that the systems use low-speed, and hence low-cost, analog and digital lines makes MICOM's products attractive to its target audience: small to midsized businesses and divisions of larger companies.

The best known of the MICOM products are the Marathon Integration Multiplexers. With a Marathon unit installed at each office (Figure 6-9), MICOM customers send their data, voice, fax, and LAN traffic over a single line, eliminating the need for separate lines for each type of traffic. This also eliminates the cost of toll charges from interoffice communications, since phone calls, fax documents, and data files transmitted over leased private lines incur no PSTN toll charges.

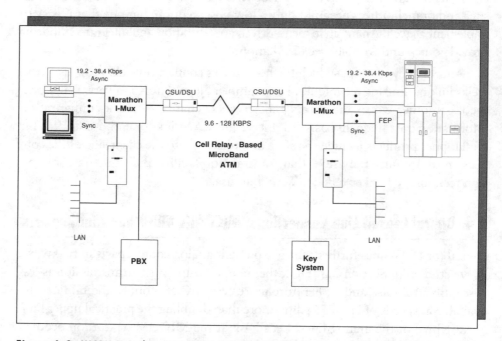

Figure 6-9. MICOM Marathon Integration Multiplexer (I-Mux) *(Courtesy of MICOM Communications Corporation)*

To fit the variety of signals on low-speed lines, MICOM uses a technology the company calls MicroBand ATM, a combination of cell relay-based fast packet technology, data/LAN/voice compression, silence suppression, and fax demodulation. MicroBand ATM allocates bandwidth as needed, rather than preallocating precious bandwidth based on fixed amounts for each data or voice channel.

Digital Signal Processors (DSPs) and microprocessors allow Marathon units to dramatically compress signals, reducing speech bandwidth requirements by up to 95 percent. Additionally, MICOM's technology does not send silent packets over the network. This silence suppression technology allows the products to fit packets of data, LAN, voice, and fax during pauses.

First introduced in 1991, the MICOM Marathon product family has grown to include several products for large and small networking applications. The Marathon products include the Marathon 20K, MICOM's most fully featured Marathon, which provides up to 41 asynchronous channels, 18 synchronous channels and eight voice/fax/modem channels, and supporting up to 12 wide-area connections. MICOM also offers modules that allow Marathons to support remote terminal server and LAN bridging/routing applications. At the other end of the networking spectrum, the branch office Marathon 1K Integration Multi-plexer (or I-Mux) offers a maximum of 41 async channels and one sync channel, four voice/fax/modem channels, and one network connection.

MICOM also offers a headquarters hub solution for all of its DVI products, the STADIA DVI hub, which offers networking capabilities for 18 links at 64 Kbps each, up to 42 links at 19.2 Kbps, or up to eight links at 128 Kbps.

In January of 1995, MICOM announced products that enhance both the Marathon and the NetRunner Integration Router product lines. MICOM's NetRunner products, which do for remote LAN internetworks what Marathon does for remote legacy data networks, are the first router products with the capability to transport voice, fax, and legacy data packets alongside LAN traffic like Novell's IPX. These products allow customers to save money on routing or bridging applications by sending toll-free phone and fax traffic alongside data/LAN traffic using one private line. MICOM's Marathon products also were enhanced in early 1995 to include routing as an option.

6.5 Designing Scalable LAN/WAN Connections

As LANs increase in their backbone transmission rate from 10 to 100 Mbps (Ethernet and fast Ethernet, respectively) or from 4 to 16 Mbps (the two Token Ring transmission rates), the amount of aggregate network traffic increases as well. When the LAN traffic increases, an increase in any LAN-to-LAN traffic follows. Therefore, scalable routers that can accommodate a variety of WAN transmission rates and protocols are required. Testing results for some of these product solutions are found in reference [6-23].

Newport Systems Solutions, Inc. (Cisco Systems, Inc., Access Business Unit) of Irvine, California manufactures a number of multi-port routers for Novell NetWare networks, designated the LAN²LAN family (Figure 6-10). LAN²LAN is a PC based multiprotocol router/bridge that can be installed either in a dedicated router or in a NetWare file server or Runtime system. The LAN²LAN router supports communication over both leased and dial-up analog and digital lines at speeds from 1200 bps to fractional or full T1/E1.

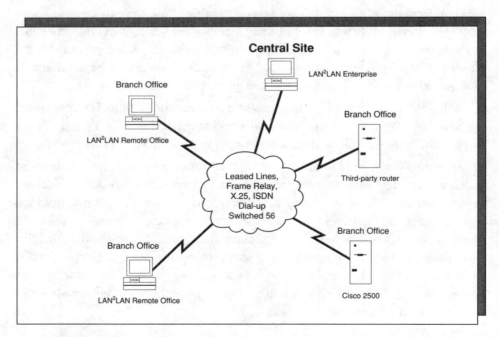

Figure 6-10. LAN²LAN WAN connectivity *(Courtesy of Cisco Systems, Inc., Access Business Unit)*

When configured as a dedicated router, the LAN²LAN products do not require NetWare. They support local and wide area routing, as well as Ethernet Transparent Bridging (ETB) and token ring Source Route Bridging (SRB). When installed in a NetWare file server or NetWare Runtime environment, such as NetWare for Systems Application Architecture (SAA) or NetWare Connect, the LAN²LAN router enables wide area routing without requiring the purchase of any additional PC hardware.

The LAN²LAN router includes many features designed to optimize routing performance and ease of use. Performance enhancements include data compression, load balancing, multipacket communication, dial backup, bandwidth on demand, and scheduled calling. Features designed to improve installation and maintenance include an automated installation utility, remote configuration, remote management and statistics viewing features, and SNMP agent support for MIB I and II.

LAN²LAN routers are available in two versions: Remote Office and Enterprise. The LAN²LAN Remote Office router, providing up to two WAN connections and four LAN ports, is an economical solution for those sites with connectivity requirements for fewer ports, such as remote offices. As requirements change or the network grows, the LAN²LAN Remote Office router can be easily upgraded to the LAN²LAN Enterprise router with a simple field upgrade. The LAN²LAN Enterprise router provides up to 24 WAN connections and 4 LAN ports for sites with larger connectivity requirements.

When installed as a dedicated router, the LAN²LAN product routes NetWare IPX and TCP/IP traffic. It also provides ETB and SRB for other protocols (such as NetBEUI, DEC LAT, LANtastic, AppleTalk, SNA, and NetBIOS) for diverse LAN platforms including LAN Manager, Banyan VINES, Apple Macintosh, and more. When installed on a NetWare file server or Runtime System, the LAN²LAN router supports IPX, TCP/IP, and AppleTalk (Phase 1 and 2) routing protocols if NetWare v4.x, v3.x, or the NetWare MPR is used as the platform.

To configure a LAN²LAN router, choose a PC with the appropriate processor and number of slots to meet your specific requirements. Install the appropriate type and number of LAN and WAN adapters, then install the LAN²LAN router software, and you have configured a LAN²LAN router customized to your specific needs and applications. The LAN²LAN router hardware consists of a Wide area Network Interface Coprocessor (WNIC) adapter, which is installed in the PC router or server to support a set number of remote sites. The WNIC contains its own central processing unit (CPU) and communications software; therefore, it handles all communications tasks independently of the PC or server, improving routing performance. Multiple WNICs can be installed in one PC, providing additional WAN ports.

Supported WAN protocols include Frame Relay, PPP, CCITT X.25, and ISO HDLC. The PPP protocol is compatible with PPP compliant routers. Frame Relay is compatible with frame relay RFC 1490-compliant routers. Data compression is available for all WAN protocols, including Frame Relay, PPP, CCITT X.25, and ISO HDLC. A scalable solution for LAN-to-WAN connections describes how the LAN²LAN product integrates easily and economically into existing internetworks.

6.6   Frame Relay Connections

RAD Data Communications of Mahwah, New Jersey has combined features from their packet switching and remote access product lines to create the LANFRAD product line. The LANFRAD connects remote PCs, LANs, and workstations to a central LAN via frame relay or X.25 networks.

The LANFRAD bridges token ring and Ethernet LANs over frame relay and X.25 networks with two different configurations. The "one-to-one" configuration operates using a single virtual circuit, and is used for point-to-point LAN interconnectivity applications. In the "many-to-one" configuration, up to 250 remote PCs or LANs can simultaneously connect into a central LANFRAD using multiple virtual circuits (Figure 6-11). The combination of bridging technology with frame relay networks is ideal. The bridging technology is simple to configure and transparent to higher-level protocols such as IP, IPX, NetBIOS, or DECNET. As we studied in Chapter 5, frame relay provides high throughput at a low cost.

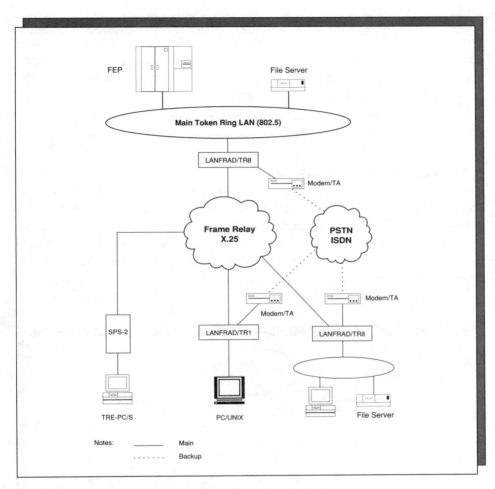

Figure 6-11. LANFRAD for token ring *(Courtesy of RAD Data Communications)*

RAD's LANFRAD is provided with two WAN links: a frame relay/X.25 main link, with data rates up to 1.024 Mbps, and a secondary link for backup or connection via dial-up modems, ISDN, or leased lines. Automatic configuration support for more than 100 popular modems is provided for this secondary port.

The high-performance hardware filtering and forwarding features of RAD's LAN-Ranger remote access bridges have been incorporated into the LANFRAD products to ensure that unnecessary LAN traffic is filtered out. Filters may be set to either block or forward based upon specific protocols, MAC addresses, or data offsets. In addition, the LANFRAD employs a unique funneling method for controlling network congestion and moderating feeder throughput speed. Packet sizes of up to 8,192 octets are supported for frame relay connections, allowing token ring or Ethernet MAC layer frames to be passed across the WAN in their entirety, without fragmentation.

The LANFRAD is unique in that it provides a simple efficient solution for connecting LANs across the WAN with minimum overhead and maximum throughput.

6.7 SMDS Network Connections

As we studied in Section 5.3.6, a number of options are available to access SMDS networks, including DS0, DS1, and DS3 transmission rates. In most cases, the customer network, such as a LAN, is connected to a router that supports the SMDS Interface Protocol (SIP) Level 3 protocol (Figure 6-12). The router takes the upper layer protocol information, such as NetWare traffic, and encapsulates it within an SIP_L3 Protocol Data Unit (PDU) for transmission over the SMDS network.

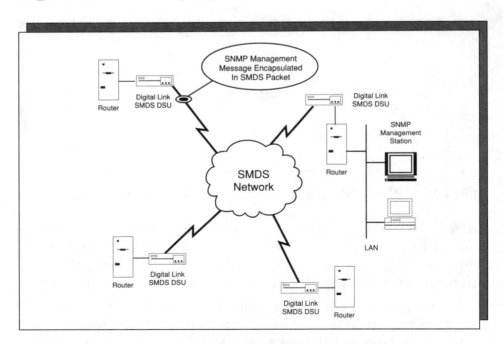

Figure 6-12. SMDS network configuration *(Courtesy of Digital Link Corp.)*

The router, in turn, connects to a Channel Service Unit/Data Service Unit (CSU/DSU) via a standard data interface such as V.35, EIA-449, or X.21. The CSU/DSU provides several key functions. The CSU portion provides maintenance, testing, and line monitoring features, while the DSU portion of the device converts the bridge/router's signal to the DS1 or DS3 format.

For SMDS applications, standard CSU/DSUs are enhanced to include protocol processing for SIP_L1 and SIP_L2 as well. Hence, the term SMDS CSU/DSU, or simply SMDSU, is used to indicate these enhanced features. The bridge/router generates an SIP_L3, which is passed via the DXI interface to the SMDSU. The SMDSU receives the L3_PDU, segments it into cells (L2_PDUs), performs the necessary Physical Layer Convergence Procedure (PLCP) operations, and sends it to the SMDS network. Thus, the bridge/router and SMDSU combine efforts to provide the three levels of SIP across the SNI [6-24].

Digital Link Corp. of Sunnyvale, California, is one of the key developers of these enhanced SMDSUs. Their product family includes the DL200 and DL200E, which operate at the DS1 and E1 rates, respectively, plus the DL3200E, which operates at the E3 rate.

The DL200 and the DL200E provide a wide range of electrical interfaces for the DTE, including V.35, RS-449, and X.21. Software upgrades may be downloaded using the Trivial File Transfer Protocol (TFTP), or via the serial port and a connection to a PC. The channel extension mode allows the use of the HDLC interface and converts to SMDS for customers that do not support DXI.

The DL3200E is a RISC-processor based design, which permits either HSSI or V.35-compatible DTEs to access the SMDS network at speeds ranging from 2.5–34 Mbps. Thus it supports SMDS access classes 1 through 5, respectively, for the U.S. domestic model, and SMDS access classes 1 through 4 for the international model.

The internal diagnostics included with these products provide L2 PDUs, L3 packet generators, terminal patterns, test configuration setups, and the most complete and user-friendly statistical log screens in the industry today.

6.8 ATM Network Connections

FORE Systems, Inc. of Warrendale, Pennsylvania, was the first to offer ATM LAN solutions commercially, and currently has one of the largest installed bases of ATM LAN solutions. ATM is the first technology designed for use in both LANs and WANs. Examples of new applications benefiting from the use of ATM include: high speed data transfer, data visualization, distributed computer-aided design, digital video production and conferencing, distance learning, networked medical imaging, and distributed image analysis.

FORE Systems offers a comprehensive ATM LAN product line including the ForeRunner series of ATM switches, LAN access products, network adapter cards, video products, and ForeView network management software (Figure 6-13). All of FORE Systems' ATM products are compatible with ForeThought internetworking software, an integrated suite of intelligent software components designed to deliver high-performance, transparent ATM internetworking.

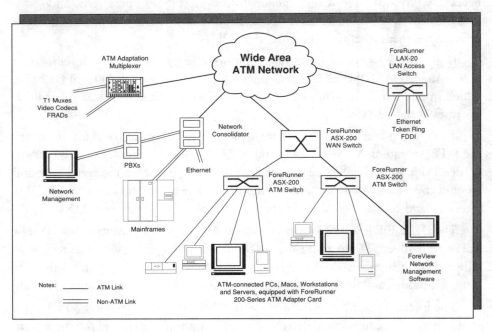

Figure 6-13. LAN-WAN ATM networking *(Courtesy of FORE Systems, Inc.)*

FORE's ATM products focus on the needs of the LAN workgroup, LAN backbone, and WAN access. To support cross-WAN, private line ATM connectivity for new data applications, FORE offers switch interfaces for DS3 (45 Mbps), E-3 (34 Mbps), and 155 Mbps SONET/SDH with singlemode fiber. FORE's switches also include other features necessary to support WAN ATM connections such as switched virtual circuit (SVC) tunneling across carrier ATM services, multiple priority queues, dual-leaky bucket traffic policing, and EFCI rate-based flow control.

ForeRunner ATM switches deliver high-performance ATM connectivity for LAN workgroups, LAN backbones, and WAN access. The ForeRunner ASX-200 ATM switch family supports from 2 to 96 connections and a full range of interface speeds from 1.5 Mbps to 155 Mbps. It provides from 2.5 Gbps to 10 Gbps switching capacity, and features an integral RISC-based processor. Modular in design, the ASX-200 ATM switch family is standards-compliant, and offers advanced connection and bandwidth management capabilities. ForeRunner LAN access switches enable conventional Ethernet, Token Ring, and FDDI LANs to connect to ATM networks. The ForeRunner LAX-20 LAN Access Switch, which provides ATM connectivity for Ethernet and FDDI LANs, offers an integral ATM interface plus LAN switching or routing on a per port basis.

The ForeRunner family of ATM network adapter cards provides high-performance ATM connectivity for the broadest range of workstations and computer platforms of any vendor. Adapters are available for Sun, Hewlett-Packard, Silicon Graphics, and DEC workstations, IBM workstations and PCs, and Macintosh computers. The ForeRunner 200-Series ATM adapters feature transparent TCP/IP, NetWare, or Windows NT support, an advanced cell processing architecture with on-board i960 processor, and physical interfaces for single and multimode fiber and Category 5 UTP and STP copper media.

The ForeRunner ATM video products enable high-quality audio and video to be carried between conventional video devices and the ATM network. The ForeRunner AVA-200 ATM video adapter multicasts real-time, high-quality video and audio from video sources to ATM-connected workstations and PCs. The ForeRunner AVD-200, in combination with the ForeRunner AVA-200 ATM video adapter, displays full motion real-time video and CD quality audio transmitted over the ATM network on standard monitors, televisions, and large screen displays. Both the AVA-200 and AVD-200 utilize ATM adaptation layer 5, taking advantage of ATM's variable bandwidth capability.

ForeThought internetworking software is a suite of software components that work in concert with ForeRunner ATM products. ForeThought supports all current ATM standards, including the user-to-network interface (UNI) 3.1, Q.2931 for switched virtual circuit (SVC) signaling, IETF RFCs 1483 and 1577 for the transport of TCP/IP over ATM, LAN Emulation and standards for congestion management, and the ILMI and AToM network MIBs. Additionally, ForeThought software includes the added value of SPANS (Simple Protocol for ATM Network Signaling), which includes NNI signaling, and enables advanced networking features such as IP multicasting, automatic network configuration, intelligent optimized routing, link load balancing, alternate routing, and SVC tunneling.

ForeView network management software provides a complete solution for managing ForeRunner ATM networks using standard SNMP-based management systems. ForeView features an easy-to-use graphical interface for configuring, controlling, monitoring, and troubleshooting ATM networks. ForeView integrates with widely-used network management platforms such as Hewlett-Packard's OpenView, SunConnect's SunNet Manager, and IBM's NetView/6000.

In addition, FORE is establishing partnerships with telecommunications equipment vendors and manufacturers to accelerate the deployment of wide area ATM services, to ensure interoperability by using a common software platform, and to provide a high level of functionality.

FORE Systems and Northern Telecom, a leading global manufacturer of telecommunications equipment, partnered to deliver seamless, end-to-end ATM solutions. The agreement capitalizes on each company's respective strengths and includes technology transfer, joint development, and joint sales and marketing. As part of this agreement, FORE Systems' ForeThought software will be added to Northern Telecom's Magellan Passport and Concorde switches. This effectively moves FORE's advanced local area network and wide area access ATM functions into the wide area backbone network. Additionally, elements of FORE's Fore-View network management software will be incorporated into Northern Telecom's carrier network management system.

Under another agreement, FORE Systems and Sprint—a leading vendor of wide-area ATM services—entered into a multiyear partnership. Under the agreement, Sprint will market, service, and support the FORE Systems ATM switch product line as an integral part of its ATM service offering.

FORE has witnessed the rapid evolution of ATM networks. ATM moved from pilot projects to support for high performance workgroups. Today, FORE's customers are building full-scale ATM networks supporting core business applications. Now, with several major carriers and PTTs already offering ATM services, and numerous others announcing trials, FORE is seeing ATM quickly expand from the LAN and campus backbone to the WAN.

6.9   References

[6-1]   Fitzgerald, Susan. "Manage and Enhance Bandwidth." *STACKS* (March 1994): 27–30.

[6-2]   Held, Gilbert. "Selecting a WAN Operating Rate." *Network Administrator* (September/October 1994): 4–16.

[6-3]   ADC Kentrox. *The WAN Managers Guide to Fast Packet Services*, 1994.

[6-4]   ADC Kentrox. *Demystifying WAN Connections*, 1994.

[6-5]   Heckart, Christine. "Carriers Extend a LAN Interconnectivity Hand." *Network World* (January 9, 1995): 35–42.

[6-6]   Ellis, Robert. *Designing Data Networks*. New York: Prentice-Hall, Inc. 1986.

[6-7]   Kornblum, Deborah F. "Interconnecting Remote LANs to Build Wide Area Networks." *Journal of Network Management* (Summer 1990): 26–37.

[6-8]   Retix. *Local Bridge Application Guide*. Document 1040187-00, 1989.

[6-9]   Irvin, David R. "Second Generation Token Ring LANs: Evaluating the Need for High Speed." *Data Communications* (March 21, 1989): 47–50.

[6-10]   ADC Kentrox. *Network Profiles*, 1994.

[6-11]   Vitalink Communications Corp. *Wide Area Network Configuration Guidelines*. Technical Note 013581F, April 1988.

[6-12]   Finn, Chris and Chris Heckart. "Frame Relay Grows Up." *Network World* (February 7, 1994): 33–40.

[6-13]   Eicon Technology Corp. *Frame Relay and Mission-critical Networking*, 1994.

[6-14]   Frame Relay Forum. *Business Applications at Work Today*, October 1994.

[6-15]   Fitzgerald, Susan. "Designing Your Frame Relay Network." *Network Computing* (January 15, 1995): 152–154.

[6-16]   Bell Communications Research, Inc. *Frame Relay User's Guide*, document PB2332-1, November 1994.

[6-17]   Briere, Daniel. "SMDS: the Silent Contender." *Network World* (November 29, 1993): 39–49.

[6-18] SMDS Interest Group. *SMDS Product and Service Guide*, Fall 1994.

[6-19] Bell Communications Research, Inc. *SMDS User's Guide*. May 1994.

[6-20] The ATM Forum/Enterprise Network Roundtable. *Mock ATM RFI White Paper*, October 1994.

[6-21] Freed, Les. "Asynchronous Communication Servers." *PC Magazine* (May 16, 1989): 227–228.

[6-22] Marks, Howard. "Asynchronous Communication Servers." *LAN Technology* (January 1990): 7–46.

[6-23] Tolly, Kevin and David Newman. "PC-Based Routers: Ready for Remote Sites." *Data Communications* (October 1993): 91–100.

[6-24] Digital Link Corporation. *Applications Document*, 1994.

7 TCP/IP and the Internet Protocols

The Transmission Control Protocol/Internet Protocol (TCP/IP) suite is perhaps the best known of all the internetworking protocols. TCP/IP was developed in the 1970s, and funded by the U.S. Government's Defense Advanced Research Projects Agency (DARPA), now known simply as ARPA. The government's objective was to develop a mechanism to link the dissimilar computers of the various military agencies, defense and research contractors, and universities into a wide area network. (Preceding the TCP/IP development was the establishment of the ARPANET [Advanced Research Projects Agency Network], also funded by DARPA. ARPANET demonstrated the first available application of packet switching technologies. Some interesting background information on ARPANET is found in references [7-1] and [7-2].)

Today, hundreds of hardware and software vendors incorporate the TCP/IP into their products, which range in size from PCs to mainframes. In addition, the Internet has grown extensively, with a large suite of applications available (see references [7-3] and [7-4]). We'll begin our study of TCP/IP by looking at the history of the Internet.

7.1 The Birth of the Internet

The history of the TCP/IP protocols dates back to the mid 1960s when DARPA initiated research into the viability of packet switching technology. A contract was awarded to Bolt, Baranek and Newman (BBN) of Cambridge, Massachusetts to develop ARPANET. The project proved successful, and ARPANET began operation in 1969 connecting four locations: the University of California at Los Angeles (UCLA), the University of California at Santa Barbara (UCSB), the University of Utah, and Stanford Research Institute (SRI). From that beginning, ARPANET developed into a worldwide packet switching network connecting hundreds of dissimilar computers. In addition, in 1975 BBN initiated Telenet, which became the first commercial packet switching network.

The ARPANET research engendered additional networks that are collectively referred to as the ARPA Internet, TCP/IP Internet, or simply the Internet [7-5]. (Following conventional nomenclature, we will use the term Internet [capital I] when referring to the worldwide Internet, and the term internet [small i] when discussing generic internetworks.) The collection of interconnected networks within the Internet is now quite diverse (see Figure 7-1). ARPANET was dismantled in June 1990, and replaced with the Defense Research Internet (DRI) which is based upon a T1 (1.544 Mbps) backbone instead of ARPANET's 56 Kbps transmission rate. Military traffic now has its own network (MILNET), which is part of the Defense Data Network (DDN). The National Science Foundation Network (NSFNET) was originally built to provide access to the NSF supercomputers, but now provides connectivity at the DS3 rate (44.736 Mbps) to a number of state-supported and regional networks as well [7-6].

The diversity of ARPANET node locations and organizations necessarily brought with it a diversity of hardware platforms and operating systems. Research into the development of a protocol suite that would overcome these differences began in the mid-1970s with papers on the subject published by Vinton Cerf in 1974 [7-7]. Implementation of these protocols throughout the Internet was mandated by DARPA in 1983; if you wanted to do business with the U.S. Government over the ARPANET, your computer needed to implement TCP/IP. Thus, a commercial interest in the TCP/IP protocols was born [7-8].

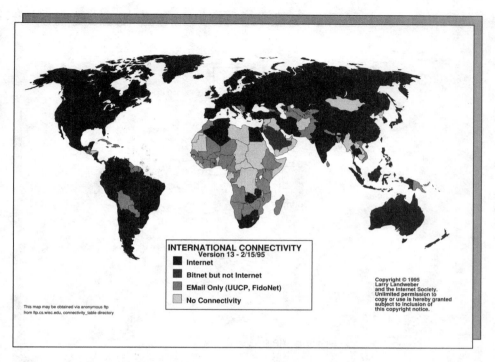

Figure 7-1. International connectivity

The architectural model of the Internet protocols uses terminology that is a slight variation from the OSI Reference Model [7-9]. Hosts (which run application programs) connect to a local network (either LAN or WAN) by means of a network access protocol. Each network connects to at least one gateway (actually a router in the OSI terminology, but old names are difficult to revise) which connects to other networks, as shown in Figure 7-2.

Gateways must contain at least three protocols: two to connect to each of the attached networks (e.g. LAN and WAN), and another (an internet protocol) which relays the network-to-network information.

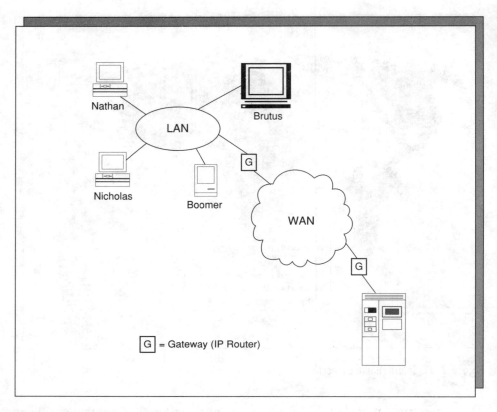

Figure 7-2. Internet connectivity

Hosts are more complex, and must have at least four distinct protocols. The network access and internet protocols are required to communicate with the routers. An OSI Transport Layer (or ARPA Host-to-Host Layer) protocol must assure reliable communication between hosts, since neither the network access nor internet protocols are of an end-to-end nature. Finally, the Application protocols—such as file transfer or electronic mail—are required for actual communication. We'll look at the details of these protocols in Section 7.2.

Information on the Internet architecture and related protocols is published in reports known as Request for Comments, or RFCs, that are circulated among the Internet community. These RFCs are available electronically via the Internet [7-10]. Of special interest is the INDEX.RFC file, which is a numerical index to the RFCs. Another helpful reference is the Assigned Numbers document (currently RFC 1700), which is a lengthy compilation of protocol parameters [7-11]. For readers needing introductory material on the Internet protocols, Charles Hedrick's "Introduction to the Internet Protocols" [7-12] is an excellent reference.

7.2 The ARPA Protocol Suite

The ARPA protocol suite (also known as the Internet protocols or the Department of Defense (DoD) protocols) follows a four-layer architecture. This includes the Network Access Layer (or Local Network Layer), the Internet Layer, the Host-to-Host Layer, and the Process/Application Layer. When comparing ARPA and OSI Reference Model architectures (Figure 7-3), the Network Access Layer includes the OSI Physical and Data Link Layers. The Internet Layer includes the OSI Network Layer functions. The Host-to-Host Layer provides OSI Transport Layer functions, and the Application/Utility Layer includes the OSI Session, Presentation, and Application Layer functions.

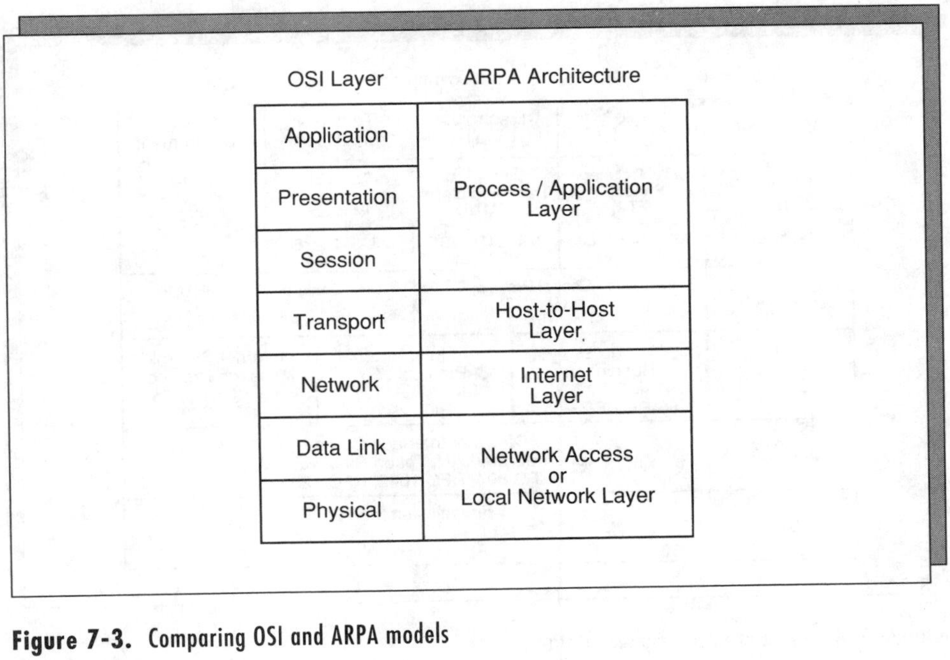

OSI Layer	ARPA Architecture
Application	Process / Application Layer
Presentation	Process / Application Layer
Session	Process / Application Layer
Transport	Host-to-Host Layer
Network	Internet Layer
Data Link	Network Access or Local Network Layer
Physical	Network Access or Local Network Layer

Figure 7-3. Comparing OSI and ARPA models

Of specific interest to our study of internetworking is the manner in which these layers are implemented. The Network Access Layer, as its name implies, controls access to the locally-attached LAN or WAN. This layer is network-specific, and may have multiple implementations throughout the internet. (We will look at Network Access protocols specific to LANs in Section 7.3.) The Internet Protocol (IP) resides on both hosts and gateways (actually routers) and relays data from the source host to the destination host. The Transmission Control Protocol (TCP) resides only on the hosts, and assures reliable data delivery. The various utilities and applications such as the File Transfer Protocol (FTP) and Simple Mail Transfer Protocol (SMTP) also reside only on the hosts.

As we discussed in Section 7.1, all of the ARPA protocols are specified by Request for Comments (RFC) documents, which are openly available on the Internet. The most prevalent of these protocols are shown in Figure 7-4 in relationship to the OSI model. Also shown are the associated RFC numbers, which are referenced throughout the remainder of this chapter. Further details on TCP/IP and the Internet protocols is available in the companion text *Troubleshooting TCP/IP* [7-13].

OSI Layer	Protocol Implementation			
Application	File Transfer	Electronic Mail	Terminal Emulation	Network Management
Presentation	File Transfer Protocol (FTP)	Simple Mail Transfer Protocol (SMTP)	TELNET Protocol	Simple Network Management Protocol (SNMP)
Session	MIL-STD-1780 RFC 959	MIL-STD-1781 RFC 821	MIL-STD-1782 RFC 854	RFC 1157
Transport	Transmission Control Protocol (TCP) MIL-STD-1778 RFC 793		User Datagram Protocol (UDP) RFC 768	
Network	Address Resolution ARP RFC 826 RARP RFC 903	Internet Protocol (IP) MIL-STD-1777 RFC 791	Internet Control Message Protocol (ICMP) RFC 792	
Data Link	Network Interface Cards: Ethernet, StarLAN, Token Ring, ARCNET RFC 894, RFC 1042, RFC 1201			
Physical	Transmission Media: LAN, MAN or WAN			

Figure 7-4. ARPA protocol implementations

7.3 ARPA Network Interface Layer Alternatives

Because of the diverse number of LAN and WAN implementations, the ARPA architecture does not specify a single Network Interface Layer (or OSI Physical and Data Link Layer) protocol to be used. Standards exist, however, supporting a number of networking options, including Ethernet (RFC 894), IEEE 802 (RFC 1042), FDDI (RFC 1188) and ARCNET (RFC 1201) LANs, Public Data Networks by means of the X.25 protocols (RFC 877), plus Metropolitan Area Networks (MANs) and broadband WANs. As shown in Figure 7-5, the host process (e.g. FTP, SMTP, TELNET) data is passed to the TCP Layer, then the IP Layer, and finally the Network Access Layer, which then completes the local network frame header and trailer for transmission on the internetwork or Internet. We'll look at several of these implementations in the following sections.

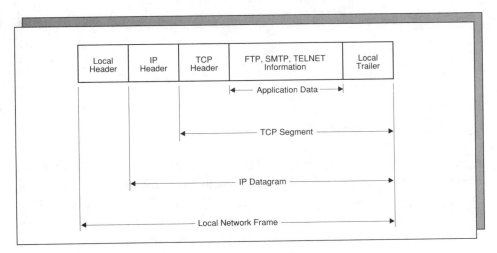

Figure 7-5. TCP/IP headers within a Data Link Layer frame

7.3.1 Ethernet

Ethernet (the DEC, Intel, and Xerox Blue Book version) was developed around the same time (1970s) as the DoD protocols, and as a result, has been used extensively for TCP/IP implementations. RFC 894 [7-14] specifies a type (or Ethertype) of 0800H for IP datagrams. Other Ethertypes used for ARPA protocols include 0806H (ARP) and 8035H (RARP). (We'll discuss these protocols further in Section 7.4.) Also noted in RFC 894 is the fact that IP must control the Ethernet Data field size (46–1500 octets) shown in Figure 7-6. For frames with less than 46 octets of data, the Data field is padded with zeros. At the upper limit, gateways (IP routers) must be able to accept and fragment maximum length (1500 octet) frames that exceed the typical 576-octet IP datagram limit.

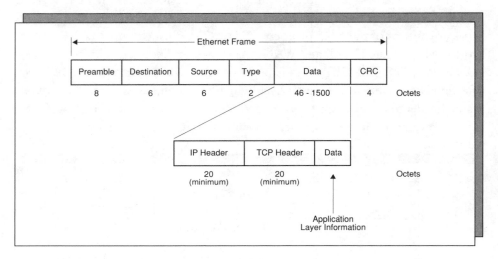

Figure 7-6. TCP/IP Headers within an Ethernet frame

A mapping between 32-bit Internet addresses and the 48-bit Ethernet addresses can be accomplished with either static tables within the host, or dynamically using two specific protocols. The Address Resolution Protocol (ARP), described in RFC 826 [7-15], converts the IP addresses to Ethernet addresses. A second protocol, the Reverse Address Resolution Protocol (RARP), described in RFC 903 [7-16], converts Ethernet addresses to IP addresses.

7.3.2 IEEE 802

IP datagrams can be encapsulated within 802.3, 802.4, or 802.5 frames, and the techniques are described in detail in RFC 1042 [7-17]. Most significant is an extension to the IEEE 802.2 Logical Link Control (LLC) header known as the Sub-Network Access Protocol (SNAP). From Figure 7-7, note that the 802.X Medium Access Control (MAC) header is transmitted first. Transmitted next are the 802.2 LLC header fields containing the Destination and Source Service Access

Point (DSAP and SSAP) addresses, set to AAH. The 802.2 Control Field is set to 03H (for Unnumbered Information). The SNAP Header consists of a 3-octet Protocol ID or Organizational Code, followed by a 2-octet Ethertype (0800H for IP). RFC 1042 may be consulted for further details.

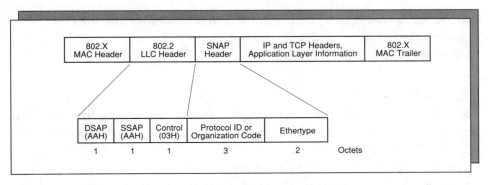

Figure 7-7. Sub-Network Access Protocol (SNAP) header encapsulated within an IEEE 802.X frame

7.3.3 ARCNET

Both IP and ARP datagrams can be encapsulated within an ARCNET frame, as shown in Figure 7-8. Several unique points, elaborated in RFC 1201 [7-18], are noted here.

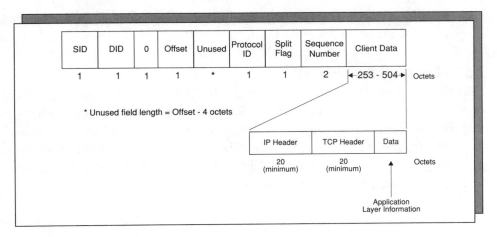

Figure 7-8. ARCNET long frame format

First, Internet addresses (32 bits) can be mapped to ARCNET addresses (8 bits) using the Address Resolution Protocol (ARP) discussed in Section 7.3.1. Second, the System Code field, assigned by Datapoint Corporation, is the first octet within the ARCNET data field. The value for IP is 240 decimal (F0H), and for ARP is 241 decimal (F1H). The maximum ARCNET frame of 508 octets is less than the maximum IP datagram length of 576 octets, thus requiring fragmentation and reassembly at the IP level. More details on the fragmentation/reassembly function follow in Section 7.4.

7.3.4 FDDI

The Fiber Distributed Data Interface (FDDI) is formalized by the American National Standards Institute (ANSI), and described in ANSI documents X3.139, X3.148, X3.166, X3.184 and others. FDDI networks operate at 100 Mbps over either fiber optic or twisted pair transmission media, using a counter-rotating, redundant, dual-ring topology. The total length of the dual ring may not exceed 100 kilometers (or 200 kilometers when wrapped or connected during a fault condition), with a maximum of 500 attached stations. With its high transmission capacity and large geographical coverage, FDDI is ideally suited for campus-wide or metropolitan area network (MAN) applications.

Support for TCP/IP over FDDI networks is very similar to the earlier standards defined for Ethernet and IEEE 802 LANs, including the use of 802.2 LLC and SNAP (Figure 7-9). Mapping between the 48-bit FDDI addresses and IP addresses is done using ARP, using the hardware type code for Ethernet. Further details on FDDI support are provided in RFC 1188 [7-19].

7.3.5 Broadband Networks

Because of its broad popularity, support for the TCP/IP protocol suite has been developed for many broadband technologies. These include Switched Multimegabit Data Service—SMDS (RFC 1209), Frame Relay (RFC 1490), and Asynchronous Transfer Mode—ATM (RFC 1577). As future transmission technologies emerge, one can be assured that TCP/IP-based applications will be one of the first protocol suites to be documented.

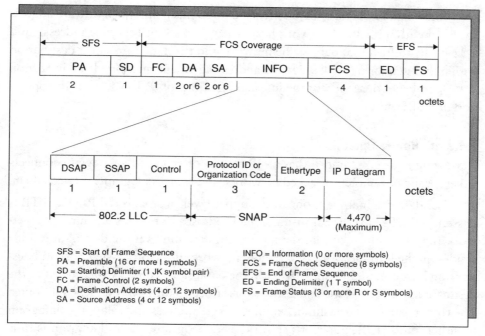

Figure 7-9. FDDI frame with IP datagram *(Courtesy American National Standards Institute)*

7.4 The ARPA Internet Layer

The ARPA Internet Layer (or OSI Network Layer) functions include routing and switching of the datagram through the communications subnetwork or subnet. The Internet Protocol (IP) provides this fundamental function, forwarding the datagram based upon the network address contained within the IP header [7-20]. Each datagram is an independent entity, not related to any other datagram. In addition, delivery of that datagram is not guaranteed by IP; therefore, the service provided by that protocol is considered an unreliable service. The next highest layer, TCP, provides the reliability that IP lacks. A secondary IP function is the fragmentation and reassembly of the datagram to match the frame size specified by the Data Link Layer protocol (e.g. Ethernet, IEEE 802.5, etc.) in use.

Notice that two addresses are involved up to this point: the hardware address specified within the local network header (e.g. the 48-bit Ethernet address); and a 32-bit IP address that defines the network and the datagram's host destination within that network. (We'll study the addressing scheme in more detail in Section 7.4.3.) To begin our study of the internal functions of IP, let's look at the operation of an IP router.

7.4.1 IP Router Operation

Reviewing Figure 7-2, recall that an IP router (often called a gateway) connects either locally or remotely attached networks, and routes datagrams between them.

User data originating at one of the upper layer protocols (ULPs), e.g. FTP, is passed to the IP Layer for transmission. The host's IP process examines the network (i.e. IP) address of that datagram and determines if the destination node resides on the local network or a remote network. If the processing host and destination host are on the same network, the datagram is directly forwarded to the destination host. If not, the datagram is forwarded to the locally attached IP router. The router, in a similar fashion, examines the IP address and relays the datagram to either another IP router or network, as appropriate. Each datagram is thus routed individually, based upon a table lookup within each router.

In order for these routing tables to be established and maintained, the various IP routers exchange information with each other detailing the current network topology. Another protocol, known as the Internetwork Control Message Protocol (ICMP), is used for this purpose. RFC 792 [7-21] is devoted to ICMP.

7.4.2 The IP Header

Again reviewing Figure 7-5, note that the IP header is the first subfield within the local network (Ethernet, 802.X, ARCNET, etc.) Information field. The minimum length of the IP header is 20 octets (assuming no options or padding). Following that header is the information that the datagram is carrying, such as the TCP header and ULP data. Note also that the structure of the ARPA protocols and their fields are based upon a 32-bit word, the width of the original ARPANET processors. Referring to Figure 7-10, let's examine the IP header fields in more detail.

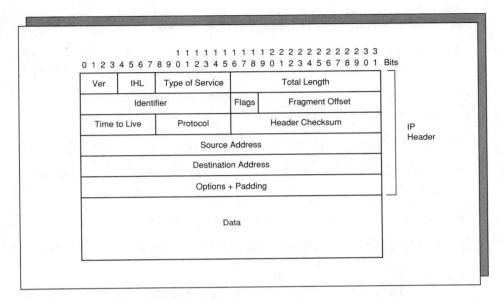

Figure 7-10. The IP Header and Data

⊗ Version (4 bits): the IP version number (currently 4).

⊗ Internet header length (4 bits): the length of the header in 32 bit words (minimum of 5 words or 20 octets).

⊗ Type of service (8 bits): flags to specify reliability, precedence, delay, and throughput parameters.

⊗ Total length (16 bits): total length of the IP datagram, given in octets, including the IP header.

⊗ Identification (16 bits): provides a unique identifier for this datagram.

⊗ Flags (3 bits): options that indicate if fragmentation is permitted and/or used.

⊗ Fragment offset (13 bits): indicates where in the entire datagram this fragment belongs; measured in 64-bit units from the beginning of the datagram.

⊛ Time to live (8 bits): measured in gateway hops or seconds.

⊛ Protocol (8 bits): identifies the next protocol that follows the IP header, e.g. TCP.

⊛ Header checksum (16 bits): a checksum on the IP header that may be recomputed at each gateway.

⊛ Source address (32 bits): the internet address of the originating host.

⊛ Destination address (32 bits): the internet address of the destination host.

⊛ Options (variable): options from the sender, e.g. a route specification.

⊛ Padding (variable): provided so that the IP header ends on a 32 bit boundary.

⊛ Data (variable): a multiple of 8 bits, not to exceed 65,535 octets for IP header plus data (TCP header, TCP data, etc.).

Note that the limits on the IP datagram are 576 octets minimum and 65,535 octets maximum.

7.4.3   IP Network Addresses

When a network joins a TCP/IP-based internet, an administrative agency, such as the InterNIC, assigns an IP network number [7-6].

The internet address consists of two parts: a Network ID, assigned by the administrative agency; and a Host ID, assigned by the local administrator. These 32 bit addresses are typically displayed as four decimal integers, separated by a period (e.g. 95.0.0.1). Each of these fields represents 8 bits of the 32 bit address and can have a value from 0 to 255. There are five classes (A, B, C, D, and E) of IP addresses (see Figure 7-11).

Class A networks are used for very large networks, and begin with bit 0 = 0. Examples would be the ARPANET (now extinct), where the network address = 10, and MILNET, where the network address = 27. Class B networks are medium-size networks —such as campuses—that have the first octet begin with a 10, and network addresses that range between 128 and 191 (decimal). Class C networks are used for small networks, and have a very large Network ID field (24 bits) and a small Host ID field (8 bits). The first octet begins with a 110, and the network addresses range from 192 to 254. Class D addresses begin with a 1110, and are used for IP multicasting, as defined in RFC 988. Class E addresses begin with 1111 and are reserved for experimental use. For all classes, addresses 0 and 255 are reserved, with 0 representing the originating entity—"this network" or "this host"—and 255 used for broadcast messages.

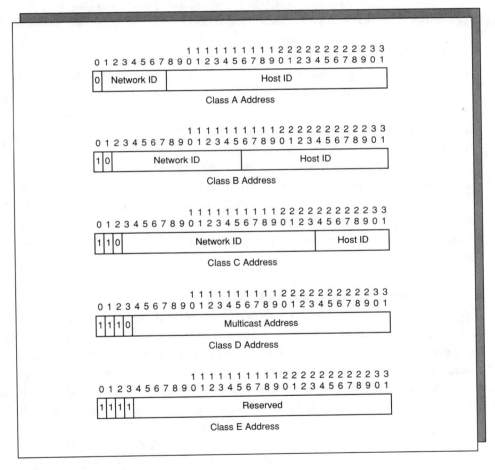

Figure 7-11. IP address fields

7.4.4 IP Routing Protocols

As we have seen, routers receive the IP header information, look at the destination network address, and make a routing decision for that particular datagram, based upon a real-time table lookup. The question is, then, how do these tables get established and maintained? The answer lies in the IP routing protocols, which are a dynamic process providing a mechanism for the routers to exchange status information regarding the various transmission paths between them. Two different protocols are commonly used for this purpose. The first, Routing Information Protocol (RFC 1058), was originally designed by Xerox in its Xerox Network Systems (XNS) implementation (see Section 8.5.1). It was then modified for TCP/IP and incorporated into the Berkeley UNIX systems. The routing metric is the hop count, which is limited to 16 hops (a hop being a transmission through an intermediate router). The hop count is not always efficient, as it cannot consider the cost factor of the path, only the number of hops.

The second standard—designed for greater internetwork efficiency—is called Open Shortest Path First (OSPF), defined in RFC 1247. OSPF is an improvement on RIP, because it allows the path to be selected based upon cost or delay factors—a process known as least-cost routing. Other capabilities include multi-path routing for load balancing, and network management functions. Instead of a routing metric based solely upon hops, the OSPF metric is a 16-bit user-configurable field. The network manager defines the factors that are most applicable (e.g. delay, transmission cost, bandwidth) and the router then makes the path choice based upon that metric [7-22].

7.4.5 Internet Control Message Protocol

ICMP also operates at the ARPA Internet Layer (or OSI Network Layer), and is used for communication between the various IP entities. ICMP messages provide intra-network communication and diagnostics, telegraphing notices of network congestion or an unreachable port. This protocol uses IP services; an ICMP message is sent using IP, with the ICMP message occupying the IP Data field (see Figure 7-12). The ICMP Header is 8 octets in length, and contains the following fields:

⊗ Type (8 bits): indicates the type of ICMP message. Currently defined are destination unreachable, time exceeded, parameter problem, source quench, redirect, echo, echo reply, timestamp, and timestamp reply.

⊚ Code (8 bits): specifies parameters of the message that can be briefly encoded.

⊚ Checksum (16 bits): checksum of the ICMP message.

⊚ Data (variable): additional information that is related to the message.

RFC 792 [7-21] describes the operation of ICMP in greater detail.

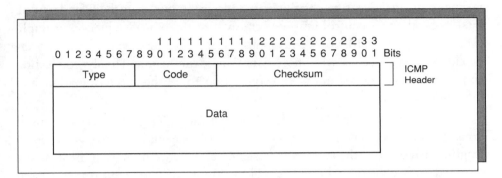

Figure 7-12. ICMP Header and Data

7.4.6 ARPA Internet Layer Summary

Reviewing Figure 7-4, notice that ARP, RARP, and ICMP all operate at the ARPA Internet Layer, but provide different functions. ARP and RARP are providing services to IP, while ICMP is a user of IP services. We will next discuss how the ARPA Host-to-Host Layer uses these three different protocols.

7.5 ARPA Host-to-Host Layer Protocols

Two protocols are defined at the ARPA Host-to-Host (or OSI Transport) Layer: Transmission Control Protocol (TCP) [7-23] and User Datagram Protocol (UDP) [7-24]. Both protocols have unique applications: TCP provides reliability with high overhead, while UDP provides unreliable service with much less overhead. We'll look at each of the protocols separately.

7.5.1 Transmission Control Protocol

TCP provides a virtual circuit service between end-user applications—reliable data transfer—that was lacking in the datagram-oriented IP. Additional functions are also present in TCP that support the end-to-end connection between host processes. First, the ULP process must be identified to TCP by a port address, sometimes known as a socket. Examples of port numbers (in decimal) would be FTP (21), TELNET (23), or SMTP (25). The Upper Layer Protocol connection is thus completely identified by this port address (16 bits) plus the IP address (32 bits). Second, error control must detect any missing, out-of-sequence, or duplicate information. Third, flow control must assure that a fast sender does not overwhelm a slower receiver with more data than it can handle. Finally, connection control must provide for end-to-end connection establishment, termination, and interruption.

TCP treats the higher-layer information (from SMTP, FTP, etc.) as a continuous stream of data. This stream is divided into segments of up to 65K octets in length. Each octet of the segment is assigned a sequence number to provide the required error control and flow control functions. Each segment is then passed to the IP Layer, which creates and passes the datagrams to the LAN, MAN, or WAN in use. At that layer, the local network protocol (e.g. IEEE 802.3, X.25) adds the local network header and trailer, and sends the bits over the transmission medium. At the remote host, a similar, but opposite, process occurs.

To support the reliability functions defined for TCP, a header with a minimum length of 20 octets is required (see Figure 7-13). These fields are described below:

- ⊛ Source port (16 bits): the number of the calling port.

- ⊛ Destination port (16 bits): the number of the called port.

- ⊛ Sequence number (32 bits): a sequence number assuring the correct arrival and sequentiality of the data. This number indicates the sequence number of the first octet in this TCP data block, and is incremented according to the number of octets transmitted in each TCP segment.

◎ Acknowledgment number (32 bits): a piggyback acknowledgment of the next expected TCP octet.

◎ Data offset (4 bits): the number of 32 bit words in the TCP header.

◎ Reserved (6 bits): set to zero.

◎ Flags (6 bits): control functions such as the setup and termination of a session, expedited or urgent data flow, reset of a connection, or indication of the end of the data.

URG: urgent pointer field significant

ACK: acknowledgment field significant

PHS: push function

RST: reset connection

SYN: synchronize sequence numbers

FIN: no more data from sender

◎ Window (16 bits): the receive window size, indicating the number of octets—beginning with the one in the acknowledgment field—that the sender (of Window) is willing to accept.

◎ Checksum (16 bits): a checksum based upon the IP address fields plus the TCP header and its length.

◎ Urgent pointer (16 bits): points to the first octet that follows the urgent data, and allows the receiver to determine how much urgent data is coming.

◎ Options (variable): one option (maximum TCP segment size) is currently defined.

TCP provides reliable delivery, but does so at the expense of higher overhead. Two TCP/IP connection protocols that support serial lines, SLIP (Serial Line IP), reference [7-25], and PPP (the Point-to-Point Protocol), reference [7-26], are also defined. For situations where reliability is not as critical, another Host-to-Host protocol is available.

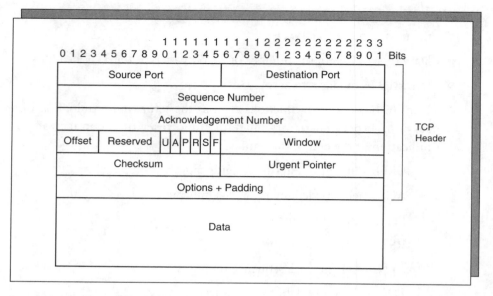

Figure 7-13. The TCP header and data

7.5.2   User Datagram Protocol

Some applications do not require the extensive error control functions provided by TCP. One example is the Simple Network Management Protocol (SNMP) that is used to communicate status updates and parameter values between a remote device and a network management workstation. For such applications, absolute reliability is not a requirement, thus the lower overhead User Datagram Protocol (UDP) can be used. The UDP header, shown in Figure 7-14, has four fields:

- ⊗   Source port (16 bits): the number of the calling port.
- ⊗   Destination port (16 bits): the number of the called port.
- ⊗   Length (16 bits): length of the UDP datagram.
- ⊗   Checksum (16 bits): checksum for the UDP header.

Note the absence of the reliability-related fields such as the Sequence and Acknowledgment numbers. Since guaranteed delivery is not a UDP requirement, the header is shortened accordingly.

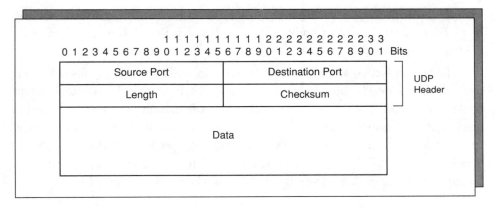

Figure 7-14. The UDP header and data

7.5.3 ARPA Host-to-Host Layer Summary

Both the TCP and UDP headers begin with 16-bit Source and Destination port addresses. Values between 0–255 are reserved and designated Well-Known ports. The other port numbers, known as Ephemeral Ports, are available. The *Assigned Numbers* document (currently RFC 1700) [7-11] contains a listing of the reserved port numbers. Software developers may be interested in the TCP/IP implementation of the NetBIOS Application Program Interface (API). Reference [7-27] contains those details.

7.6 ARPA Higher Layer Protocols

Extensive literature exists on the Application protocols used within the Internet (see references [7-13] and [7-28] through [7-31]). A brief summary is presented here.

Simple Mail Transfer Protocol (SMTP) is an electronic messaging utility. SMTP is only concerned with the destination of the message, not its contents, and as such requires local host processing for message editing. See RFC 821 [7-28] for further details. TELNET is a protocol for virtual terminal operation, providing a facility to log-in to remote hosts. Once logged-in, the user appears to be connected locally. RFC 854 [7-29] details the TELNET protocol.

File Transfer Protocol (FTP), as its name implies, specifies how users can transfer files from a remote host without regard to the hardware or operating system involved. Both text and binary files are supported. Provisions also exist to restrict access by use of passwords. Further details are found in RFC 959 [7-30].

The Simple Network Management Protocol (SNMP) is used to manage remote internetwork devices. It uses datagram transport (UDP) to provide communications between a network management station and a network management agent in the managed object. A number of vendors have accepted SNMP as the network management protocol of choice, and have incorporated it into their products. SNMP version 1 is detailed in RFC 1157 [7-31]. SNMP version 2, which includes protocol, security, and a number of other enhancements, is described in RFCs 1441 through 1452.

7.7 The Future of TCP/IP

As we studied in Section 7.4.3, IP addresses are 32 bits in length, and uniquely identify a device on either a TCP/IP-based internetwork, the worldwide Internet, or possibly both. Due to the explosive growth of the Internet in the past few years, the number of available IP addresses in certain categories, especially Class B, is dwindling.

As a result of this projected address shortage, the Internet Engineering Task Force (IETF) chartered a committee, known as an "area," to study the problem and recommend a solution. This solution is known as IPng, for Internet Protocol—Next Generation (IPng), or IP version 6 (IPv6), the designated successor to the current IP version 4 (IPv4) (see reference [7-32]).

A number of protocols were submitted to the IETF as IPv6 proposals. The Common Architecture for Next Generation Internet Protocol (CATNIP) proposed to integrate the ISO Connectionless Network Layer Protocol (CLNP), IP, and Novell's IPX. The TCP and UDP with Bigger Addresses (TUBA) protocol proposed to replace IPv4 with the OSI CLNP, which allows variable length addresses. The Simple Internet Protocol Plus (SIPP) proposal expanded the addressing and routing capabilities of IP, simplified the IP header, and added quality of service, authentication, and privacy (encryption) functions.

After extensive debate, the IETF incorporated elements from both TUBA and SIPP into IPng, defined in RFC 1752 [7-33]. These features include a 16-octet address length, autoconfiguration, encryption, flow control, and support for wireless networks. Migration strategies, a big part of this development effort, are untested at the time of this writing. It is safe to say, however, that as TCP/IP-based internetworks in general, and the worldwide Internet in particular, migrate to IPv6, all devices that use IP, from workstations to routers, will be affected in some way. Whether this effect will be direct, as in a software upgrade, or indirect, as in the installation of a proxy or gateway device, is not known. Network managers should be aware of this change, and should educate themselves accordingly before making any major network reconfigurations [7-34].

7.8 TCP/IP Internetworking Examples

As mentioned previously, a very large number of vendors support the TCP/IP protocols for PCs, LANs, minis, and mainframes. Following are four examples of LAN internetwork products that utilize the TCP/IP protocols.

7.8.1 NetManage Chameleon

The ChameleonNFS product from NetManage, Inc. of Cupertino, California, is a desktop communications software package designed for multivendor internetworking from Windows environments. Windows users are thus able to easily access TCP/IP- and UNIX-based hosts, using the familiar Windows icons instead of the more rigorous UNIX command line. The TCP/IP stack is called NEWT (NetManage Enhanced Windows TCP/IP). It allows the more than 24 applications, including the Network File System (NFS), to run on top of Windows (Figure 7-15).

The product applications fall into five groups: terminal emulation, electronic mail, file and printer sharing, network utilities, and communications protocol. With these five functions, a single product incorporates the major desktop applications that are needed in the corporate environment. The terminal emulation group includes TELNET, TN3270 and TN5250 with Visual Script Editor and Player, which allow the user to create and edit custom terminal emulation scripts.

SMTP mail application with Multipurpose Internet Mail Extensions (MIME) allows users to attach graphics, spreadsheet and word processing documents to Internet mail. Internet front end applications provide tools that facilitate Internet information access. This includes Gopher for information retrieval, NewsReader for subscribing to newsgroups, and WhoIS for locating individual Internet subscribers.

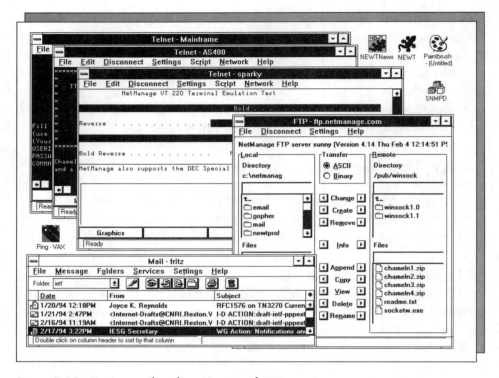

Figure 7-15. NetManage Chameleon *(Courtesy of NetManage)*

File utilities include NFS for remote file access, plus Line Printer Remote (LPR) and Line Printer Domain (LPD) for remote file printing. Chameleon users may also create their own file server using the Anonymous FTP server. Standard network utilities such as PING, Finger, and Bind applications are included also. Additionally, RMON and SNMP support is bundled in—allowing the applications to be managed as well.

For the dial-up user, Internet Chameleon provides a suite of TCP/IP internet applications, including SMTP mail, Telnet, FTP, NewsReader, Gopher, Mosaic, Archie, Instant Internet (instant Internet provider setup), WhoIs, Ping, and Finger.

In summary, the Chameleon product line from NetManage provides the software needed to turn your Windows desktop into a fully functioning TCP/IP desktop, for both internetworking and Internet connectivity.

7.8.2 Wollongong Pathway

The Wollongong Group, Inc. of Palo Alto, CA, specializes in software-based, open systems solutions. The firm's core technologies include open protocols, such as TCP/IP; network and systems management, such as SNMP; and network applications, such as advanced terminal emulations and Internet access. As an early pioneer of TCP/IP technology, Wollongong encouraged the evolution of this technology from its complex, UNIX-oriented background in the 1980s to its current acceptance as the standard enterprise-wide and Internet-connectivity protocol.

PathWay, Wollongong's flagship product line, is an integrated suite of desktop TCP/IP applications and services that deliver multi-platform communications across diverse computing platforms. PathWay products connect DOS, Windows, Macintosh, and OpenVMS clients to IBM, DEC, UNIX, and other hosts across TCP/IP corporate and public networks (Figure 7-16).

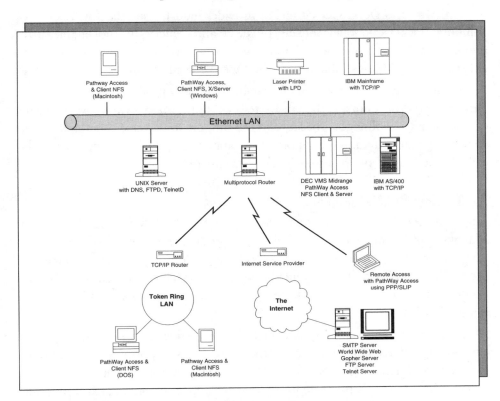

Figure 7-16. PathWay connectivity *(Courtesy of the Wollongong Group, Inc.)*

PathWay Access includes desktop TCP/IP applications for LAN and remote use. Applications include a MIME-enabled electronic mail client, Internet News-Reader, advanced terminal emulation suite including IBM TN3270 and TN5250, DEC VT100-340 and others, FTP client/server, SNMP management support and print redirection.

PathWay Client NFS provides access to open distributed file systems and printing services in use in a multi-vendor network environment based on Sunsoft's ONC/NFS protocols. This product is available for DOS/Windows, Macintosh, and OpenVMS platforms. PathWay Server NFS provides ONC/NFS services on DEC's OpenVMS platform and Microsoft Windows NT.

PathWay Runtime is Wollongong's TCP/IP stack which provides the interface to the underlying transport protocols. Core protocols include TCP, IP, ICMP, ARP, BOOTP, and NetBIOS, plus PPP/SLIP for remote access.

PathWay API Developer's Tool Kit provides industry-standard APIs such as Windows Sockets, Berkeley Sockets, plus FTP and Telnet. This tool enables programmers to write applications that access remote network services, and is available on DOS/Windows, Macintosh, and OpenVMS platforms.

Wollongong has been successful in selling PathWay products into workgroup and enterprise accounts as they move to TCP/IP internetworking. Many of its customers pick Wollongong because of the support for diverse client and server computing platforms and the simple-to-use applications for accessing host applications and files in an open standards environment.

7.8.3 Novell's LAN WorkPlace

The Advanced Access Applications Division of Novell's Information Access and Management Group, in San Jose, California, produces a family of software products that brings TCP/IP connectivity to both stand-alone and NetWare-connected users. The LAN WorkPlace product family provides TCP/IP-based communications for all of the popular desktop systems: DOS/Windows, and Macintosh (Figure 7-17a).

Principal features of the product include: terminal emulation, providing concurrent TELNET connections to multiple hosts; FTP support for file transfers between NetWare, DOS, UNIX or any other FTP servers; NFS client, for transparent access to UNIX file systems; utilities for remote command execution, file and print services; and Finger, Ping and Talk utilities for querying the network and communicating with other networked users. LAN WorkPlace simplifies connectivity for the end user by bringing these features together in a familiar graphical interface and by automating host connection and file transfer tasks with built-in scripting capability.

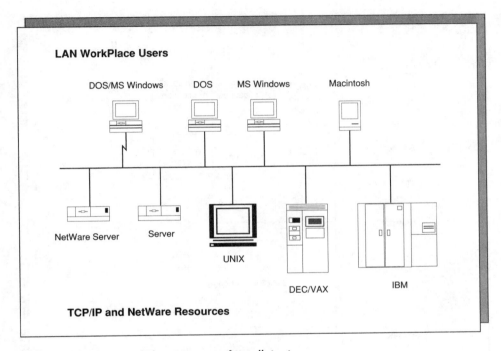

Figure 7-17a. LAN WorkPlace *(Courtesy of Novell, Inc.)*

Mobile computing is supported with Point-to-Point Protocol (PPP) and Serial Line IP (SLIP) drivers for remote access to both IPX and TCP/IP networks, using a standard dial-up connection. In addition, the MS Windows version comes with a special graphical dialer interface. LAN WorkPlace also includes several utilities for monitoring and managing networks using Simple Network Management Protocol (SNMP), as well as a Reverse Address Protocol (RARP) server, which facilitates assignment of IP addresses to other nodes on the network.

LAN WorkPlace supports a wide range of networking hardware, using Novell's Open Data-Link Interface (ODI) technology. It also accommodates any combination of networking software that conforms to the NDIS standard (including NetWare, Microsoft LAN Manager, Banyan VINES, and UNIX NFS environments). LAN WorkPlace supports a large number of third-party applications, including those compatible with the X Window System, the SQL database language, and the Windows Socket API Specification (WinSock) (Figure 7-17b).

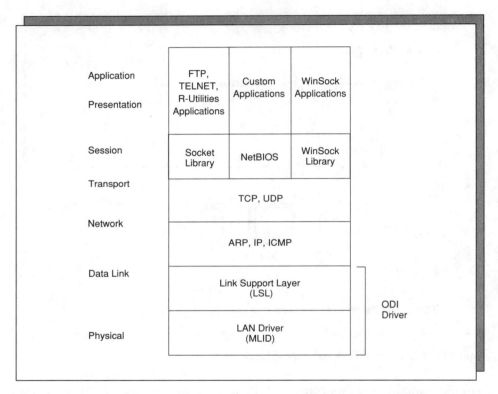

Figure 7-17b. LAN WorkPlace architecture *(Courtesy of Novell, Inc.)*

The LAN WorkGroup product provides the same connectivity features as LAN WorkPlace, with the added convenience of centralized installation and configuration over a NetWare network. Consisting of a NetWare Loadable Module (NLM) package and a complete set of client applications, LAN WorkGroup makes it easy and inexpensive to install TCP/IP on a company-wide basis. It also streamlines the task of managing large networks by automatically configuring and assigning IP addresses using the Bootstrap Protocol (BOOTP). Network administrators save time and money, and end users work with the same interface they would find in their platform-specific versions of LAN WorkPlace.

LAN WorkShop is a software development kit for programmers writing TCP/IP-aware applications using the LAN WorkPlace TCP/IP protocol stack. It provides all of the tools a developer might need to create TCP/IP-enabled applications and includes TCP/IP development libraries, plus full documentation and numerous example programs. It also includes NetWare TI-RPC, an enhanced implementation of the NetWare Transport Independent Remote Procedure Call (TI-RPC) toolkit.

The LAN WorkPlace family of products from Novell is well-suited for enterprises that want to standardize their network environment using TCP/IP and at the same time accommodate the widest possible variety of existing systems. Noted for its cross-platform, multi-vendor flexibility, its reliability is proven. LAN WorkPlace has the largest installed base of any desktop TCP/IP product. And perhaps most importantly, it comes from the makers of NetWare, the most popular network operating system.

Both LAN WorkPlace and LAN WorkGroup are available in native language versions, including English, French, German, Spanish, Portuguese, and Japanese.

7.8.4 Xyplex Access Server

During the past few years, there has been an increased need to provide geographically-dispersed remote users and branch offices with access to computing resources at headquarters locations. Historically, this requirement was provided by terminal servers with multiple serial ports through which dial-up, asynchronous connections could be made. Technology innovations in the early 1990s created a new device, called the remote access server, which provides remote access to both remote users and remote branch offices. These servers combine the flexibility of a terminal server for connecting individual computers with the ability to provide a remote client with seamless access to the corporate LAN. For remote clients, the connection is typically made using a dial-up analog telephone line using modems. For remote branch offices, dial-up or dedicated circuits may be used based upon the traffic requirements between locations.

Xyplex, Inc. of Littleton, Massachusetts, developed the Access Server product line as a result of their experience with terminal servers. This family of products provides network access both locally and remotely via dial-up connections for a variety of devices, including terminals, PCs, bar code readers and data acquisition devices. Server configurations range in capacity from 8 to 40 ports, with port speeds up to 115.2 Kbps (see Figure 7-18).

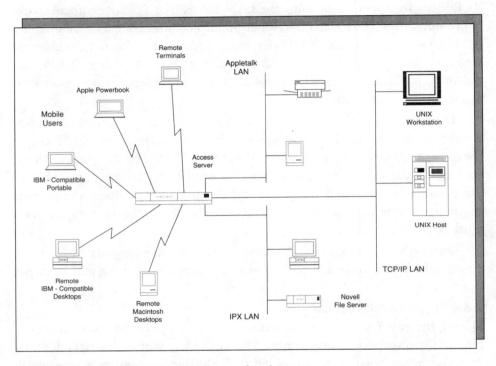

Figure 7-18. Xyplex Access Server *(Courtesy of Xyplex, Inc.)*

Most corporate networks combine multiple systems from different vendors, many of which use different transport protocols. For example, the AppleTalk Remote Access Protocol (ARAP) is required to dial into an AppleTalk LAN; IPX support is the key to NetWare LAN access; and IP is used for dial-in access to UNIX-based servers and hosts. Remote access servers have widely adopted the Point-to-Point Protocol (PPP), an adjunct to the TCP/IP suite, to transport multiprotocol traffic over WAN links. PPP defines and controls the establishment and configuration of remote links, and can encapsulate multiple protocols within its frame format. PPP also includes network management and security functions, including standard messages for Link Quality Monitoring (LQM), password security and user authentication. This contrasts with the Serial Line Internet Protocol (SLIP), which supports only serial IP connections.

Xyplex includes an industry-first feature, known as the Auto Protocol Detection function, into their remote access server. The algorithm automatically detects and configures itself to the remote user's protocol, whether it be dial-in or local, terminal or workstation. This eliminates the need for preconfigured ports to support specific protocols. With Auto Protocol Detection, network managers don't have the cumbersome task of assigning and updating dedicated ports for the variety of protocols utilized in the enterprise network. Thus any port may accept traffic from any protocol, be that AppleTalk, IPX or TCP/IP, relieving network managers from yet another configuration responsibility.

To summarize, the worldwide Internet has experienced meteoric growth in the past few years. As references [7-35] through [7-37] attest, growth in this international communication medium is steadily increasing. Business use of the Internet, using such tools as the World Wide Web [7-38], is furthering its popularity. With that growth has come a greater interest and appreciation for the Internet protocols, TCP and IP. In the next chapter, we will study another protocol suite that provided significant contributions to internetworking, the Xerox Network Systems, or XNS.

7.9   References

[7-1]   Schultz, Brad. "The Evolution of ARPANET." *Datamation* (August 1, 1988): 71–74.

[7-2]   Padlipsky, M. A. "A Perspective on the ARPANET Reference Model." IEEE Infocom 83 Proceedings: 39–253.

[7-3]   Daniel C. Lynch and Marshall T. Rose, editors. *Internet System Handbook*. New York: Addison-Wesley Publishing Co., 1993.

[7-4]   Paxson, Vern. "Growth Trends in Wide-Area TCP Connections." *IEEE Network* (July–August 1994): 8–17.

[7-5]   Comer, Douglas. *Internetworking with TCP/IP Principles, Protocols and Architecture*. 2nd ed. New York: Prentice-Hall, 1991.

[7-6]   Further information on the Internet may be obtained from the InterNIC, telephone (703) 742-4777, or email info@internic.net.

[7-7]   Cerf, Vinton and R. Kahn. "A Protocol for Packet Network Interconnection." *IEEE Transactions on Communications*, May 1974.

[7-8]   Retz, David. "TCP/IP: DoD Suite Marches into the Business World." *Data Communications* (November 1987): 209–225.

[7-9]   Cerf, Vinton G. and Edward Cain. "The DoD Internet Architecture Model." *Computer Network* Vol. 7, no. 5 (October 1983): 307–318.

[7-10] Request for Comments (RFC) documents may be obtained via anonymous FTP from the following hosts:

ds.internic.net, directory rfc
nis.nsf.net, directory internet/documents/rfc
nisc.jvnc.net, directory rfc
ftp.isi.edu, directory in-notes

[7-11] J. Reynolds and J. Postel. *Assigned Numbers*. RFC 1700, October 1994.

[7-12] Hedrick, Charles L. "Introduction to the Internet Protocols." Rutgers the State University of New Jersey, September 1988. Available via anonymous FTP on host nic.merit.edu, directory introducing.the.internet, file intro.to.ip.

[7-13] Miller, Mark A. *Troubleshooting TCP/IP*. New York: M&T Books, Inc., 1992.

[7-14] Hornig, C. *A Standard for the Transmission of IP Datagrams over Ethernet Networks*. RFC 894, April 1984.

[7-15] Plummer, D.C. *An Ethernet Address Resolution Protocol*. RFC 826, November 1982.

[7-16] Finlayson, R., et. al. *A Reverse Address Resolution Protocol*. RFC 903, June 1984.

[7-17] Postel, J.B. and J.K. Reynolds. *A Standard for the Transmission of IP Datagrams Over IEEE 802 Networks*. RFC 1042, February 1988.

[7-18] Provan, D. *Transmitting IP Traffic over ARCNET Networks*. RFC 1201, February 1991.

[7-19] Katz, D. *A Proposed Standard for the Transmission of IP Datagrams over FDDI Networks*. RFC 1188, October 1990

[7-20] Postel, J.B. *Internet Protocol*. RFC 791, September 1981.

[7-21] Postel, J.B. *Internet Control Message Protocol*. RFC 792, September 1981.

[7-22] Moy, John. "OSPF: Next Generation Routing Comes to TCP/IP Networks." *LAN Technology* (April 1990): 71–79.

[7-23] Postel, J.B. *Transmission Control Protocol*. RFC 93, September 1981.

[7-24] Postel, J.B. *User Datagram Protocol*. RFC 768, August 1980.

[7-25] Jacobson, V. *Compressing TCP/IP Headers for Low-Speed Serial Links*. RFC 1144, February 1990.

[7-26] Simpson, W. *The Point-to-Point Protocol*. RFC 1661, July 1994.

[7-27] DARPA IAB NetBIOS Working Group, *Protocol Standard for a NetBIOS Service on a TCP/UDP Transport: Concepts and Methods*, RFC 1001, March 1987; Detailed Specifications, RFC 1002, March 1987.

[7-28] Postel, J.B. *Simple Mail Transfer Protocol (SMTP)*. RFC 821.

[7-29] Postel, J.B. and J.K. Reynolds. *TELNET Protocol Specification*. RFC 854.

[7-30] Postel, J.B. and J.K. Reynolds. *File Transfer Protocol (FTP)*. RFC 959.

[7-31] Case, J.D. et. al. *Simple Network Management Protocol*. RFC 1157, April 1989.

[7-32] Gross, Phil. "Charge to IPng Area: A Direction for IPng." *ConneXions, the Interoperability Report—Special Issue on IP—the Next Generation*, May 1994.

[7-33] S. Bradner and A. Mankin. "The Recommendation for the IP Next Generation Protocol." RFC 1752, January 1995.

[7-34] Johnson, Johna Till. "Doubts about IPng Could Create TCP/IP Chaos." *Data Communications* (November 1994): 55-60.

[7-35] Krol, Ed. *The Whole Internet—User's Guide and Catalog*. O'Reilly & Associates, Inc., 1992.

[7-36] Malamud, Carl. *Exploring the Internet*. New York: Prentice-Hall, 1993.

[7-37] Tom Badgett and Corey Sandler. *Internet: from Mystery to Mastery*. New York, MIS:Press, 1993.

[7-38] December, John and Neil Randall. *The World Wide Web Unleashed*. New York: Sams Publishing, 1994.

8 XNS Protocols

Unlike TCP/IP, the Xerox Network Systems (XNS) protocols may not be an internetworking protocol suite that comes immediately to mind. XNS has, however, made a very significant—albeit quiet—impact on the architecture of many LAN operating systems. XNS was developed at Xerox Corporation's Palo Alto Research Center during the late 1970s in conjunction with research into Ethernet. (Recall that DEC, Intel and Xerox collaborated on the Ethernet development, which was announced in 1973.) With interest in Ethernet networks growing in the late 1970s, the need for many more internetworking capabilities—such as network address formats—evolved, and research extended toward developing a mechanism to internetwork multiple LANs. The culmination of the effort was the Xerox Network Systems architecture and protocols, first published in 1980.

XNS was initiated as an open architecture, and was designed with multivendor internetworking in mind. As a result, major networking vendors, including Novell, 3Com, and Banyan, have implemented the XNS protocols within their respective software architectures, at one point in time or another. We will investigate these XNS derivatives in Section 8.7. First, however, let's study the architecture of an XNS internetwork.

8.1   XNS Internetwork Architecture

The XNS architecture makes two basic assumptions about its users: the internetwork's underlying LAN technology is Ethernet, and multiple Ethernets exist. These Ethernets are connected by various communication channels, such as dial-up or leased lines (see Figure 8-1), and the intelligence to communicate between them resides in an internetwork router. The unit of information transferred via the internetwork is known as an internet packet, which must necessarily contain additional addressing to assure proper delivery of the packet to the desired destination network and host. This packet is delivered on a datagram (not virtual circuit) basis, in which neither delivery nor sequentiality is guaranteed. To provide for those situations requiring reliable transfer, a number of Transport Layer protocols (which we will study in Section 8.5) are used.

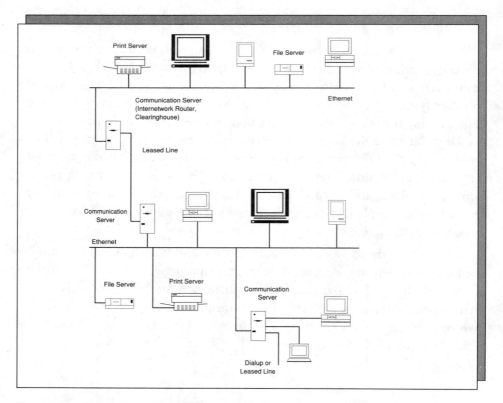

Figure 8-1. An internetwork of Ethernet LANs *(Courtesy of Xerox Corporation)*

The XNS Architecture defines five different layers (zero through four), and corresponds closely to the OSI model (see Figure 8-2)—so closely, in fact, that XNS is credited, in part, as being the inspiration behind the OSI layered structure.

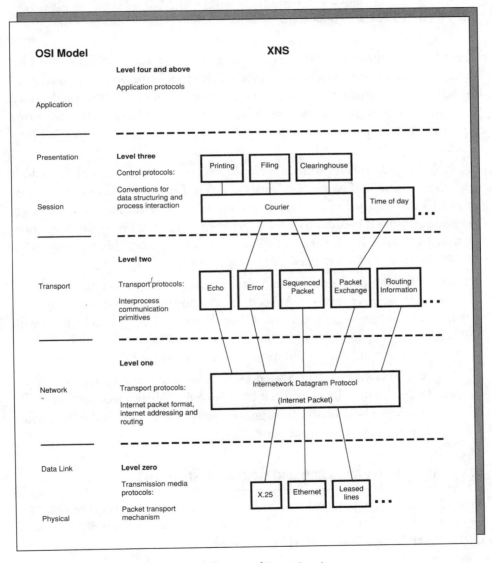

Figure 8-2. XNS protocol architecture *(Courtesy of Xerox Corp.)*

XNS Level 0 defines the transmission media protocols that provide the physical mechanism for packet transport. This level corresponds to the OSI Physical and Data Link Layers, and includes internetworking options such as Ethernet (naturally!), X.25, leased and dial-up lines. Typical interfaces such as RS-232-C, RS-449, and X.21 are supported.

XNS Levels 1 and 2 are collectively known as the Transport protocols. XNS Level 1 defines the destination of the datagram (or packet), and how it will get there. The Internetwork Datagram Protocol (IDP) is defined, as well as an addressing scheme to designate the various networks, hosts, and sockets through which that packet will originate, traverse, or terminate. (We'll look at the addressing and routing schemes in Section 8.2. XNS Level 1 corresponds to the OSI Network Layer.)

XNS Level 2 provides structures for the stream of datagrams. This level deals with the multitude of issues such as sequencing, flow control, and retransmissions that are required of the OSI Transport Layer. Five different protocols are defined at this level in order to satisfy varying user requirements: Routing Information Protocol (RIP); Error Protocol (Error); Echo Protocol (Echo); Sequenced Packet Protocol (SPP); and Packet Exchange Protocol (PEP).

XNS Level 3 provides structures for the actual data that was transmitted, and also controls various processes. As such, Level 3 covers the OSI Session and Presentation Layers, and is designated the Control Protocols. XNS Level 4 deals with the various Application Protocols, similar to the OSI model. We will briefly discuss the XNS Control and Application protocols in Section 8.6.

Xerox offers two excellent references on Ethernet [8-1] and the XNS development [8-2]. A third, [8-3], written by a Novell software architect, provides some interesting XNS history. To begin our study, we'll look at the addressing schemes that facilitate router operation.

8.2 Datagram Addressing and Routing Within XNS

The XNS packet (or datagram) must be delivered to the correct destination to assure meaningful communication. Since the source and destination may be on different networks, additional addressing is required.

The Internet packet includes three specific address fields. The Host address is a 48-bit number that identifies any system that is connected to a network. The host address numbering is a flat scheme (not hierarchical) and uniquely identifies each hardware element. By implementing a flat Host address (which can be burned into a ROM), Xerox allowed for that host to be moved from one network to another without requiring the revision of its address. The 48-bit field can address up to 281,474,977 different hosts [8-4].

A Network address identifies a specific network (e.g. LAN) within an internet. This number is required for internetwork routing and is a 32-bit field. All networks within an internet have a unique Network address; a host may be connected to multiple networks, each of which would have a unique identity.

A Socket address locates a specific host process that can send and receive packets. Of the 65,536 possible socket numbers, the first 3000 are reserved for well-known sockets that are defined within the internet. All other socket numbers can be re-used.

To illustrate the process of packet addressing and routing within an XNS internet, consider Figure 8-3, taken from reference [8-5]. The Source host (s) exists on an Ethernet (Network A), and needs to communicate with the Destination host (d), which exists on some other type of network (B). The Destination socket (p) is also specified by the source process. The routing table within the Source host determines that the Destination host is not known on its network (A), and encapsulates the packet for transmission on network A to the internetwork router (r). At the router, the packet is decapsulated, and the full destination address (Network B, host d, Socket p) is read. Router (r) performs another table lookup and determines that the desired host (d) exists on network B. Another encapsulation of the packet occurs (for transmission on network B, to network-specific host m) and the packet then reaches the desired host (d). Additional routing within that host provides packet delivery to the appropriate socket (p).

With this introduction to the XNS architecture and addressing scheme, let's now look at the protocols in detail.

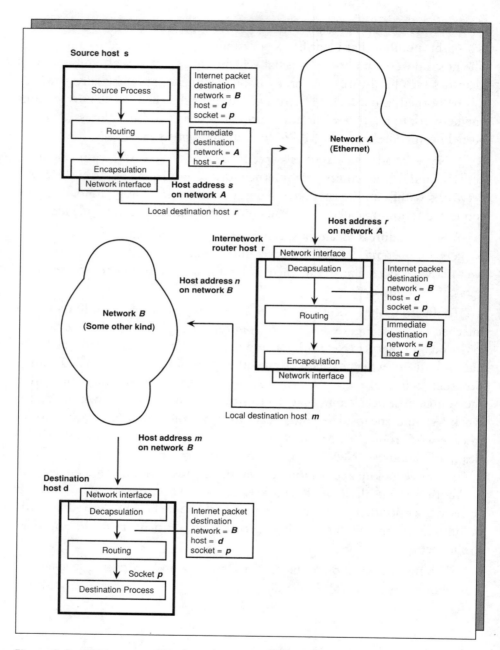

Figure 8-3. XNS Internetwork Packet Delivery *(Courtesy of Xerox Corp.)*

8.3   XNS Level 0 Transmission Media Protocols

Referring again to Figure 8-2, note that several options, including Ethernet, X.25, and leased line connections are available for the XNS Level 0 protocols. The function of these protocols is to move the data across the transmission medium, which may be a coaxial cable (in the case of Ethernet), or twisted pair used with either analog or digital private lines. Since the transmission (or Data Link Layer) frame format may differ in length from the internet packet, provisions must also be made to fragment the packet prior to encapsulation within that frame. The specific frame header and trailer must also be added as required by the transmission media protocol of choice. Ethernet is the most obvious choice for XNS LAN implementations, and thus a brief description of the Ethernet frame and its addressing scheme is in order.

As discussed in Section 8.2, a 48-bit flat address is used for both Destination and Source addresses (see Figure 8-4). These 48 bits are divided into six octets—A, B, C, D, E, and F—transmitted in that order with the least significant bit (LSB) of each octet being transmitted first. Octets A, B, and C are considered a block number, with blocks assigned to individual manufacturers. Each of the 8,388,608 (2 to the 23rd power) blocks contains 16,777,216 (2 to the 24th power) Host address numbers (octets D, E, and F). The LSB of octet A is reserved for the multicast bit, indicating that the address is destined for more than one host. Multicasts to all hosts (known as broadcasts) are indicated with all 48 bits of the Destination address set to 1. Note that the multicast bit is set to zero within the Source address, since a multicast transmission is meaningless.

A Type field (sometimes called an Ethertype) follows the Source address, and this two-octet field indicates the type of higher-layer protocol encapsulated within the Data field. The value 0600H is assigned to the XNS protocols. From 46 to 1500 octets of data may be transmitted with each frame; values outside of these ranges are considered invalid and rejected by the intended receiver. A 32-bit Cyclic Redundancy Check (CRC) completes the frame [8-4].

An encapsulated packet within an Ethernet frame is illustrated in Figure 8-5. In the next section we'll look in detail at the packet format.

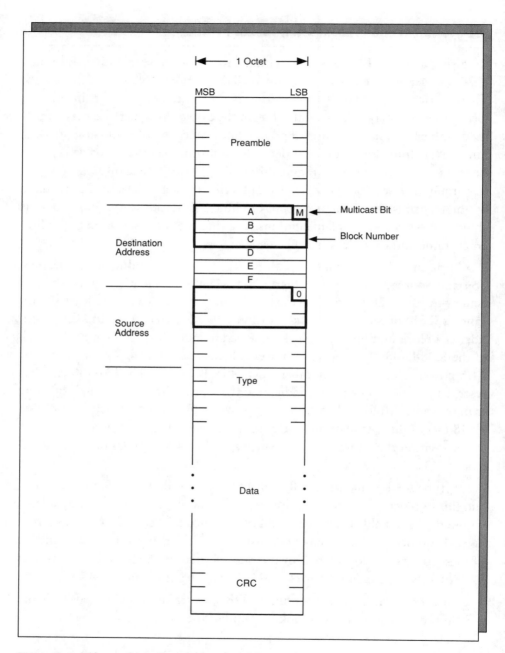

Figure 8-4. Ethernet frame format *(Courtesy of Xerox Corp.)*

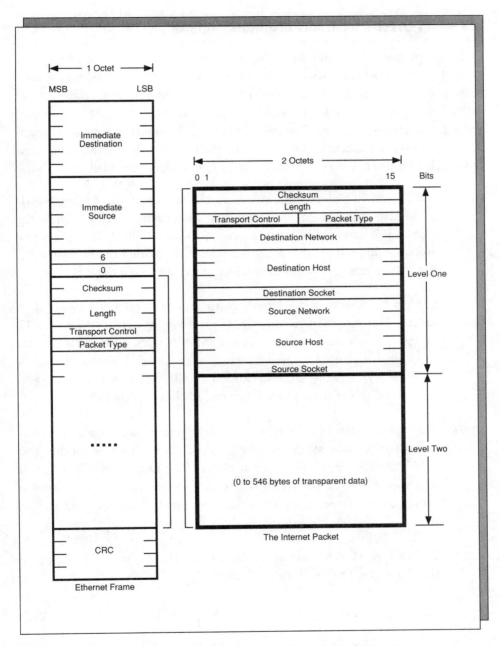

Figure 8-5. The Internet packet within an Ethernet frame *(Courtesy of Xerox Corp.)*

8.4 XNS Level 1 Transport Protocols - Internet

Only one protocol, the Internet Datagram Protocol (IDP), is defined by XNS Level 1. IDP's function is to address, route, and deliver internet packets on a best-effort basis. Recall that this type of service is termed an unreliable datagram. The term "unreliable" is used because delivery of that data is not guaranteed. The term "datagram" is used because each packet is routed independently of all other packets within the data stream. Figure 8-6 shows the format of the XNS Internet Packet. The individual fields are described below:

- ⊗ Checksum (2 octets) is a software checksum of the 16-bit words within the internet packet (excluding the checksum field). Since the Data Link Layer also provides a checksum (CRC), many vendor software implementations replace this field with FFFFH indicating that the internet packet is unchecksummed (although the frame is).

- ⊗ Length (2 octets) is the length of the internet packet measured in octets. This length is nominally 576 octets: 30 octets of header, 12 octets of Sequenced Packet Protocol (SPP) header, 512 octets of data (a typical disk page), plus 12 octets for Level 3 protocol use. A garbage byte (octet) may be added to fill the data to an integral number of 16-bit words, but is not included in the length count.

- ⊗ Transport Control (1 octet) is used by the internetwork routers, and is initialized to zero by the Source process. As the routers modify this field, they also recompute the Checksum. The Hop Count (bits 4–7) is incremented as the packet traverses each router. A packet requiring a hop count of sixteen would be discarded. Bits 0–7 are reserved and set to zero.

- ⊗ Packet Type (1 octet) identifies the format of the Data field, similar to the Ethertype. Defined types include:

Protocol	Packet Type (hexadecimal)
Unknown	00
Routing Information	01
Echo	02
Error	03
Packet Exchange	04
Sequenced Packet	05
Experimental	10–1F

⊛ Destination and Source addresses (12 octets each) define the internet addresses, and specify the Network (4 octets), Host (6 octets), and Socket (2 octets). Socket numbers may also be assigned, and two are reserved: zero (unknown) and all ones (all). Other well-known sockets are:

Function	Well-Known Socket (hexadecimal)
Routing Information	01
Echo	02
Router Error	03
Experimental	20–3F

⊛ Data (0–546 octets) contains information from the higher layers.

⊛ Garbage byte (optional 1 octet) allows the data to occupy an integral number of 16-bit words.

Note that the various internetwork routers may modify the Destination and Source network numbers via table lookups as the packet moves through the internetwork (we saw an example of this in Figure 8-3). Our next topic of study will be the various Level 2 protocols that fill the Data field of the internet packet. Reference [8-6] gives a summary of these protocols, and [8-7] provides extensive details.

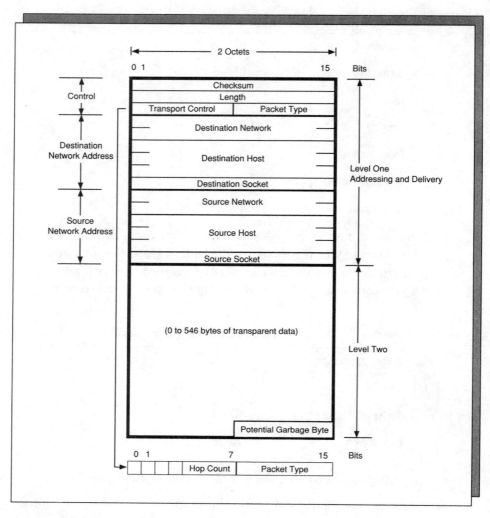

Figure 8-6. The XNS Internet packet *(Courtesy of Xerox Corp.)*

8.5 XNS Level 2 Transport Protocols—Interprocess

From Figure 8-2 we saw that five different protocols are implemented at the Interprocess level. We'll study each of these separately.

8.5.1 Routing Information Protocol

Each router contains a table that performs a lookup to determine the correct route for each internet packet. This table is maintained with information transmitted or received at the well-known Routing Information socket, as the various routers inform each other of the changes in the internetwork topology. The Routing Information Protocol (RIP) is used for this purpose.

The RIP packet is specified by the Packet Type field of the IDP header (see Figure 8-7). The first field (two octets) of the RIP packet indicates the Operation—either a request for routing information (Operation = 1), or a response containing routing information (Operation = 2). The Contents portion of the RIP packet contains one or more tuples (six octets each). Each tuple consists of a 32-bit Object Network number, and a 16-bit Internetwork Delay, measured in hops. For a request, the Object Network defines the network of interest, and the Internetwork Delay is set to 16 hops (defined as infinity). Requested information regarding all Object Networks would use the "all" address and set the Internetwork Delay to infinity (16 hops).

Response packets indicate the number of hops required to reach any host on that network via the responding router. The delay to reach a router on a directly connected network is defined as zero hops.

8.5.2 Error Protocol

The Error Protocol (see Figure 8-8) is used for diagnostic purposes, and is sent from the well-known router error socket to the source socket that caused the error. The Error Number (two octets) indicates the kind of error:

Error Number (octal notation)	Description
0	An unspecified error is detected at destination.
1	The checksum is incorrect, or the packet has some other serious inconsistency detected at destination.
2	The specified socket does not exist at the specified destination host.
3	The destination cannot accept the packet due to resource limitations.
1000	An unspecified error occurred before reaching destination.
1001	The checksum is incorrect, or the packet has experienced some other serious inconsistency before reaching destination.

333

1002	The destination host cannot be reached from here.
1003	The packet has passed through 15 internet routers without reaching its destination.
1004	The packet is too large to be forwarded through some intermediate network. The Error Parameter field contains the length of the largest packet that can be accommodated.

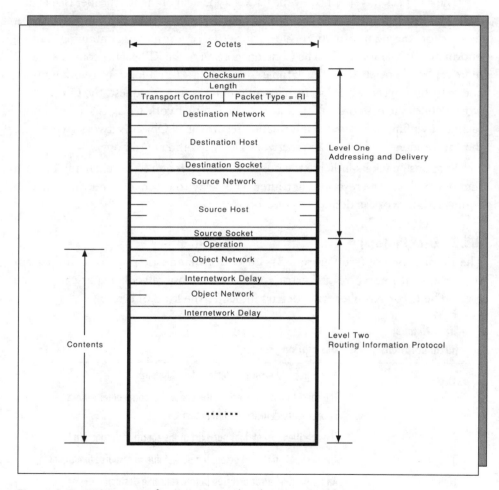

Figure 8-7. XNS Routing Information Protocol packet *(Courtesy of Xerox Corp.)*

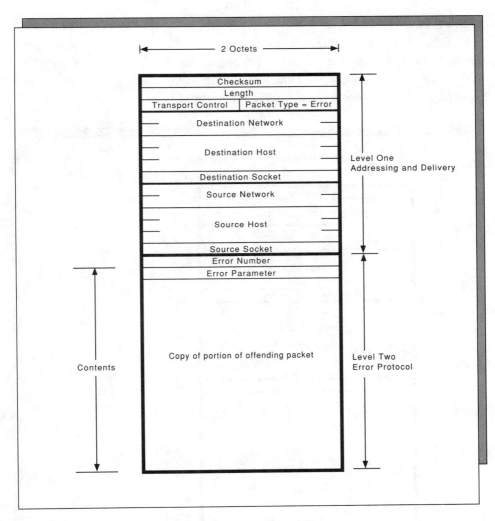

Figure 8-8. XNS Error Protocol packet *(Courtesy of Xerox Corp.)*

Certain kinds of errors are elaborated upon within the Error Parameter field (2 octets). The Error packet contents contain a copy of the first portion (IDP header plus higher-layer headers) of the offending packet.

335

8.5.3   Echo Protocol

The Echo Protocol is a simple protocol used to verify the existence of, and transmission path to, a designated host. Two operations are defined (see Figure 8-9): Echo Request (Operation = 1) and Echo Reply (Operation = 2). The data portion of the Echo Protocol packet will contain the data of the arriving packet.

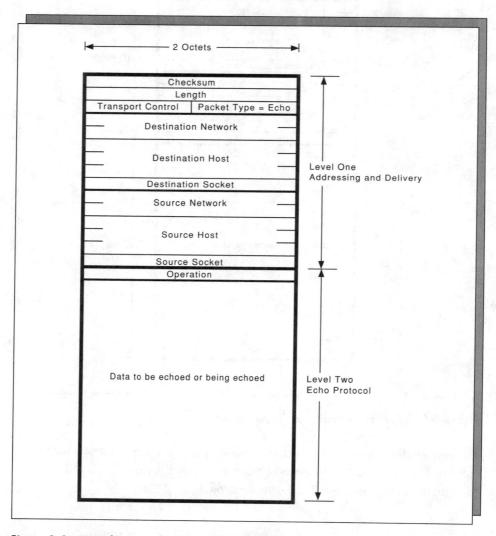

Figure 8-9. XNS Echo Protocol packet *(Courtesy of Xerox Corp.)*

8.5.4 Sequenced Packet Protocol

The Sequenced Packet Protocol (SPP) is the workhorse of the XNS Transport Layer (Levels 1 and 2), providing reliable transmission of data from the various higher-layer processes. All transmissions include sending and receiving sequence numbers for message reassembly, flow control, and error control. The basis of the process-to-process communication is a connection that is opened between two sockets. Packets are then exchanged between the two sockets via that connection.

The SPP header (see Figure 8-10) is a 12-octet field that is transmitted immediately after the IDP header. Up to 534 octets of data may complete the datagram. Fields in the SPP header include:

- Connection Control (1 octet) includes four subfields plus four reserved bits (set to zero). System Packet determines if that packet contains system (control) information or client process data. Send Acknowledgment is a request from sender to receiver requesting an acknowledgment. Attention provides a signal to the client process that this packet has arrived. End-of-Message indicates that this packet terminates one message and that the subsequent packet will begin another message.

- Datastream Type (1 octet) is used by the higher-layer protocols to define the type of information contained within that packet's data field. Examples would be data, interrupt, or end-of-data types.

- Source and Destination Connection ID (2 octets each) are specified at each end of the connection at the time of connection establishment. All subsequent transmissions will reference these same ID numbers.

- Sequence Number (2 octets) is the send sequence number that provides the receiver packet with sequencing, duplicate suppression, and flow control. Packet sequencing always begins at zero, and extends to a maximum of 65,536.

- Acknowledge Number (2 octets) indicates the sequence number of the next expected packet from the other end of the link.

- Allocation Number (2 octets) indicates the maximum packet sequence number that will be accepted from the other end of the link.

The Data field of the SPP packet (0 to 534 octets) is the higher-layer information. Note that Data packets must not have the System Packet bit set. Packets with the Attention bit set will have only one octet of data.

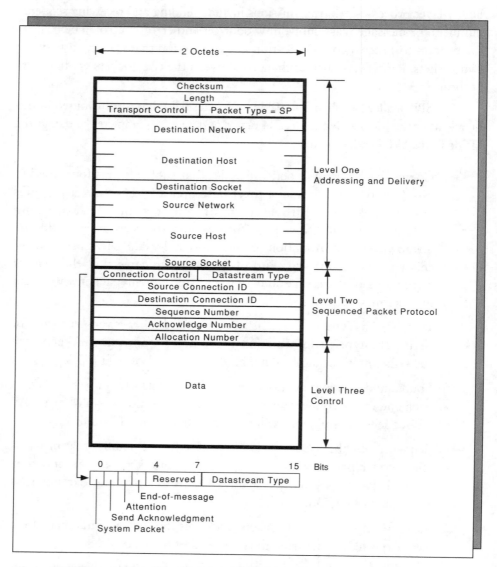

Figure 8-10. XNS Sequenced Packet Protocol packet *(Courtesy of Xerox Corp.)*

8.5.5 Packet Exchange Protocol

The Packet Exchange Protocol (PEP) is used to transmit packets with reliability greater than that of independent packets, but without the overhead associated with SPP. Its purpose is somewhat analogous to the DoD User Datagram Protocol (UDP) that we studied in Section 7.5.2. (Recall that UDP provides some Transport Layer reliability without the extensive header overhead required by TCP.) PEP is similar, and operates on a single packet basis, using any socket as source and destination locations.

Two fields are included in the PEP header (see Figure 8-11). The ID field is a 32-bit number that identifies the transaction (a pair of packets) between sender and receiver. The Client Type field defines the higher-layer client protocol.

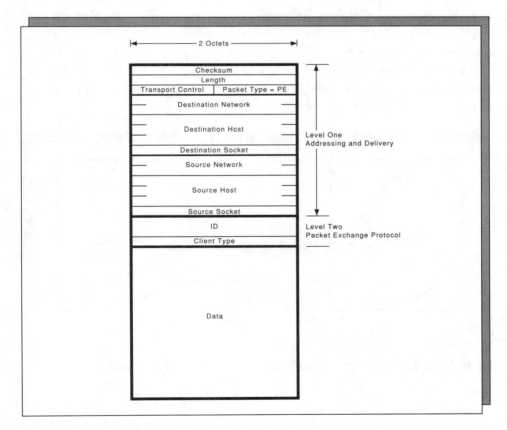

Figure 8-11. XNS Packet Exchange Protocol packet *(Courtesy of Xerox Corp.)*

8.6 XNS Levels 3 and 4

Reviewing Figure 8-2, note that XNS Level 3, the Control Protocols, perform OSI Session and Presentation Layer functions, and that XNS Level 4 contains the Application Layer procedures. (Since these higher layers are somewhat implementation-specific, we won't go into great detail.) One protocol, the XNS Courier, has been used extensively in LAN operating systems such as Banyan VINES and will be studied here.

8.6.1 XNS Courier Protocol

The Courier protocol, which is subtitled the Remote Procedure Call (RPC) protocol, defines a mechanism for transmission between various entities. The underlying assumption in Courier is that two types of elements exist within the network (see Figure 8-12). The Active System Element issues the Call requests with the necessary arguments that request an action. The other element, called the Passive System Element, is a provider of the requested service. The Remote Program responds with the Return results or an error statement in the event that the requested function could not be completed.

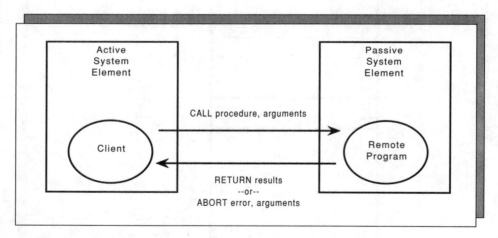

Figure 8-12. XNS Courier Remote Procedure Call model *(Courtesy of Xerox Corp.)*

Most importantly, it is assumed that the Active System Element (or Client) and the Passive System Element (or Remote Program) may not be located on the same physical network. As a result, the Courier protocols rely upon the underlying Internetwork Transport protocols (XNS Levels 1 and 2) to facilitate the required communication between Client and Remote Program.

The Courier protocol interfaces with the Sequenced Packet Protocol (SPP) at XNS Level 2 to move the request or response to the appropriate network destination (review Figure 8-2). Courier also interfaces with the higher-level Control and Application protocols to translate the specific service request into call messages and the resulting Return or Abort messages. To facilitate the Application Layer interface, the Courier protocol has its own language—described further in reference [8-8].

8.6.2 Clearinghouse Protocol

As we saw, the Courier protocol provides Remote Procedure Call functions so that services on a remote host can be requested and obtained. A mechanism must be established, however, to identify the location of that remote host containing the desired information. The Clearinghouse protocol provides this directory service. Clearinghouse is a database of objects, with each entry including various properties associated with that object. The naming of those objects follows a three-level hierarchy—Local Name: Domain: Organization. An example would be John Doe:Accounting:Denver. The database can also be distributed throughout several locations, and for larger networks many Clearinghouse servers would exist.

A Clearinghouse request example is shown in Figure 8-13, taken from reference [8-2]. The user needs to locate a particular resource, such as a printer, and issues a request for the Clearinghouse address. The Courier and Internet protocols are invoked in turn, and result in an Ethernet broadcast message. The Clearinghouse server responds and identifies itself. The user then interrogates the Clearinghouse database to determine the specific address of the printer in question. See reference [8-9] for further details on the Clearinghouse protocols.

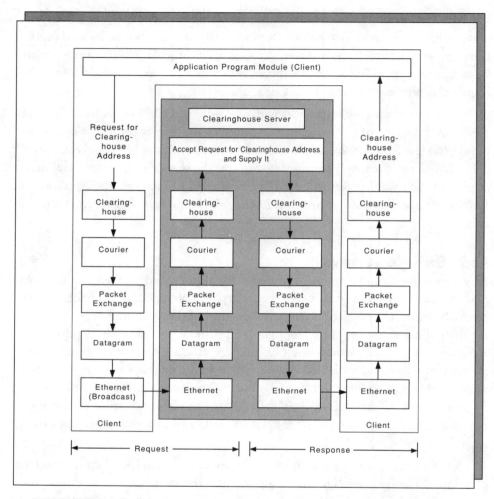

Figure 8-13. XNS Clearinghouse request and response operation *(Courtesy of Xerox Corp.)*

8.7 XNS Implementations

As described earlier and in reference [8-3], the XNS protocols have been implemented extensively in various networking software architectures in addition to Xerox's. We'll briefly describe three of these implementations, from Novell, Inc., Banyan Systems, Inc., and 3Com Corp.

The most well-known XNS implementation is Novell's NetWare, which has made extensive use of the XNS protocols in both the Network and Transport Layer implementations. NetWare's Network Layer protocol, the Internetwork Packet Exchange (IPX), is identical to the XNS IDP packet format. Reviewing Figure 8-6, the Transport Control field is used by the NetWare internetwork routers. Defined Packet Types are 0 (Unknown Packet), 4 (Packet Exchange), 5 (Sequenced Packet Protocol), or 17 (NetWare Core Protocol). The Destination/Source Network numbers are assigned by the network administrator, and the Destination/Source Host numbers are assigned by the specific node hardware (either within a ROM or by DIP switches).

Xerox has assigned five sockets for NetWare use:

0451H	File Service Packet
0452H	Service Advertising Packet
0453H	Routing Information Packet
0455H	NetBIOS Packet
0456H	Diagnostic Packet

File servers identify themselves using the Service Advertising Protocol (SAP), socket 0452H. File service requests are addressed to socket 0451H.

The Data field is not always limited to 546 octets. For throughput optimization, Novell extends this field based upon the local network hardware (Ethernet, Token Ring, etc.) in use.

NetWare's Transport Layer, the Sequenced Packet Exchange (SPX) protocol, is based upon XNS SPP and uses IDP Packet Type 5. The SPX header also uses the various SPP fields that were discussed in Section 8.5.4. Another higher-layer option is the NetWare Core Protocol (NCP), which uses IPX Packet Type 18. NCP is Novell's proprietary protocol, used for file access, printer sharing, and application program communication.

Banyan Systems' VINES (Virtual Networking System) also has strong roots in XNS. At the Network Layer, VINES defines four protocols. One of these, the VINES Internet Protocol (IP), is structured similarly to XNS IDP. The Checksum (set to FFFFH), Length, Transport Control and Protocol Type fields are similar to their XNS IDP counterparts. The Addressing fields differ, with XNS IDP using

12 octets each for Destination and Source, and VINES IP using 6 octets each. As a result, the VINES IP header requires 18 octets, not the 30 octets specified by XNS IDP.

The VINES Transport Layer also has a number of protocols defined for specific functions. Two of these, the Interprocess Communications Protocol (IPC) and the Sequenced Packet Protocol (SPP) are similar, but not identical, to the XNS SPP. In view of the network addressing scheme differences discussed above, the VINES IPC and SPP headers (16 octets in length) include Source/Destination port addresses, similar to the XNS SPP socket addresses. For VINES IP, IPC, and SPP protocols, the VINES headers thus occupy a total of 34 octets, instead of the 42 octets defined by XNS. All differences aside, however, it is clear to see the influence that the XNS protocols had on the VINES architecture.

3Com Corporation utilized the XNS protocols in their previously-marketed DOS-based 3+ and the OS/2 LAN Manager-based 3+Open network operating systems. The 3Com Network Layer was based upon XNS IDP, and supported four of the five XNS Transport Layer protocols (the Error Protocol was not used). The XNS IDP header, as well as the RIP, Echo, PEP, and SPP header formats were identical to their XNS counterparts. Like Novell, 3Com also extended the maximum length of the IDP packet to accommodate the Data Link Layer hardware in use.

In summary, Xerox has thus had a dramatic influence on the shape of today's LANs and internetworks. Both the Ethernet network and the XNS protocol suite developments have made significant contributions to distributed computing.

8.8   References

[8-1]   DEC, Intel, and Xerox. *The Ethernet, A Local Area Network-Data Link Layer and Physical Layer Specification, Version 2.0*. DEC document no. AA-K759B-TK, November 1982.

[8-2]   Xerox Corp. *Xerox Network Systems Architecture General Information Manual*. Document no. XNSG 068505, April 1985.

[8-3]   Neibaur, Dale. "Understanding XNS: The Prototypical Internetwork Protocol." *Data Communications* (December 21, 1989): 43 –51.

[8-4]   Dalal Y. K. and R. S. Printis. "48-bit Absolute Internet and Ethernet Host Numbers." Reprinted in *Office Systems Technology*, Xerox document OSD-R8203A, January 1984, pp. 161–166.

[8-5]   Y. K. Dalal, "Use for Multiple Networks in the Xerox Network System." Reprinted in *Office Systems Technology*, Xerox document no. OSD-R8203A (January 1984): 150–160.

[8-6]   White, J. and Y. K. Dalal. "Higher-level Protocols Enhance Ethernet." Reprinted in *Office Systems Technology*, Xerox document no. OSD-RS203A (January 1984): 167–175.

[8-7]   Xerox Corp. *Internet Transport Protocols*. Document no. XNSS 028112, December 1981.

[8-8]   Xerox Corp. *Courier: The Remote Procedure Call Protocol*. Document XNSS 038112, December 1981.

[8-9]   Xerox Corp. *Clearinghouse Protocol*. Document no. XSIS 078404, April 1984.

9 Networking Software, Internetworking, and Interoperability

Recall your first Network Operating System (NOS). If yours was like mine, it was probably a basic file-sharing system that required any network printer to physically reside on a single server. Communication with the outside world was limited to a proprietary electronic mail application which was built into the system and handled only a small amount of data transfer, such as one line (80 characters). You probably wished that the network's limited communications capabilities could be expanded. Perhaps you needed to access a mini-computer at your facility or a remote host via the TCP/IP protocols. Earlier NOSs lacked these capabilities, but as users (like us) demanded greater performance, vendors rose to the challenge.

That challenge to expand NOS capabilities has been addressed in three ways. First, hardware platforms and peripherals have been advanced to the point where 32-bit computing and hundreds, if not thousands, of megabytes of storage capacity are commonplace. Second, support for standard internetworking protocols—such as X.25 and TCP/IP—is being added to the core systems of most NOSs. In addition, capabilities to address legacy systems, such as DEC's DECnet or IBM's SNA, may also be standard. And, with the advent of internetworking and standardized protocols comes a third, ever-evolving internetworking solution—interoperability.

Interoperability is the antithesis of incompatibility. Let's define the term by example. Users need the flexibility to employ whatever hardware platform (PC, Macintosh, Sun workstation) or operating system (DOS, OS/2, UNIX, NetWare) best suits their requirements. Further, a constraint exists at the Application Layers: users require seamless (i.e. transparent) access between applications. For example, an electronic mail program for a Macintosh should be able to send and receive a message from another package running on a UNIX-based minicomputer. (If we throw the WAN variable into the equation, the Macintosh and UNIX-minicomputer would be across the country from each other.)

In this chapter, we will discuss the internetworking and interoperability of the key networking software implementations: Apple Computer AppleTalk; Banyan Systems VINES; Novell NetWare; Microsoft Corporation Windows NT; and IBM OS/2 LAN Server. In Chapter 10, we'll discuss the interoperability issue further by exploring various gateway products. Miller-Freeman, Inc., publisher of *LAN Magazine* and *STACKS, the Network Journal*, periodically publishes a supplement called *Interoperability* [9-1]. Readers facing interoperability challenges should consult this excellent reference for solutions.

9.1 Apple Computer AppleTalk

In 1985, Apple Computer, Inc. of Cupertino, California, developed the AppleTalk architecture which became known as AppleTalk Phase 1. An extension of this architecture, known as AppleTalk Phase 2, was released in 1989 [9-2]. The AppleTalk protocol suite (Figure 9-1a) was examined in detail in a companion volume (reference [9-3]); we'll briefly summarize it here.

9.1.1 AppleTalk Protocols

The AppleTalk Physical and Data Link Layers support a variety of hardware connections. Phase 1 networks support Ethernet and LocalTalk (the 230 Kbps Macintosh-based network). Phase 2 added IEEE 802.2, 802.3, and 802.5 support. Links to IBM's SNA and DEC's DECnet architectures are also available through third-party products.

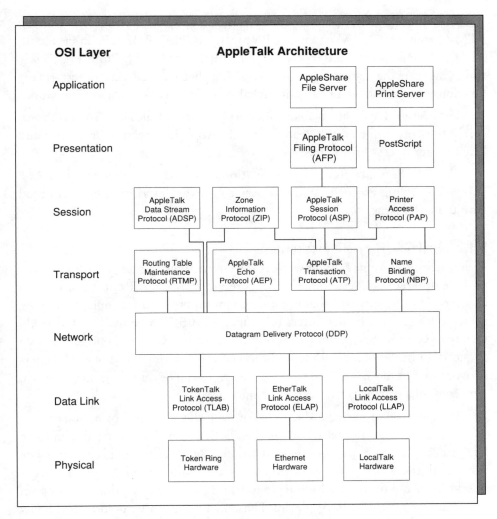

Figure 9-1a. Comparing the AppleTalk architecture with OSI *(Courtesy of Apple Computer, Inc.)*

The Network Layer is implemented with the Datagram Delivery Protocol (DDP), the core protocol operating within the internet routers. The channel between the routers can be a dial-up or leased telephone line; a LAN backbone (such as Ethernet or token ring); or some other network (such as DECnet).

The AppleTalk Transport Layer implements a number of protocols, including RTMP (Routing Table Maintenance Protocol); AEP (AppleTalk Echo Protocol); ATP (AppleTalk Transaction Protocol); and NBP (Name Binding Protocol). Closely tied to these are the Session Layer protocols. Together, these two layers perform the functions of establishing and assuring reliable communications over the network.

The Session Layer protocols include ADSP (AppleTalk Data Stream Protocol); ZIP (Zone Information Protocol); ASP (AppleTalk Session Protocol); and PAP (Printer Access Protocol).

The OSI Presentation and Application Layers are implemented in AFP (AppleTalk Filing Protocol) and PostScript—a page description protocol used with the LaserWriter printers.

9.1.2 AppleTalk Network Architecture

The heart of the AppleTalk network is the internetwork router, which can exist in three different configurations (see Figure 9-1b). A Local Router (Configuration A) connects networks that are in close proximity—for example, within the same building. Two Half Routers (Configuration B) can be used with a WAN facility to connect two remote locations. A Backbone Router (Configuration C) connects a LocalTalk network to an Ethernet or token ring backbone. The internetwork that results from these router connections can be quite large, and as such, may contain a number of third-party components.

An AppleTalk node (e.g. Macintosh or router) is identified by a 2-octet Network number and a 1-octet Node number, both of which are carried within the DDP packet. In Phase 1, nodes that existed on a single cable could communicate using only the 8-bit Node number. Two of these addresses (0 and 255) were reserved (for unknown and broadcast addresses, respectively), thus allowing up to 254 nodes per cable. In AppleTalk Phase 2, a node is always identified by its Network number and Node number in what is known as extended addressing. The complete Phase 2 internet can thus support 65,536 networks and over 16 million nodes, although the Apple Internetwork Router can support a maximum of 1,024 networks.

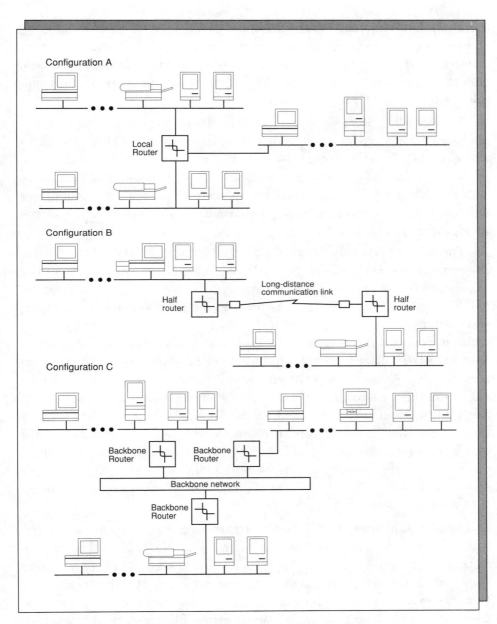

Figure 9-1b. AppleTalk router configurations *(Courtesy of Apple Computer, Inc.)*

9.1.3 AppleTalk Interoperability Products

Apple markets a variety of products that enhance AppleTalk and Macintosh connectivity to other systems. These include products supporting remote access, connections to SNA environments, TCP/IP-based internetworking, plus support for X.25 and OSI protocol suites.

The AppleTalk Remote Access (ARA) Personal Server and Client products allow remote Macintosh users to communicate with another Macintosh or an entire AppleTalk network over dial-up, cellular, X.25, or ISDN connections. Both the server and client software install on a Macintosh, and require an adjunct modem. Communication enhancements, such as data compression, user name and password authentication, predetermined callback numbers, and activity logs simplify user operations.

The SNA*ps Gateway, SNA*ps 3270, and SNA*ps 5250 products provide connections into SNA environments. The SNA*ps Gateway software turns a Macintosh into an integrated 3270, 5250, Advanced Program-to-Program (APPC), and Advanced Peer-to-Peer Networking (APPN) gateway. The gateway software runs on an intelligent NuBus token ring, SLDC or coax DFT card, which frees the main processor of the Macintosh to run other applications. The SNA*ps 3270 software provides full-function 3270-display terminal emulation, allowing a Macintosh or PowerBook computer to communicate with IBM mainframes. The emulation software works with the Apple Coax/Twinax Card, the Apple token ring 4/16 NB card, or the Apple Serial NB card to provide a direct connection to the SNA host. As an alternative, the terminal emulator may be connected over an AppleTalk network to a Macintosh that is running the SNA*ps Gateway software. In a similar way, the SNA*ps 5250 software emulates an IBM 5250 display terminal, for access to applications running on IBM AS/400 systems.

Products supporting TCP/IP-based internetworks include the Apple IP Gateway, TCP/IP Connection for Macintosh, and MacSNMP. With the Apple IP Gateway, Macintosh users with Apple Remote Access, LocalTalk, or any other AppleTalk connection can connect to an Ethernet-based TCP/IP network. The Gateway may be installed in three different configurations. First, it may be used as a stand-alone product, allowing AppleTalk-networked Macintosh computers to connect to the IP network. Second, it may be used in conjunction with the Apple Internet Router software, providing IP access to any Macintosh computer that is also part of the router's network. Third, it may be used in conjunction with an Apple Remote Access Server, providing ARA clients with remote access to both AppleTalk and IP services.

The TCP/IP Connection for Macintosh provides the software needed to connect a Macintosh to a TCP/IP-based network. The protocol stack that runs on the workstation is called MacTCP, which implements IP, UDP, TCP, ARP, RARP, ICMP, BOOTP, RIP, and DNS, as discussed in Chapter 7. MacSNMP, which is Apple's implementation of the Simple Network Management Protocol on the Macintosh, allows both current and future AppleTalk products to be managed using SNMP. The MacSNMP architecture includes both manager and agent functions, and also allows Macintosh computers to be managed by a number of SNMP-based consoles, including those from Hewlett-Packard, IBM, and SunSoft.

The MacX25 and OSI Connection for Macintosh products provide for connections into other protocol suites. MacX25 provides the software to link a Macintosh to an X.25-based network, or to use a Macintosh as a gateway to an X.25-based network. The software consists of two components: a server side which connects to the X.25-based network, and a client side, called Mac-PAD. The MacX25 software may also be used in conjunction with two other products, the MacX25 Router Extension and the Apple Internet Router, to interconnect remote AppleTalk LANs across public or private X.25-based networks. The OSI Connection for Macintosh software provides for connections to OSI-based networks. The software includes an OSI stack called MacOSI Transport. It may also be used in conjunction with the MacX25 software for access to X.25-based networks, and with the MacTCP software, to run OSI services over TCP/IP-based networks.

A number of innovative connectivity enhancements have come with AppleTalk Phase 2. The Macintosh is no longer just a fine computer known for its graphics capabilities but is now a full-fledged participant in SNA, TCP/IP, X.25, and OSI-based environments.

9.2 Banyan VINES

Banyan Systems, Inc. of Westboro, Massachusetts, is the developer of VINES, an operating system that strongly supports both LAN and WAN connections. (As we investigate the architecture, we'll discover why.)

The company name and logo provide some insight into the characteristics of VINES capabilities. The Banyan tree, native to India, consists of a main trunk and broad foliage. As the tree grows, slender vines form from the branches and extend to the ground. These then root and develop another trunk system. After a few years, a single Banyan tree proliferates to become a small forest. The VINES (Virtual Networking System) software is similar, having a number of "branches" that communicate with dissimilar systems and protocols.

For example, VINES servers can communicate using block asynchronous, HDLC, X.25, TCP/IP, or IEEE 802.2 protocols. For SNA environments, the Banyan SNA Communications Service (BSCS) provides both traditional 3270/SNA emulation and LU 6.2 peer protocol support. BSCS is based on the DCA (Digital Communication Associates, Inc., now part of Attachmate Corp.) IRMALAN/EP SNA Gateway, and provides 3270 emulation for Microsoft Windows, DOS, and Macintosh workstations. We'll begin our study of VINES internetworking by looking at the VINES protocols.

9.2.1 VINES Protocols

The VINES operating system is based upon UNIX System V, and consists of both workstation and server modules (see Figures 9-2a and b). (References [9-4] and [9-5] cover these protocols in detail.) Physical and Data Link Layers (as we will see) allow for almost all protocol possibilities, including asynchronous, HDLC, IEEE 802.X and X.25. Device drivers are used to communicate with the various Network Interface Cards. The VINES Network Layer supports the DoD IP, ARP, and ICMP protocols, plus four proprietary VINES protocols: IP (Internet Protocol), RTP (Routing Update Protocol), ARP (Address Resolution Protocol), and ICP (Internet Control Protocol). The Transport Layer implements the DoD, TCP, and UDP protocols, plus the VINES proprietary IPC (Interprocess Communications Protocol) and SPP (Sequenced Packet Protocol).

Higher-layer (Session, Presentation, and Application) support includes a variety of VINES and third-party applications. The Microsoft SMB (Server Message Block) protocol is also available.

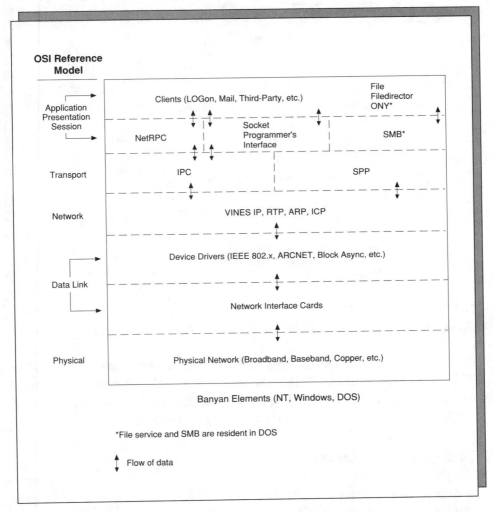

Figure 9-2a. Banyan VINES elements and the OSI model (Workstation Side) *(Courtesy of Banyan Systems, Inc.)*

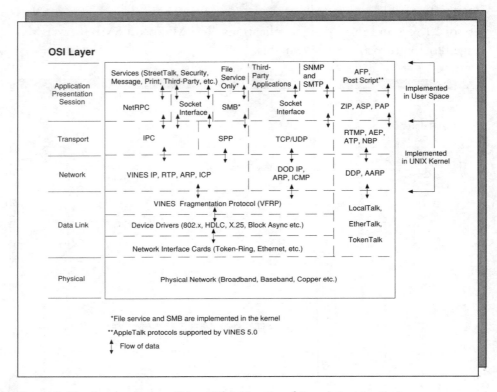

Figure 9-2b. Banyan elements (Server Side) *(Courtesy of Banyan Systems, Inc.)*

A device driver communicates with the hardware. A socket interface, the UNIX Transport Layer Interface (TLI), or Named Pipes connect to the higher layers. A variety of protocol stacks, including TCP/IP, VINES, and AppleTalk, are presently available. The UNIX kernel is at the core of the VINES system.

9.2.2 VINES Serial Communications

VINES contains a number of WAN connection alternatives. This strength becomes evident when the architecture of the ICA (Intelligent Communications Adapter) Card is considered. The ICA is a six-port high-performance serial communications card that is available for the PC-AT and Micro Channel hardware platforms. Two of the ports operate at up to 115 Kbps, and the other four operate at up to 38.4 Kbps. When installed in a VINES server, the ICA card can support a mixture of protocols including asynchronous, HDLC, SDLC, BSC (Bisynchronous), and X.25 (see Figure 9-2c). VINES Communication software for the specific application is also required. With a single ICA card, the VINES server can simultaneously maintain one IBM SNA connection, an X.25 connection, two connections to a DEC VAX, and two dial-in connections. An aggregate of 1.7 Mbps data throughput is allowed.

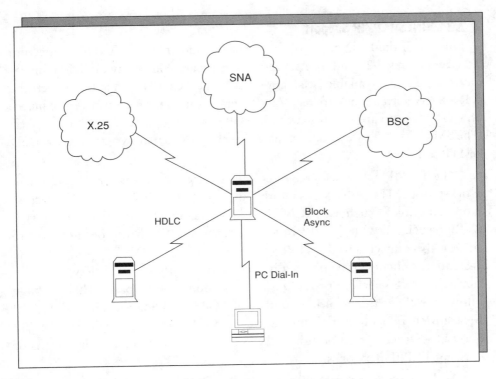

Figure 9-2c. VINES Communications Options *(Courtesy of Banyan Systems, Inc.)*

The X.25 option allows server-to-server or server-to-host connections via Packet Switched Public Data Networks (PSPDNs). Both Permanent Virtual Circuits (PVCs) or Switched Virtual Circuits (SVCs) are supported. The EiconCard (discussed in Section 4.9.2) is an alternative to Banyan's ICA Card. The IBM 3270/SNA server support allows host connectivity from any workstation on the VINES network. Each server can support 16, 32, 96, or 128 concurrent sessions with up to 4 concurrent host sessions and one DOS session per PC. The communication channel between server and host is a synchronous line into an SDLC interface on the IBM front end processor.

The flexible connections into VINES support the claim for both a WAN and LAN operating system. The wide range of speed and protocol options makes for a very powerful communications server.

9.2.3   VINES TCP/IP Support

A number of the DoD protocols have been included in the VINES architecture (review Figures 9-2a and b). As a result, five separate internetwork communications options are available (see Figure 9-2d). The TCP/IP Routing Option lets the VINES server act as an IP router. When communication between servers is required, the VINES software encapsulates the TCP/IP message within a VINES packet. The SMTP Mail Gateway option integrates the VINES mail system with the DoD SMTP standard.

The TCP/IP option uses IPSwitch, Inc.'s software package on VINES client workstations. This software is tightly integrated with VINES to provide access from data links—such as ARCNET or dial-up connections—that are not typically associated with TCP/IP. In addition, the VINES client does not have to be directly connected to the VINES server running the VINES Routing Option. Instead, the client can be physically located on another VINES network, with the two VINES servers providing the communications path. This package allows the client to perform a number of TCP/IP applications, including FTP file transfer, Telnet terminal emulation, and SMTP electronic mail. The TCP/IP Server-to-Server option permits VINES servers to be connected by means of existing TCP/IP networks.

At the sender's end, VINES data is encapsulated within TCP/IP packets and forwarded to a foreign IP router. The receiver strips the TCP/IP headers and places the packet on the remote VINES network. Lastly, the TCP/UDP API (Applications Programming Interface) allows developers to combine TCP/IP host applications and VINES services. References [9-6] and [9-7] provide further details on VINES TCP/IP connectivity options.

In summary, VINES incorporates a number of popular protocols—including the AppleTalk, X.25, and TCP/IP suites—into its operating system to provide the maximum flexibility in server-to-server and server-to-gateway applications.

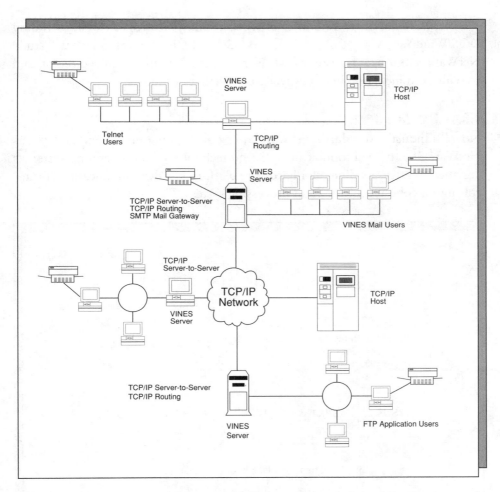

Figure 9-2d. VINES TCP/IP Options *(Courtesy of Banyan Systems, Inc.)*

9.3   Novell NetWare

Volumes could be (and have been) written about the NetWare operating system from Novell, Inc. of Provo, Utah. Although NetWare is based on Intel Architecture (80386 CPU and above), it has been ported to several different server platforms, including DEC VAX/VMS minicomputers and UNIX-based hosts.

NetWare supports a number of workstation platforms as well, including DOS/Windows, Macintosh, UNIX, and OS/2 [9-8]. In this section, we will study NetWare 3 and new features of NetWare 4, including the client redirector, and we will examine a number of Novell's connectivity products.

9.3.1 NetWare 3

Novell's industry standard, NetWare 3, began shipping in September 1989 as NetWare 386, named to indicate its 32-bit technology. This operating system is designed to integrate dissimilar hardware platforms and communications protocols into a cohesive information processing system (Figure 9-3a).

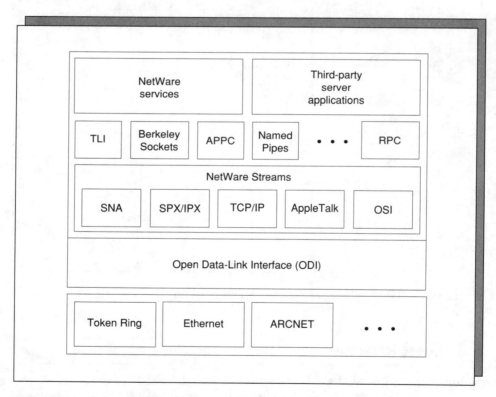

Figure 9-3a. NetWare 3 Multivendor Connection Services *(Courtesy of Novell, Inc.)*

A number of hardware configuration options, for both LANs and WANs, are available. The Open Data-Link Interface (ODI) facilitates communication between these adapters and the higher protocol layers of the architecture. ODI allows multiple protocols and frame types to exist on a single adapter as well as multiple adapters in the same PC. OSI Network and Transport Layer protocol choices include Novell's Internetwork Packet Exchange/Sequenced Packet Exchange (IPX/SPX, derived from the XNS protocols discussed in Chapter 8), TCP/IP, AppleTalk, and OSI TP4 (Transport Protocol, Class 4). ODI protocol stacks support several industry-standard programming interfaces, including: AT&T Streams and the Transport Level Interface (TLI), Berkeley Sockets interface library, NetBIOS, LU 6.2, and DOS Named Pipes.

The NetWare Loadable Module (NLM) architecture allows the Network Operating System (NOS) to be divided into modular components and to be dynamically loaded and linked at run-time. NetWare provides open APIs to extend hardware support such as LAN and disk (DSK) drivers, while other NLMs can actually provide new APIs and define new services on NetWare. All NLMs undergo thorough testing and certification to assure interoperability. Several important products for interoperability and internetworking are, in fact, a set of NLMs. These include NetWare for NFS, NetWare for SAA, NetWare for Macintosh, and the MultiProtocol Router (MPR). References [9-9] through [9-11] discuss the architecture of NetWare 3 in greater detail.

9.3.2 NetWare 4

NetWare 4, released in 1993, is built on a foundation of multi-platform connectivity that was initiated with NetWare 3 (Figure 9-3b). All of the capabilities of previous NetWare versions are included in NetWare 4, along with some significant enhancements, including: internationalization, auditing, burst or large packet support, disk compression, sub-allocation, and a global directory. References [9-12] through [9-14] describe these enhancements in greater detail, and references [9-15] through [9-17] provide industry reaction to these enhancements.

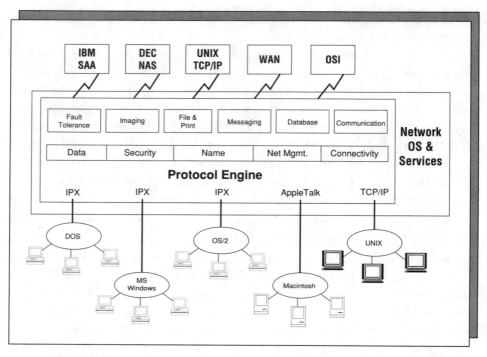

Figure 9-3b. NetWare 4 architecture *(Courtesy of Novell, Inc.)*

The NetWare Directory Services (NDS) maintains a global, distributed database of network resources, such as users, groups, servers, printers, volumes, applications, and all other resources. This information can be used as a "yellow pages" to find resources based on user criteria. NDS facilitates resource management by rules rather than by exceptions. Users will also log in to the network directory instead of a specific server. Once logged into the network, users can then navigate the directory to find and use any permitted network resource.

9.3.3 NetWare Client Products

Novell's client products provide access to NetWare services from DOS, Windows, OS/2, Macintosh, NT, and UNIX platforms. With NetWare 4.0, Novell introduced a new client architecture called Virtual Loadable Modules, or VLMs. The VLM architecture brings much of the same modular NLM dynamic load and link functionality to the client. The basic set of Redirector, NETX, File I/O, Print, RSA encryption, IPXNCP, Bindery, and NDS functions are implemented as VLMs. One new feature is autoreconnect (auto.vlm), which will maintain a client connection when a routing or network problem occurs. Only the VLMs that are necessary at each workstation are loaded, thus optimizing performance and conserving memory.

Novell's client strategy is to offer NetWare access and network resources from within the local desktop operating system. This provides a consistent and familiar interface to the user, independent of where the resource actually resides (see Figure 9-3c, taken from Reference [9-18]). The traditional NETX shell and the new VLM redirector are both supported for DOS and Windows. Once logged in to NetWare, all the drives appear in the File Manager menu and can be accessed just like the local hard drive. The Apple Macintosh Chooser lists all the NetWare servers and printers and can be accessed when you log in. The OS/2 and NT Requesters use installable file systems to provide the same seamless network integration. These Requesters also support Universal Naming Convention (UNC) paths, which bypass drive letters and specify a server and volume followed by the full directory path. Lastly, UNIX clients can take full advantage of the NetWare resources through the NetWare UNIX Client File System. The NUCFS.NLM allows UNIX clients to mount a NetWare volume, and it coordinates user IDs, locking, and access and file rights.

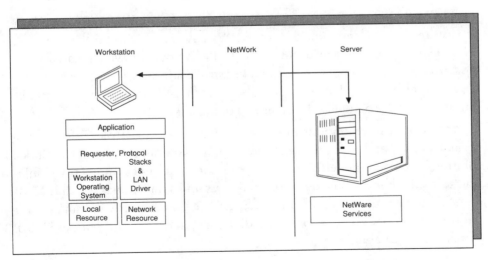

Figure 9-3c. Novell client strategy *(Courtesy of Novell, Inc.)*

9.3.4 Novell Network Access Products

Novell markets a number of network access products, both stand-alone and Net-Ware adjuncts, which facilitate internetworking and interoperability between dissimilar systems. The capabilities of six of these products are summarized below.

NetWare MultiProtocol Router (MPR) is a software-based bridge/router product that operates on a regular NetWare 3.12 or NetWare 4.1 server, or on a run-time NetWare kernel. MPR offers a modular, cost-effective way to build global internetworks with standard PCs and NetWare. In a remote office configuration, MPR can be installed on the local NetWare server with a LAN/HUB adapter and a WAN link back to the central office. MPR routes IPX, TCP/IP, OSI (CLNP), and AppleTalk Phase 1 and 2 protocols and bridges IBM SNA and NetBIOS traffic using the source-route bridging. LAN topology options include Ethernet, fast Ethernet, token ring, FDDI, and ATM. WAN link options include leased lines up to 2.048 Mbps, the Point-to-Point Protocol (PPP) over X.25, frame relay, SMDS, and ISDN.

NetWare Connect allows remote users of DOS, Windows, or Macintosh workstations to remotely access NetWare resources such as files, printers, mainframes, databases, and electronic mail via dial-up lines. In addition, network users may dial out from the network to access remote workstations, hosts, bulletin boards, or other services.

NetWare Connect clients can use Apple Remote Access Service, Remote Node Service, and NASI Connection Service. NetWare Asynchronous Services Interface (NASI) software, such as Carbon Copy or PC Anywhere, were created when modems were slow and only screen and key stroke information was sent over the wire. This also required an application server or host workstation that actually ran the DOS or program at the other end of the link.

However, as the amount of screen, mouse, and key stroke information became greater and the speed of modems increased dramatically, remote node solutions become more efficient. A remote node does not require any emulation software, but does include modem drivers and a dialer over which IPX, IP, and AT can be routed. At the host side, NetWare Connect provides support for data compression, security login and dial-back, auditing, and remote SNMP management capabilities.

NetWare NFS integrates UNIX systems with NetWare systems, allowing UNIX users to transparently mount a NetWare volume on their desktop. The product runs on a NetWare 3 or NetWare 4 server, and allows the UNIX users to access NetWare resources as part of their desktop. Other related products allow for NetWare IPX clients to gain access to UNIX volumes through the NFS gateway. Flex-IP allows bi-directional print capabilities, allowing UNIX and NetWare users access to the printer best suited for the job.

NetWare/IP is a client and server NLM that allows NetWare 3 or NetWare 4 servers to integrate in a TCP/IP backbone or WAN environment. NetWare/IP is commonly installed where multiple protocols are used locally, but only TCP/IP is routed over the WAN. This allows native IPX-based NetWare file, print, database and other applications to communicate over the TCP/IP link transparently.

NetWare for SAA runs on a NetWare 3 or NetWare 4 server, and integrates SNA traffic over LAN protocols (Figure 9-3d). NetWare clients can thus access IBM mainframe or AS/400 data using any of the standard NetWare protocols, including IPX/SPX, AppleTalk, or TCP/IP. Host applications such as PC/3270, IND$FILE, Client Access/400, and Logical Link Control (LLC-2) traffic such as NetBIOS are thus enveloped and routed across the LAN or WAN. NetWare for SAA uses native NetWare security, administration, and management and can ease the host configuration and user access control and management. NetWare for SAA also provides a platform for integrating database, email, scheduling, and other applications between the host and LAN environments. References [9-19] and [9-20] explore the capabilities of this product in greater detail.

NetWare for DEC Access runs on a NetWare 3 or NetWare 4 server, providing bidirectional support for DEC's Local Area Transport (LAT) protocol. The software is implemented as a set of NLMs, and functions as a communication server (Figure 9-3e). The package supports multiple terminal emulators, including Telnet, and enables up to 128 simultaneous users to access DEC applications over any NetWare-supported topology. Reference [9-21] discusses additional applications for NetWare for DEC Access.

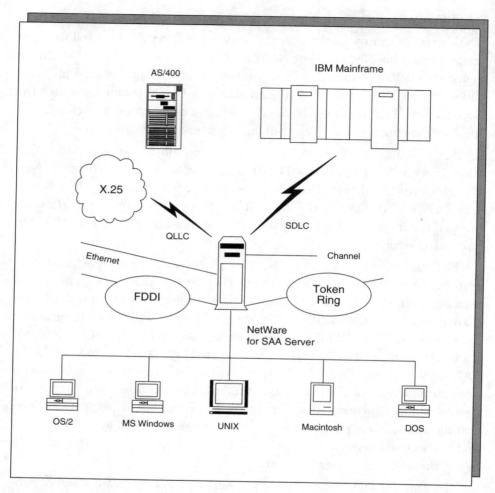

Figure 9-3d. NetWare for SAA 2.0 *(Courtesy of Novell, Inc.)*

By incorporating support for third-party hardware and software platforms, Novell has improved the internetworking and interoperability functions of its NetWare product line. References [9-22] and [9-23] illustrate the favorable response that industry analysts have made to these enhancements.

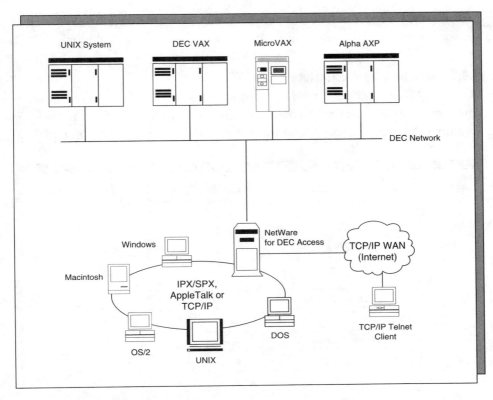

Figure 9-3e. NetWare for DEC Access *(Courtesy of Novell, Inc.)*

9.4 Microsoft Windows NT

Microsoft Corp.'s Windows NT products began shipping in July 1993, and were built upon experience gained from Microsoft's earlier network operating system, OS/2 LAN Manager. Rather than being an upgrade of the previous product, however, Windows NT was designed as a new product, featuring compatibility with existing file systems and applications, portability across both Intel 80386 and RISC processing systems, scalability to symmetric multiprocessing systems, with high security, reliability, and robustness. The operating system consists of two components: the Windows NT Workstation, a workstation operating system designed for ease of use and productivity; and the Windows NT Server, which provides the base services, connectivity, and administrative functions required to support distributed computing applications (see references [9-24] through [9-26]).

9.4.1 Windows NT Architecture

Windows NT is a modular architecture which is composed of several components. These modules include the Hardware Abstraction Layer (HAL), the Kernel, the Executive, and various subsystems (see Figure 9-4a, taken from reference [9-27]).

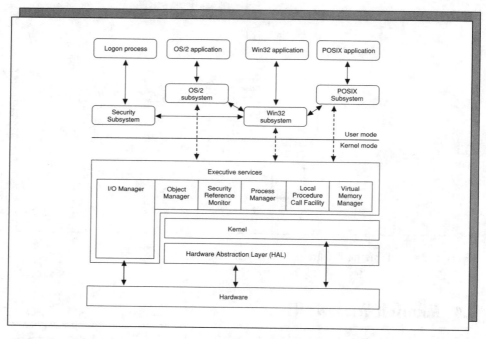

Figure 9-4a. Windows NT modular architecture *(From Windows NT Networking Guide.Copyright © 1995, Microsoft Corporation. Reprinted with permission of Microsoft Press. All rights reserved.)*

The Hardware Abstraction Layer (HAL) is a software layer that abstracts (or hides) differences in hardware from the upper layers of the operating system. Different types of hardware, such as Ethernet and token ring, thus look alike to the operating system. The Kernel is the heart of Windows NT, scheduling computing activities and processes. The Executive includes the Kernel and the HAL, and provides a set of common services that the environment subsystems can use. These Executive components include: the I/O Manager, the Object Manager, the Security Reference Monitor, the Process Manager, the Local Procedure Call Facility, and the Virtual Memory Manager. A layer at the top of the Executive, called the System Services, provides an interface between the user-mode environment subsystems and the kernel-mode. The environment systems are Windows NT processes, which emulate different operating system environments in support of the user applications.

9.4.2 Windows NT Networking

The Windows NT Networking Model provides support for all layers of the OSI model (see Figure 9-4b, taken from reference [9-28]). This model includes two interfaces, the Network Driver Interface Specification (NDIS) and the Transport Driver Interface (TDI). The NDIS was developed in 1989 by Microsoft and 3Com Corporation to facilitate communication between the MAC layer and the upper layer protocols. The NDIS is a software interface which allows any NDIS-compatible network adapter card to communicate with any NDIS-conformant protocol, and vice versa. By using NDIS, the need for a unique interface driver to support each network adapter is eliminated. In a similar manner, the TDI provides a communication interface to protocols residing at the Session layer and above.

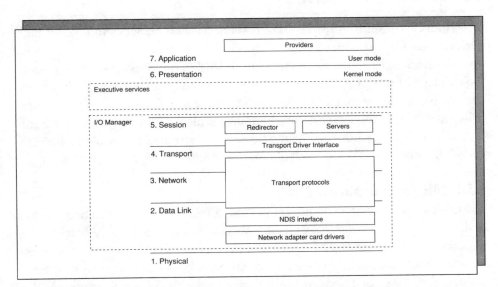

Figure 9-4b. Windows NT networking model *(From Windows NT Networking Guide. Copyright © 1995, Microsoft Corporation. Reprinted with permission of Microsoft Press. All rights reserved.)*

Windows NT supports a variety of Transport protocols, including NetBEUI Frame (NBF), Microsoft Data Link Control (DLC), NWLink and TCP/IP. NBF is an implementation of the NetBIOS Extended User Interface (NET-BEUI) protocol, and provides compatibility with existing LAN Manager, LAN Server, and MS-Net networks. DLC provides an interface for accessing mainframes and network-attached printers that use the IEEE 802.2 Logical Link Control (LLC) protocol. NWLink is an NDIS-compliant version of Novell's IPX/SPX protocols.

At the highest layer of the networking model are two additional software components, the servers and the redirector, which provide server and work-station functions. The redirector is a software component that redirects client requests for network resources—such as file access or printing—to the network. The server component provides the clients with the access to these requested resources.

References [9-29] through [9-32] are examples of recent trade press arti-cles that discuss the capabilities and applications for Windows NT.

9.5 IBM OS/2 LAN Server

Now in its sixth release, IBM's OS/2 LAN Server 4.0 provides full 32-bit high performance file and print serving for IBM's OS/2 Warp solution server platform, and is considered an integral component in IBM's connectivity strategy (Figure 9-5a). The two versions of LAN Server 4.0, Entry and Advanced, provide a range of networking solutions, from solutions for business environments to large enter-prise networks. LAN Server networking now scales to all of IBM's major hard-ware and software platforms. At the time of this writing, it is available for AIX RS/6000, AS/400—LAN Server/400, and the ES9000 with MVS and VM.

9.5.1 LAN Server Architecture

The OS/2 LAN Server is a component of IBM's OS/2 LAN communication support environment. Two elements make up the LAN components: the OS/2 LAN Requester, the client side; and the OS/2 LAN Server, the server side (Figure 9-5b). Different requester configurations allow each workstation to be optimized for specific mem-ory and operating conditions. A third product is the DOS LAN Services for DOS clients, included in the OS/2 LAN Server. Note that LAN Server 4.0 provides internetworking support for a broad set of clients, including: OS/2 Warp Connect, DOS LAN Services, Macintosh, DOS/Windows, Windows NT 3.5, and Windows for Workgroups. Ethernet networks are also supported (Figure 9-5c).

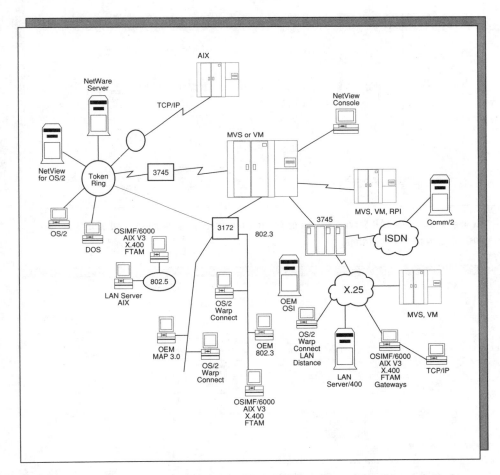

Figure 9-5a. IBM interconnectivity *(Reprinted by permission of International Business Machines Corporation)*

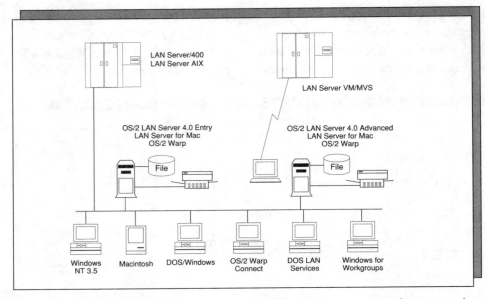

Figure 9-5b. IBM LAN Server/Requester Architecture *(Reprinted by permission of International Business Machines Corporation)*

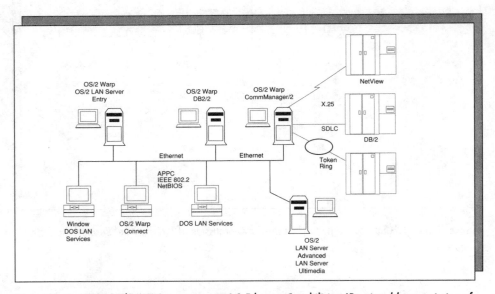

Figure 9-5c. IBM OS/2 LAN Server version 4.0 Ethernet Capabilities *(Reprinted by permission of International Business Machines Corporation)*

Support for distributed computing is also fundamental to the LAN Server architecture. The LAN Server domain-based directory architecture allows users to view network resources from a "single system" perspective across multiple domains. In the future, the domain concept will be extended with an optional "global directory service" based on Distributed Computing Environment (DCE) technology. This, then, will form the foundation for open distributed computing across IBM and non-IBM hardware and software platforms.

9.5.2 Multi-Protocol Transport Networking

With many computing architectures, a strong tie exists between applications and the underlying transport protocols. For example, an application written to the BSD Sockets interface and destined for TCP/IP transport is not easily ported to the Net-BIOS interface for transport over a LAN. To address this challenge, IBM has developed the Multi-Protocol Transport Networking (MPTN) Architecture. MPTN provides an architectural framework that allows applications written to one API to run over another (non-native) transport protocol. MPTN is based upon a software layer called the Common Transport Semantics, or CTS (see Figure 9-5d plus references [9-33] and [9-34]). This layer allows the APIs above CTS to access any of the protocols below CTS. MPTN provides the definitions for network address mapping, function compensation, and transport gateway connectivity.

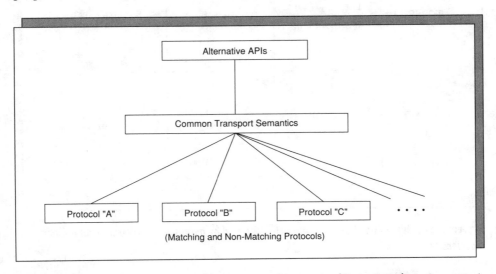

Figure 9-5d. MPTN Schematic *(Reprinted by permission of International Business Machines Corporation)*

Many combinations of APIs and protocols are thus available (Figure 9-5e). APIs include the Network Control Block (NCB) within NetBIOS, BSD Sockets, plus SNA interfaces. Note that the "AnyNet/2" series of products is a generic name that IBM has associated with a family of products conforming to MPTN to support APIs over non-matching protocols. Figure 9-5f illustrates a dual API environment using both NetBIOS and Sockets over TCP/IP transport.

Protocol \ API	NetBIOS NCB	BSD Sockets	APPC/CPI–C
NetBIOS	(Native)	LAN Server 4.0 DCE or DSOM ——— AnyNet/2 – Sockets over NetBIOS	
TCP/IP	LAN Server 4.0 RFC 1001 / 1002	(Native)	AnyNet/2
SNA	AnyNet/2 – NetBIOS over SNA	AnyNet/2	(Native)

Figure 9-5e. IBM API and protocol support *(Reprinted by permission of International Business Machines Corporation)*

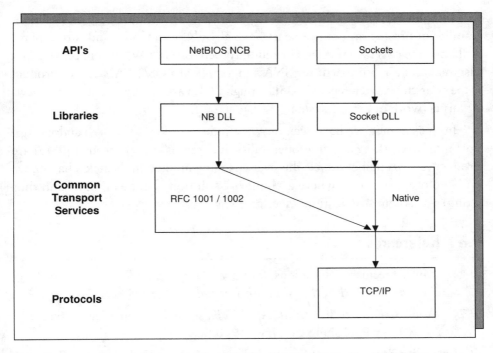

Figure 9-5f. Client With Dual API Support *(Reprinted by permission of International Business Machines Corporation)*

The implementation of MPTN on LAN Server 4.0 is called Multiprotocol Transport Services, or MPTS. It allows for easy integration into a number of networking environments (including Distributed Computing Environment—DCE) when available for LAN Server. These services execute when the network is installed, and allow the network administrator to select from a variety of transport protocols, including full TCP/IP support and NetBIOS over TCP/IP, which is called TCPBEUI.

TCPBEUI is LAN Server's implementation of RFC 1001/1002 standards. It allows applications requiring a NetBIOS interface to utilize TCP/IP for communication. Because NetBIOS is not inherently routable, TCPBEUI includes three extensions that enable efficient routing. The methods utilized by TCPBEUI for routing are: Name files, which map NetBIOS names with IP addresses, thus minimizing broadcast traffic; Broadcast files, which optimize IP broadcast traffic; and TCP/IP domain name servers, which maintain tables of NetBIOS names and IP addresses.

In summary, IBM is implementing multi-protocol support progressively. A number of product announcements have already been made, and future plans will unify the coverage further. For multiprotocol LAN or WAN connectivity that also includes a requirement for SNA support, IBM's OS/2 LAN Server product is the clear choice. References [9-35] through [9-38] are examples of recent reviews of this network operating system.

In this chapter, we have seen how the industry's key software vendors support internetworking and interoperability. References [9-39] through [9-43] are product reviews that chronicle this ever-changing market. In the next chapter, we will explore a situation where a "built-in" solution is not available, and thus requires use of an Application Layer gateway.

9.6   References

[9-1]   Miller-Freeman Publications. *Interoperability, a Supplement to LAN Magazine and STACKS, the Network Journal*, May 1994.

[9-2]   Apple Computer, Inc. *Inside AppleTalk*, second edition. New York: Addison-Wesley Publishing Co., Inc., 1990.

[9-3]   Miller, Mark A. *LAN Protocol Handbook*. New York, NY: M&T Books, 1990.

[9-4]   Banyan Systems, Inc. *VINES Architecture Definition*. Document no. 002645, 1993.

[9-5]   Banyan Systems, Inc. *VINES Protocol Definition*. Document no. 003673, 1993.

[9-6]   Banyan Systems, Inc. *TCP/IP Guide*. Document no. 001891, 1992.

[9-7]   Kapustka, Paul. "VINES Gets Native TCP/IP Client Support." *Open Systems Today* (February 6, 1995): 22–24.

[9-8]   Novell, Inc. *Novell Products and Programs Guide*. Document 461-000028-011, March 1995.

[9-9]   Novell, Inc. *NetWare 386 Theory of Operations*. Document 479-000042-001, August 1989.

[9-10] Novell, Inc. *NetWare 386 Technical Overview*. Document 471-000011-002, July 1989.

[9-11] Novell, Inc. *NetWare 3 and NetWare 4—Features Comparison Reference.* Document 461-000226-002, December 1994.

[9-12] Novell, Inc. *Novell Application Notes, Special NetWare 4.0 Edition* (April 1993): 1–240.

[9-13] Novell, Inc. *Novell Application Notes, Special NetWare 4.1 Edition* (January 1995): 1–136.

[9-14] Novell, Inc. *NetWare 4.1 Implementation Guide.* Document 482-000219-001, December 1994.

[9-15] Wittman, Art and James E. Drews. "With NetWare v4.1, Novell Finally Lives Up To Its Promises." *Network Computing* (November 1, 1994): 48–49.

[9-16] Williams, Dennis. "NetWare 4.1 Ready (Finally)." *LAN Times* (December 5, 1994): 1, 129.

[9-17] Wittman, Art and James E. Drews. "NetWare 4.1 Puts Novell In The Spotlight." *Network Computing* (January 15, 1995): 50–60.

[9-18] Drake, Dawn and Prakash Rao. "NetWare Clients: Overview and Strategy." *Novell Brainshare 1995 Presentation Book* (Volume 15): 1–4.

[9-19] Arra, Dan. "NetWare for SAA 2.0: Current Features and Future Directions." *Novell Brainshare 1995 Presentation Book* (Volume 3): 1–7.

[9-20] Jewell, Brian R. "NetWare for SAA 2.0: An Overview of Novell's Next Generation SNA Connectivity Product." *Novell Application Notes* (March 1995): 85–116.

[9-21] Combs, Ray. "Introduction to NetWare-to-Digital Connectivity." *Novell Brainshare 1995 Presentation Book* (Volume 3): 8–13.

[9-22] Kalman, Steve. "Leveraging the Modularity of NetWare." *STACKS, The Network Journal* (July 1994): 25–29.

[9-23] Croes, Tony. "Novell Paves Road to ATM." *Network World* (September 19, 1994): 60–62.

[9-24] Microsoft Corp. *Microsoft Windows NT Workstation 3.51 Reviewer's Guide,* March 1995.

[9-25] Microsoft Corp. *Microsoft Windows NT Server 3.51 Reviewer's Guide,* February 1995.

[9-26] Microsoft Corp. *Microsoft Windows NT Server Concepts and Planning Guide*, version 3.5. Document no. 58004-0794, 1994.

[9-27] Microsoft Corp. *Windows NT Resource Guide.* Microsoft Press, 1995.

[9-28] Microsoft Corp. *Windows NT Networking Guide.* Microsoft Press, 1995.

[9-29] Baker, Steven. "NT on the WAN." *Interoperability, Supplement to STACKS, The Network Journal* (May 1994): 61–73.

[9-30] Bahr, Daniel. "NT's Promise Fulfilled." *LAN Magazine* (February 1995): 139–144.

[9-31] Streeter, April. "NT Forges Corporation Foothold." *LAN Times* (February 27, 1995): 56–61.

[9-32] Wong, William. "Windows NT 3.5: Ready for Prime Time." *STACKS* (March 1995): 33–37.

[9-33] IBM. *IBM LAN Server 4.0 Reviewer's Guide*, 1994.

[9-34] Yeung, Leo and Brice Bartek. "Networking Support for the IBM LAN Server—Becoming a Protocol Independent Network Operating System." *IBM LAN Systems Development*, January 1995.

[9-35] Petreley, Nicholas. "IBM cleans up LAN Server's Act." *InfoWorld* (August 22, 1994).

[9-36] Shimmin, Bradley F. "LAN Server Redefined." *LAN Times* (September 19, 1994).

[9-37] Rash, Wayne. "LAN Server 4.0 Eases Net Mgm't." *Communications Week* (January 30, 1995): 12.

[9-38] Wong, William. "Stepping Out." *LAN Magazine* (March 1995): 142–149.

[9-39] Chernicoff, David P. "The Big Three Now Work Better Together." *PC Week* (November 14, 1994): 126–136.

[9-40] Morse, Stephen. "The NOS Report Card." *Network Computing* (October 1, 1994): 75–79.

[9-41] Wong, William. "OS Update: Peer-to-Peer." *STACKS* (October 1994): 25–33.

[9-42] Wong, William. "OS Update, Part II: Dedicated Server." *STACKS* (November 1994): 41–52.

[9-43] Wong, William. "OS Update III: Enterprise Systems." *STACKS* (December 1994): 51–55.

10 Gateways

The last stop on our tour of internetworking devices is at the highest level of the OSI Reference Model—the Application Layer. Recall from Figure 1-9 that gateways operate at all layers of the OSI Model and that protocol conversions may be required at each of these layers.

In practice, however, it would be more appropriate to consider the interconnectivity architecture as two "half gateways." This is because two dissimilar systems are being linked, and one half of the gateway is required to communicate with each. At some level within the gateway (most likely the Application Layer), the protocols of each half are equivalent. The other layers communicate with their peer protocols on either "one-half" of the gateways.

While this theory may be interesting to academics, most readers are responsible for making two or more dissimilar systems communicate, and are therefore more interested in gateway application. Many gateway products are available for specific purposes; a listing of representative vendors is given in Appendix F. In this chapter we will study twelve products for linking dissimilar systems. This is by no means an exhaustive study. Instead, it is intended as a survey of representative products that can be used for linking dissimilar LANs, such as Novell's NetWare and Banyan Systems' VINES; or a LAN and a minicomputer, such as a NetWare network and a Hewlett-Packard HP3000.

Each of these examples is relatively independent; pick and choose those that apply to your internetwork. For further information on gateways and their applications, consult references [10-1] through [10-13].

10.1 BLAST Software from BLAST, Inc.

BLAST, developed by BLAST, Inc. of Pittsboro, NC, stands for BLocked ASynchronous Transmission. It began as a program to transfer files between dissimilar hosts. Let's suppose that you wanted to transfer an ASCII file from an IBM mainframe to a DEC VAX minicomputer; you would need two different BLAST packages—BLAST for IBM Mainframe and BLAST Professional for DEC VAX. Each package would run under the native operating system (i.e., VM/MVS and VMS respectively). The common denominator linking the two systems is the proprietary BLAST protocol.

The program was named for its transmission format, which uses a proprietary sliding window protocol. The protocol specifies a full-duplex transmission format, with data blocks of up to 4096 characters in length (Figure 10-1a). Each block is provided with a Cyclic Redundancy Check (CRC) for error detection, plus a sliding window for additional accuracy. The sliding window performs two key functions: it provides a sequence number for each data block, and it assures that one computer with a fast transmitter will not overwhelm a slower computer with too much data. Each end of the transmission link maintains a "window" indicating how many more data blocks can be sent or received.

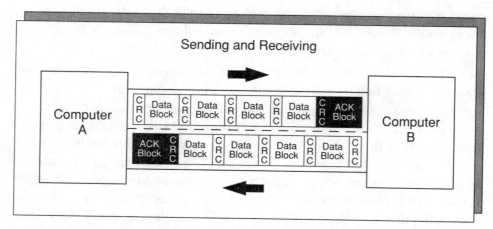

Figure 10-1a. BLAST full duplex protocol *(Courtesy of BLAST, Inc.)*

Acknowledgments from the opposite end of the link move the near-end's transmit window, thus permitting an additional block (or blocks) to be transmitted. Should a problem occur mid-transmission (such as a noise hit on the transmission line or a total interruption), the sliding window protocol also serves to mark the file at the point of interruption and resume the transfer after communication is re-established. Other file transfer protocols, such as Kermit and XMODEM, operate in a half-duplex mode (Figure 10-1b). These protocols operate in a less efficient manner, since each block of data must be acknowledged (ACK'd) before the transmitter forges ahead.

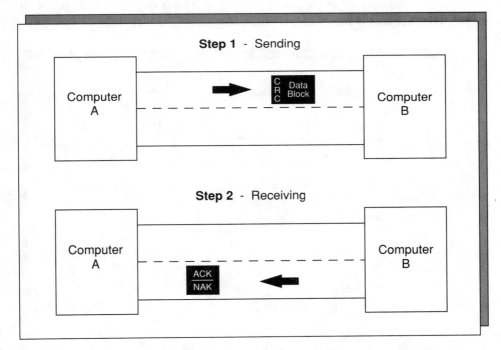

Figure 10-1b. Kermit and XMODEM half duplex ACK/NAK protocol *(Courtesy of BLAST, Inc.)*

The software was initially released in 1979 and is currently in its tenth release. It is available for more than 40 different platforms and operating systems. These include: MS-DOS, Windows, SCO UNIX, XENIX, AT&T, Interactive, Macintosh, VAX VMS, Alpha Open VMS, HP9000, SUN Solaris 1.x, SUN Solaris 2.x/x86, Data General AViiON, IBM RS6000, Silicon Graphics, Sequent, and others (Figure 10-1c). Along the development process, a number of other features were added to the software. These features are terminal emulation, remote control on the DOS product, TCP/IP and Telnet support, a scripting language, and SECURE BLAST. BLAST Professional for DOS operates with any NetBIOS-compatible LAN, and interfaces with communication server software that supports NACS (Novell Asynchronous Communication Server), ACS (IBM Asynchronous Connection Server), and AGS (AT&T Asynchronous Gateway Server). Since BLAST is a software interface, it does not care about the physical topology and is equally comfortable with Ethernet, StarLAN, or token ring networks. The physical communication channel between LAN and host could be a dial-up line or access to a PSPDN via the X.25 protocol.

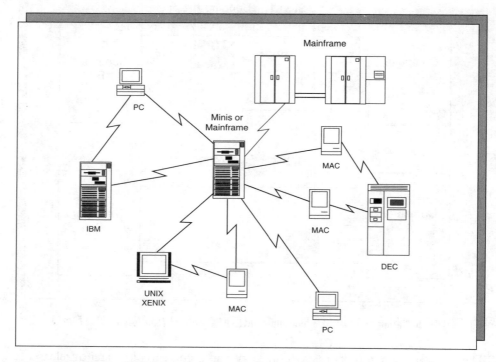

Figure 10-1c. BLAST Platform Options *(Courtesy of BLAST, Inc.)*

The terminal emulation feature permits access to local or remote host computers and allows terminal emulation and file transfer. Keyboard remapping is also available, allowing the workstation's keys to be remapped for any specific terminal function. Emulators supported include DEC VT52/100/220/320, Wyse 50/60, Data General D200/410/411/461, Televideo 920, Hewlett-Packard 2392, IBM 3101, PC ANSI Color, Ampex D80, ADM 3A, and TTY.

Remote Control permits total screen and keyboard control of LAN workstations from a remote site, or control of a remote workstation from a LAN-attached workstation via dial-up lines. For example, if a network problem occurs when the administrator is off-site, he or she can access the network console remotely and initiate troubleshooting procedures immediately.

BLAST Professional for DOS provides TCP/IP support for terminal emulation (Telnet) and file transfer (FTP) over all TCP/IP environments. BLAST Workstation products provide Telnet support for logging onto remote machines over TCP/IP networks. BLAST can be used to send and receive data over any virtual asynchronous connection including X.25 interfaces, satellite links, RS-232 connections, radio waves, cellular connections, and analog telephone lines.

A powerful script language (which is identical for all BLAST versions—PC, MAC, UNIX, DEC, etc.) allows automated logins, remote access, and file transfers. An application could be a large file transfer or backup from the LAN to a host overnight (in order to take advantage of lower dial-up telephone line charges). The BLAST script language provides for these unattended transfers and provides sample scripts for login to Value Added Networks such as CompuServe.

SECURE BLAST allows the BLAST administrator to create multiple passwords with individual security options. BLAST is then "secured" by attaching the password database to the BLAST program. All file transfer access to the "secured" system is then controlled by the permissions granted within the password database.

An impressive feature of BLAST is the vast number of workstations, minicomputers, mainframes, and LANs that are supported by the software. For file transfer, terminal emulation, and remote access functions, it's safe to assume that a BLAST product exists to connect your computing system to any other platform.

10.2 Beame & Whiteside BW-MultiConnect for Solaris

There are other protocols in addition to Internet standards like TCP/IP that can be used to interconnect disparate computing platforms. NetWare, for example, is based on the IPX/SPX (Internetwork Packet Exchange/Sequenced Packet

Exchange) networking protocol developed by Novell. Since IPX is the core protocol for NetWare, it makes sense to use IPX as the link to other computing platforms.

This is exactly what Beame & Whiteside Software (Raleigh, North Carolina) has done with its software solution to link NetWare environments to Solaris UNIX networks (Figure 10-2). Beame & Whiteside's BW-MultiConnect for Solaris is a client/server solution that provides an IPX/SPX protocol stack for Solaris to enable a seamless exchange of files and print services between NetWare and Solaris UNIX. Beame & Whiteside offers this software as both a server solution, which gives NetWare users access to Solaris files and print services, and as a client solution, which gives Solaris users access to NetWare files and print services.

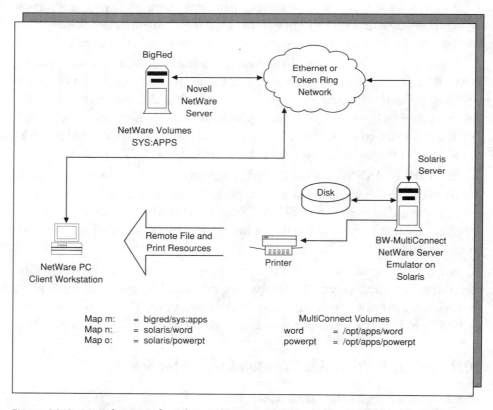

Figure 10-2. BW-MultiConnect for Solaris architecture *(Courtesy of Beame & Whiteside Software, Inc.)*

BW-MultiConnect Server for Solaris was designed to give NetWare workstations seamless access to file and print services on network servers running Solaris UNIX by adding the IPX/SPX protocol stack to Solaris. One piece of software is installed on the server, so no additional software is required on the client workstation—a practical approach if you have a large NetWare network. Using this approach, you can support multiple NetWare clients on a single Solaris machine and still use the security features of native NetWare.

BW-MultiConnect Server for Solaris uses an IPX/SPX protocol stack developed by Beame & Whiteside, complete with a TLI/TPI interface, Ethernet support (including Ethernet version 2, IEEE 802.3, and SNAP frame types), SAP (Service Advertising Protocol) advertising services, RIP (Routing Information Protocol) connections to other NetWare networks, and a complete NetWare subset Applications Programming Interface (API) programming library. The server software itself is implemented as a loadable streams driver on the Solaris host to emulate a NetWare server, making UNIX services appear as NetWare 3.x features.

Beame & Whiteside has also added a number of NetWare features to its BW-MultiConnect Server for Solaris, including: server filing system support, server print servers, support for multiple simultaneous users, queue management, and server bindery services. NetWare DOS utilities included are: LOGIN, ATTACH, MAP, SLIST, and LOGOUT. It also includes a Virtual Terminal Server that provides Telnet terminal emulation for remote access (LOGON) to UNIX services via NetWare NVT protocol services. Shared print services make it possible for NetWare users to direct their NetWare-based print output to Solaris printers. The BW-MultiConnect print server can also retrieve print jobs queued on other NetWare file servers.

BW-MultiConnect Client for Solaris gives Solaris users access to NetWare files and print services. The client software uses a mechanism similar to automount to mount Solaris UNIX workstations to a NetWare volume or directory the same way they normally mount a Solaris file system. Once mounted, the NetWare volume operates just like a Solaris directory.

BW-MultiConnect Client for Solaris includes support for automount by reference, UNIX file permission mapping, UNIX uid/gid mapping, and client printing. BW-MultiConnect Client for Solaris also offers the capability to print to NetWare printers using the UNIX lp interface, or using nprint, which is similar to the Novell MS-DOS print utility.

Many UNIX-based systems use TCP/IP at the core of their internetworking architecture, requiring other systems to communicate using these protocols. Beame & Whiteside's MultiConnect software takes a different approach—it incorporates Novell's IPX/SPX protocols into a UNIX-based environment, thus making connectivity into the NetWare world that much easier.

10.3 Innosoft International's PMDF e-Mail Interconnect

Most electronic mail systems have some means to exchange messages with other email platforms, usually through some sort of SMTP (Simple Mail Transfer Protocol) gateway. For exchanging simple text messages, an SMTP link is adequate. However, if you want to be able to exchange documents, files, and binary data, you need to be able to rely on a more powerful networking standard such as the MIME (Multipurpose Internet Mail Extensions) standard, defined in RFCs 1521 and 1522.

MIME was developed to define virtually any type of electronic message for transmission across the Internet. But even with MIME support in conventional email systems, email integration can still be a limitation. For example, network users accustomed to a LAN-based email system may need to be able to exchange email with users served by other mail systems, such as host-based mailers within the enterprise and/or Internet connections or X.400 service providers.

Innosoft International Inc. of West Covina, California, has solved this problem by creating PMDF-Interconnect, the only email routing and distribution software system based solely on the Internet MIME standards (as opposed to proprietary email systems with hooks into the Internet like SMTP gateways). Although MIME was written to make it possible to send multipart/multimedia messages across the Internet, the authors recognized that MIME is also a powerful tool capable of defining any kind of email transmission—messages could be readily translated from one email format to another by using MIME as an intermediary or canonical format. The result is an "Internet-style" email integration package.

PMDF is actually made up of a number of separate pieces of software that run on Digital hardware, specifically the OpenVMS and OSF/1 operating systems (Figure 10-3). The messaging backbone is packaged in PMDF-MTA, a MIME-based Message Transfer Agent. PMDF-MTA serves as the email integration engine that forms the backbone of the store-and-forward distribution and routing system. From PMDF-MTA, users can access a variety of email platforms, including VMS Mail, PATHWORKS, POP and IMAP clients, DECwindows mail, and Gold-Mail.

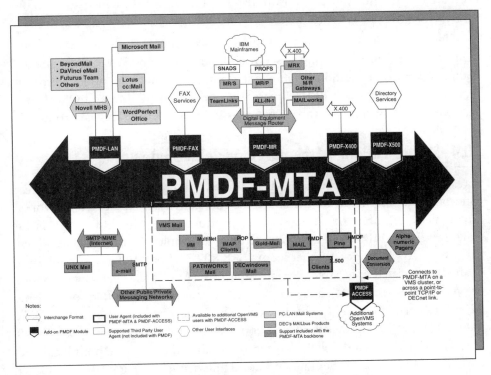

Figure 10-3. PDMF-MTA architecture *(Courtesy of Innosoft International, Inc.)*

Once PMDF-MTA is up and running, additional support software can be added to extend support to other email platforms. PMDF-ACCESS includes PMDF-MAIL, an extension of VMS Mail, and PMDF Pine, a menu-driven user agent popular among UNIX users. It extends full email integration and user agent functionality to users on other systems, such as OpenVMS or OSF/1 networks linked to the network that is running PMDF-MTA. PMDF-LAN interconnects PC LAN-based mail systems, such as Microsoft Mail, Lotus cc:Mail, Novell MHS, and WordPerfect Office. PMDF-FAX provides email-to-FAX capabilities so users can send and receive FAXes from their electronic mailbox. PMDF-MR integrates Digital's MAILbus products such as ALL-IN-1.

Innosoft has also extended support for OSI-based standards with two additional software products that augment PMDF-MTA. PMDF-X400 provides MIME-based access to X.400 mail systems, basically linking any mail system supported by PMDF to X.400. Innosoft also has PMDF-X500, which adds X.500 directory services to the enterprise.

Since the entire PMDF email system is based on MIME, it can take advantage of full multimedia support, sending binary files, PostScript files, images, audio, and video in addition to plain text as multipart, multiple format electronic mail messages. Although PMDF currently runs on OpenVMS and OSF/1, it is capable of linking email platforms from virtually any networking environment.

10.4 Shiva FastPath 5 Ethernet to AppleTalk Gateway

Shiva Corporation of Burlington, Massachusetts, is a developer of remote access solutions and peripherals that enhance the connectivity of AppleTalk networks. Shiva has a number of devices in its product line. The EtherGate is an EtherTalk/LocalTalk/Serial gateway (actually an AppleTalk router) that allows EtherTalk (AppleTalk over Ethernet or IEEE 802.3), LocalTalk (AppleTalk over unshielded twisted pair cable), Serial AppleTalk (AppleTalk over asynchronous or synchronous serial lines), and serial devices such as printers, plotters, or modems to be combined into a single internetwork. The TeleBridge provides an AppleTalk to Serial (RS-232) interface for asynchronous modems at speeds of up to 57,600 bps. The EtherGate and TeleBridge can be combined to provide both local and remote access between EtherTalk and LocalTalk networks (Figure 10-4a). Other products include modems and bridges specifically for the AppleTalk market, as well as a complete line of remote access products for Macintosh, PC, and UNIX workstations.

One of the Shiva products is the FastPath 5, an AppleTalk to Ethernet gateway (this product is truly a gateway) that supports a number of higher-layer protocols. The FastPath has an interesting history. The product was originally developed by Kinetics, Inc. of Walnut Creek, California, in 1985. Kinetics was merged with Excelan, Inc., which was then acquired by Novell, Inc. In June 1990, Novell sold the FastPath product to Shiva, where it became a natural extension to Shiva's AppleTalk product line.

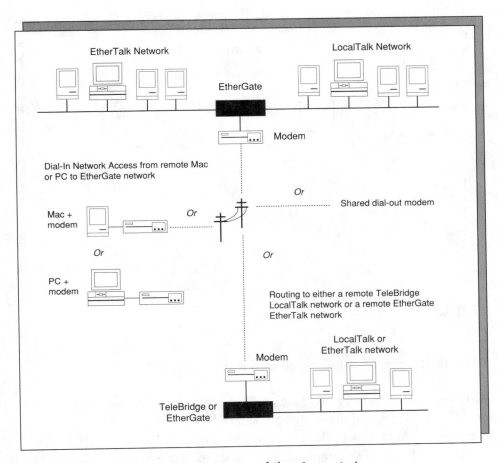

Figure 10-4a. EtherGate configuration *(Courtesy of Shiva Corporation)*

The FastPath 5 is a hardware gateway that allows connection to one Ethernet network and one LocalTalk network (see Figure 10-4b). The Ethernet connection has a variety of cabling options, including Ethernet version 2, IEEE 802.3 10BASE-T, plus thick or thin coax. The FastPath is autoconfiguring for its basic operation. If the network manager wishes to use advanced features such as the TCP/IP gateway, zone or device filtering, or AppleTalk tunneling over IP, an installation disk is used.

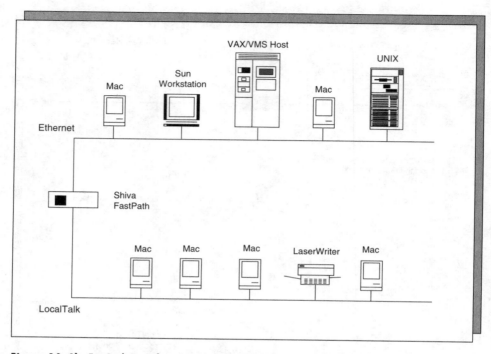

Figure 10-4b. FastPath 5 configuration *(Courtesy of Shiva Corporation)*

Most applications require that Macintosh workstations be connected to a UNIX or VAX ULTRIX-based minicomputer. For TCP/IP-based Ethernets, the FastPath 5 accepts the AppleTalk packets from the LocalTalk network, encapsulates them within a UDP (User Datagram Protocol) message, and re-transmits them on the Ethernet. Access to any IP-based services from the LocalTalk side is thus possible. In addition, since TCP/IP and DECnet are WANs, the Macintosh user has access to distributed resources anywhere on the Internet—not just the locally connected Ethernet.

Shiva Corporation has a number of interesting AppleTalk connectivity products. With the software-configurable FastPath 5 gateway, users are provided with a platform to connect their Macintosh networks with a number of other Ethernet-based minicomputers.

10.5 Andrew NetAxcess AppleTalk to AS/400 Gateway

Integrating the Macintosh into IBM midrange and mainframe systems is a technology that is somewhat limited in the number of vendor choices available. However, one solution for integrating AppleTalk to AS/400 and System/3X minicomputers is available from Andrew Corporation of Austin, Texas. Known as NetAxcess, this gateway is both a hardware and software solution. The hardware consists of the NetAxcess card which may be installed in any Macintosh II, SE-30, or LC. The physical connection is via twinaxial cable to the AS/400 and via LocalTalk-compatible unshielded twisted pair cable to the Macintosh network. Existing EtherTalk (IEEE 802.3) and TokenTalk (IEEE 802.5) cabling can be used as well. The hardware interfaces with all AppleTalk Phase 2 devices, and may also be integrated with remote access devices such as Shiva's EtherGate. Each NetAxcess card supports up to seven minicomputer connections (Figure 10-5), and up to five cards can be installed per gateway Macintosh, depending on the number of available slots. The installation of additional cards permits access to multiple minicomputers.

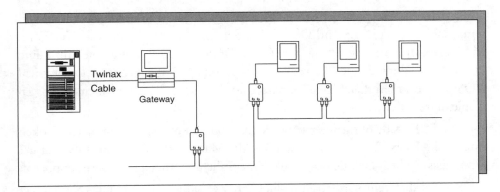

Figure 10-5. AppleTalk to AS/400 gateway *(Courtesy of Andrew Corporation)*

The software portion of the gateway offers several user functions. A terminal emulation program (TwinAxcess) provides IBM 5250 terminal emulation functions for the Macintosh. IBM 3812, 5219, 5224, 5225, and 5256 printers are also emulated, allowing use of an Apple LaserWriter as an IBM AS/400 or S/3X printer. A file transfer utility (ETU, or Emulator Transfer Utility/400) emulates

IBM's PC Support Program. It is a host-based utility, supporting all the security features of the host. An Apple HyperCard API is also available.

The Macintosh to AS/400 might not be the most common gateway product in use, but it is good to know that the functional need is being met. The NetAxcess product meets this need with a user interface that will make the Macintosh user feel very comfortable.

10.6 Miramar Systems MACLAN Connect

As you will recall from our study of the AppleTalk internetworking architecture, there was one standard missing—NetBIOS (the Network Basic Input/Output System). NetBOIS is an IBM standard Applications Programming Interface (API—widely implemented on other LAN operating systems, including Banyan Systems' VINES and Novell's NetWare). It is not built into the AppleTalk architecture.

A third party, Miramar Systems, Inc. of Santa Barbara, California, offers an interface solution with their MACLAN product family. MACLAN Connect is a Macintosh-to-PC gateway, allowing Macintosh computers to be integrated into a PC network. The package will work with a number of network operating systems, including VINES and OS/2 LAN Server plus all versions of NetWare. MACLAN operates by sitting in between DOS and AFP (the AppleTalk Filing Protocol). As long as the PC workstation presents a logical, virtual, or physical DOS prompt, then this "drive" is passed to the interconnected Macintosh as an AppleShare volume.

On the PC side of the internetwork, all topologies—including Ethernet, token ring, and ARCNET—are supported. On the Macintosh side, AppleTalk Phase 2 topologies—which include LocalTalk, EtherTalk, and TokenTalk—are supported.

Several different software products are available. The MACLAN Connect permits any PC-compatible to function as an AppleShare server. For this configuration, the PC server must have both an AppleTalk and a network (Ethernet or token ring) interface card and necessary workstation software installed (see Figure 10-6a). The physical interface is the cabling system native to that architecture, such as unshielded twisted pair for LocalTalk or token ring, or RG58A/U coax for thin Ethernet. The PC server thus becomes a dedicated AppleShare server, while the MACLAN Connect software provides an implementation of the AppleTalk Filing Protocol (AFP) for DOS. Transparent sharing of volumes, folders, and files between the AppleTalk and DOS environments thus becomes possible.

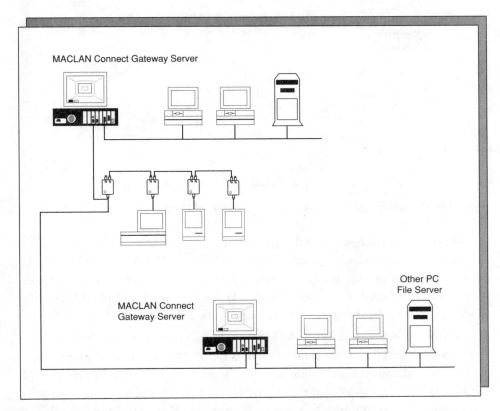

Figure 10-6a. MACLAN Connect gateway server *(Courtesy of Miramar Systems)*

A second gateway product is known as MACLAN Gold. In addition to the file service, it allows PCs and Macintoshes simultaneous access to PostScript printers (see Figure 10-6b). The print server software requires a dedicated PC/AT/386/486 workstation that is also configured as a LAN workstation. Physical connection between printer and print server may be established through the PC network, AppleTalk cabling, or serial/parallel interface.

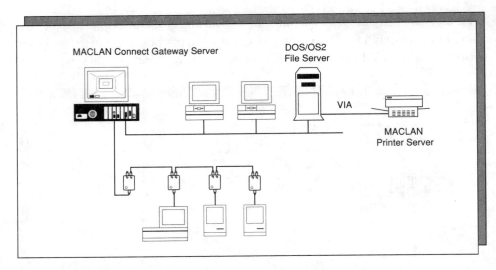

Figure 10-6b. MACLAN PostScript printer support *(Courtesy of Miramar Systems)*

In addition to supporting file and printer sharing, the MACLAN gateway offers a third application—electronic mail interoperability. MACLAN supports several popular email packages, including cc:Mail (Lotus, Inc., Cambridge, MA) Microsoft Mail, and QuickMail (CE Software, Inc., Des Moines, IA). With MACLAN's support, other applications are sure to be identified.

Another Miramar product is the Personal MACLAN Connect. This is a Windows non-dedicated product that provides full peer-to-peer file and printer sharing between Macintosh and Windows PCs (Figure 10-6c). Personal MACLAN Connect is PC Windows software that gives Macintosh and Windows users an easy-to-use full featured way to share disk drives, PostScript printers, CD-ROM drives, and other resources among a mix of computers. Sharing information between Windows and Macintosh users is as transparent as working off your own local hard drive. Print jobs go to the output device of your choice, regardless of its location on the network.

Windows users can share any local Macintosh hard drive by selecting it and assigning it an available logical disk drive letter. PCs can log in to any Macintosh, AppleShare, or AFP file server and become a full-fledged client. Using standard Apple System 7 file sharing software, each Mac user controls exactly when, where, and which users have access to their computer.

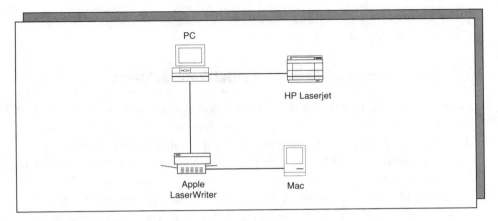

Figure 10-6c. Personal MACLAN Connect *(Courtesy of Miramar Systems)*

Windows users can share their local storage devices with any Macintosh user. All PC files and printers are accessed from the Mac using the standard Macintosh Chooser interface. Windows users can dynamically select whether to share specific directories on the fly, or to share their entire hard, floppy, or CD-ROM drive. They can control exactly when, where, and which users have access to their PC, and can allow simultaneous access of multiple Macintosh workstations.

You can also maximize expensive printing resources by putting them to work for all of your computers instead of just a few. Bi-directional printing support allows full peer-to-peer print sharing between Windows and Macintosh users. Any PostScript printers available to your PC or Macintosh computers can be shared equally between both Mac and Windows users. You can place your printers wherever it's convenient and know that everyone will still have the same access.

Windows users have the ability to print to Macintosh based LaserWriters, Linotronics, RIP publishing printers, or any other AppleTalk based output device. Windows users simply send their jobs to AppleTalk printers as if they were locally connected. The software routes print jobs to the appropriate print device regardless of its location on the network. Print Server—Printers available to the Windows PC can be shared by both Macintosh and PC users. Mac users select the desired print queue from the Chooser and spool their jobs transparently to the Windows printer. Print output is directed to a print queue or a directory on the disk for processing. PostScript printers are supported and additional drivers are available from third parties for non-PostScript devices.

For those users wishing Macintosh-to-PC LAN integration, these products are certainly worthy of consideration.

10.7 Hewlett-Packard OfficeShare-NetWare Gateway

Hewlett-Packard Company of Irving, Texas, has developed a gateway linking their HP3000 minicomputers with Novell NetWare networks. The core of the gateway is the HP OfficeShare software. Components of this software run on the client PC, the gateway, and the HP3000 minicomputer. The OfficeShare software allows an HP3000 to be used as a server for a Novell PC-based network, and provides logon access to the HP3000 from the Novell client. Let's study the operation of the gateway by first comparing the HP OfficeShare and Novell NetWare protocol stacks.

HP OfficeShare (see Figure 10-7a) is a LAN operating system that runs on both a DOS and MPE (HP's MultiProgramming Executive) platform. It supports protocols such as IEEE 802.3, Ethernet, TCP, and IP. The Session Layer protocol is known as NetIPC (Network InterProcess Communication). OfficeShare uses a Virtual Terminal (VT) program at the Presentation Layer and HP AdvanceLink terminal emulation software at the Application Layer.

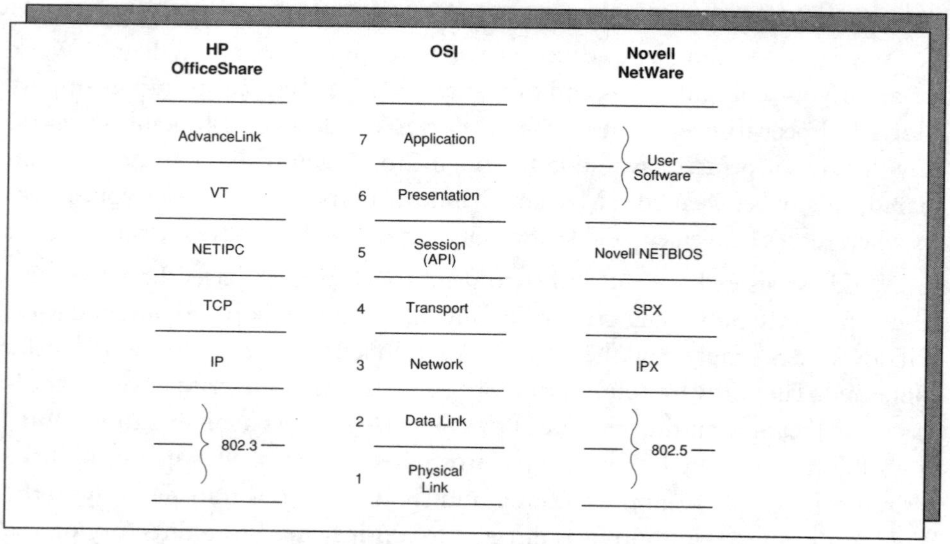

HP OfficeShare		OSI		Novell NetWare
AdvanceLink	7	Application		User Software
VT	6	Presentation		
NETIPC	5	Session (API)		Novell NETBIOS
TCP	4	Transport		SPX
IP	3	Network		IPX
802.3	2	Data Link		802.5
	1	Physical Link		

Figure 10-7a. Comparing HP OfficeShare and Novell NetWare with the OSI reference model (*Courtesy of Hewlett-Packard Company*)

Novell, on the other hand, has a variety of Physical and Data Link Layer platform options, including Ethernet, IEEE 802.3, IEEE 802.5, and ARCNET, among others (IEEE 802.5 is shown in Figure 10-7a as an example). As we discussed in Section 8.7, Novell's IPX and SPX, based upon the XNS, IDP, and SPP protocols, are used at the Network and Transport Layers. The Session Layer interface is a NetBIOS emulation, with the NetWare Core Protocols (NCP) and Application programs operating at the Presentation and Application Layers.

Clearly, HP and Novell have a different view of network architectures. Communication between these two dissimilar systems is possible with the HP-Novell gateway shown in Figure 10-7b. The OfficeShare-NetWare gateway software resides in a dedicated PC-compatible. Two network interfaces (one supporting Ethernet/IEEE 802.3 for communicating to the HP3000, and the other supporting the Novell network hardware—e.g., 802.5) are required within the gateway. Each PC on the NetWare side must also run a terminal emulation program that is compatible at both the Novell workstation and the HP3000 ends of the internetwork. HP provides one such program (known as HP AdvanceLink), although other software supporting Telnet and FTP protocols could also be used.

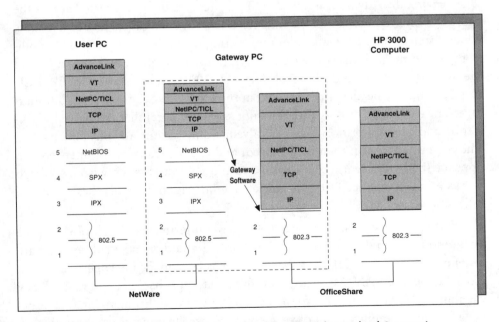

Figure 10-7b. HP-Novell gateway architecture *(Courtesy of Hewlett-Packard Company)*

Interoperability is achieved for several specific applications with the HP-Novell gateway: terminal emulation for HP2622 terminals; file transfer via FTP (both achieved with AdvanceLink); Program-to-Program communication with HP NetIPC; and other services—such as printing—defined by the HP3000 as the network server.

The data communication path inside the OfficeShare-NetWare gateway is also shown in Figure 10-7b. Note that the left-hand side of the figure shows NetWare-compatible protocols, while the right-hand side communicates with OfficeShare. Let's trace the path of the AdvanceLink message from the Novell workstation to the HP3000 server. The AdvanceLink message (such as a file transfer request) is initiated by the user, generating an IP datagram. The IP datagram is passed to the NetBIOS SPX and IPX protocols in turn, which add their Protocol Control Information (PCI), and encapsulate the AdvanceLink message. An IEEE 802.5 frame is generated at the workstation, which then waits for a free token. The frame is transmitted over the token ring network cable, through Multistation Access Units (MSAUs) and possible repeaters, until it reaches the gateway. Inside the gateway the IPX, SPX, and NetBIOS PCI are removed from the message, leaving the AdvanceLink packet. This packet is then transferred across the gateway's internal bus to the IEEE 802.3 NIC. The NIC builds an 802.3 frame, which listens to the coaxial cable transmitting during an idle period. No collisions or retransmissions occur (remember, this is theoretical and utopian!) and the 802.3 frame successfully reaches the HP3000. At the server, the IP, TCP, NetIPC, and VT headers are removed in turn, revealing the AdvanceLink message. The AdvanceLink software does not know (or care) that the Novell workstation and gateway protocol were involved; it only sees an AdvanceLink packet. The requested file can then be accessed, and the file transfer commenced. An opposite (but equivalent) process would then occur with the reply from server to workstation. Reference [10-1] is an excellent article that details these protocol interactions.

This Hewlett-Packard gateway solves several problems—most obvious, the integration of the HP and Novell architectures. Two other, more subtle issues are also involved. First, an HP MPE-based host has been made interoperable with a Novell PC-based LAN. More importantly, the storage, backup, and redundancy capabilities are now available to the PC network as well. From an internetworking and interoperability point of view, this is an excellent merger of technologies.

10.8 Attachmate LAN-Gateway and PEPGate/TCP

Attachmate Corporation of Bellevue, Washington, is a third-party vendor of peripherals and connectivity products that support a variety of mainframe environments, including IBM and Unisys. The Unisys products are produced by Attachmate's Unisys Products Group in Cincinnati, Ohio, and are available for Unisys A/V series (formerly Burroughs) and the Unisys 2200 series (formerly Sperry) systems. Two examples from that line are the LAN-Gateway and PEPGate/TCP.

In A Series environments, the LAN-Gateway provides Poll/select access to Unisys A series hosts for DOS or Windows users connected to a NetBIOS-compatible LAN. The gateway software requires an intelligent communications adapter—either an UniCard+ or a UniCard IDC—that resides in the communications server (Figure 10-8a). (The IDC—Intelligent DataComm Controller—is recommended for non-dedicated communication server applications. This allows the IDC to do the majority of the data communications processing, freeing the server's CPU for other tasks). Up to two of these cards can be installed in the same communications server. All other PCs attach to the communications server with normal LAN connections. Multiple server PCs can be used in the same network to extend the utility of the gateway to a large number of users.

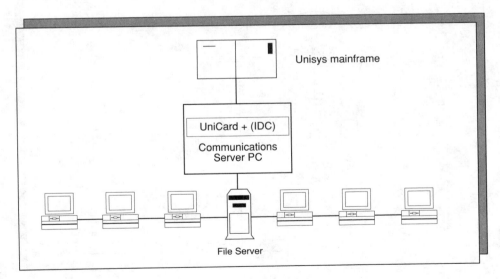

Figure 10-8a. LAN-Gateway architecture *(Courtesy of Attachmate Corp.)*

The A Series LAN-Gateway features optional address pooling, which enables a larger number of workstations to be configured with a smaller number of host terminal addresses. It also offers dynamic addressing, which further decreases otherwise heavy communication traffic.

In OS 2200 and System 80 environments, PEPGate provides host access for users of Novell, Banyan, or any NetBIOS-compatible LAN. PEPGate servers run on DOS or OS/2 and can link with the host using Uniscope, TCP/IP, or channel connections. The servers can support as many as 256 sessions for Windows, DOS, OS/2, and Unisys OFIS DSSP clients.

PEPGate/TCP is the high-speed TCP/IP network gateway developed for users of Unisys OS (2200) and OS/3 information hubs and/or mainframes (Figure 10-8b). The PEPGate/TCP Server software is installed in a PC or compatible, which manages all communications between a Unisys DCP (data communications processor) or HLC (host LAN controller) and client workstations. The server software supports several configuration options, and all Banyan, Novell, and NetBIOS compatible networks. One PEPGate/TCP server can support up to 32 simultaneous host sessions.

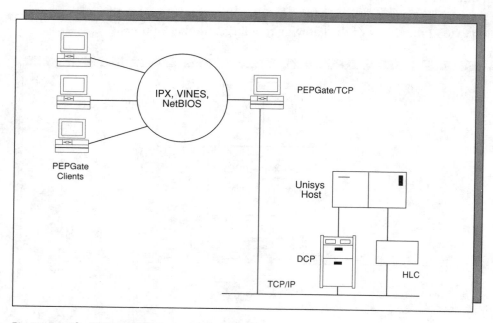

Figure 10-8b. PEPGate/TCP *(Courtesy of Attachmate Corp.)*

Attachmate's gateways are thus viable alternatives for managers and designers needing to incorporate Unisys host systems into their internetworking environments.

10.9 FEL LANLink-DECnet Gateway

FEL Computing, Inc. of Williamsville, Vermont, specializes in connectivity solutions to DEC VAX minicomputers. One FEL product of interest to LAN designers is the LANLink-DECnet Gateway.

The gateway requires a PC/XT/AT-compatible hardware platform having two adapter cards: one to communicate to the DECnet (Phase IV) Ethernet, and the other to communicate with a LAN (see Figure 10-9). LANLink-DECnet is compatible with Novell, Banyan, or any NetBIOS-compatible network software. Since it provides a software—not hardware—interface, the LAN topology does not matter. If the NIC is supported by the LAN Operating System, it can be used in the gateway and workstation platforms. LANLink-DECnet connects client workstations on the LAN to any DEC host using the DECnet LAT (Local Area Transport) protocol. Compatible platforms include: VAX/VMS, VAX/Ultrix, DEC terminal servers, or any LAT-compatible terminal servers. Up to 100 simultaneous sessions can be supported. In addition to the gateway software, a 10 KB memory-resident module is required at every workstation.

LANLink-DECnet is installed on the gateway PC after it has been configured on a normal LAN workstation. The gateway is dedicated to this purpose, and should have no extraneous hardware or software installed. The workstation software is stored on the network server, and is licensed by a set number of simultaneous sessions. Client PCs can load all of LANLink-DECnet into high memory, and the memory used can then be released without rebooting the workstation.

The two primary applications of the LANLink-DECnet gateway are emulation of DEC VT320 terminals, and menu-driven file transfers using the Kermit protocol. LANLink-DECnet supplies the industry-standard INT-14 interface and DEC's PC interface, so that LAN-based PCs can run programs based upon these interfaces. This low-cost but highly flexible product is an excellent alternative to individual PC-to-VAX attachments.

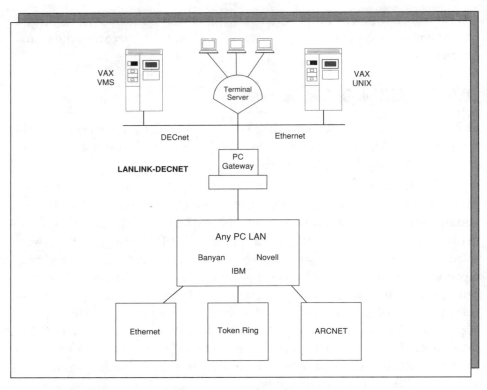

Figure 10-9. LANLink-DECnet gateway *(Courtesy of FEL Computing)*

For applications that require advanced PC and VAX integration features, FEL Computing offers another product line for VAX/VMS connections called Mobius. Mobius provides PCs with a virtual file system, printer support, VT320 terminal emulation, and transparent file transfer. Mobius Plus adds virtual process, control of the PC from the VAX, task-to-task communication, and an advanced programmer's interface. Add-on modules include Mobius ACCESS, an automatic login utility, and Task-Force, a high-level, task-description language for fast applications programming involving PC/network/VAX interactions. Mobius supports ASCII and Ethernet connections, and can be layered on top of LAN-Link-DECnet for networked PCs. Mobius requires software to be loaded on the VAX, as well as on the PC or network server.

In summary, the Mobius and LANLink-DECnet products allow a number of powerful PC network-to-DECnet applications.

10.10 InterConnections Leverage Host Services

Interconnections, Inc. of Bellevue, Washington, markets a variety of software packages to connect PC LANs with DEC AXP or VAX OpenVMS systems. The Leverage Host Services, developed in close cooperation with Novell, is a family of products that link PCs on NetWare LANs and DEC AXP/VAX OpenVMS systems. This software provides seamless integration of these two systems, making it easy for NetWare and OpenVMS users to share information and resources.

Leverage Host Services implements Novell's IPX/SPX protocols on an AXP or VAX system (Figure 10-10). These services implement three key applications: terminal emulation, file sharing, and print sharing. The terminal emulation services (TES) implements the IPX/SPX protocol on the AXP or VAX to allow NetWare users to log into the DEC system and run OpenVMS applications. Support for a number of Windows- and DOS-based terminal emulators is included, such as WRQ's Reflection which can be purchased with Leverage Host Services, EM320, Rumba for the VAX, Kermit, or any terminal emulator that supports that LAT API interface.

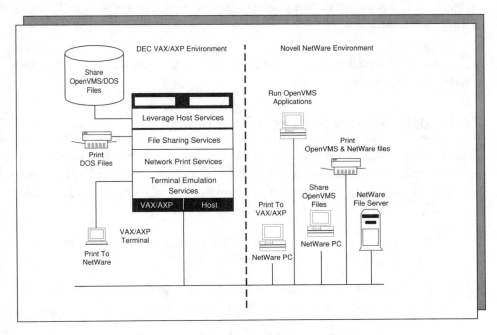

Figure 10-10. Leverage Host Services *(Courtesy of Interconnections, Inc.)*

With the File Sharing Services, NetWare users can store critical data on the DEC system, which provides secure and ample disk storage with reliable file backup. Files are transferred between PCs and AXP/VAXes at LAN speeds. To NetWare users, the AXP or VAX appears as a standard DOS drive. File Sharing Services automatically translates files to their native mode. Files copied to a network drive mapped to a File Sharing server are stored in OpenVMS as RMS files. NetWare users access them as DOS files, while DEC users access them as OpenVMS files. The PC user may also access OpenVMS print queues which direct output to DEC-attached printers. The OpenVMS queues can be accessed and managed by using the familiar NetWare PCONSOLE, NPRINT, and CAPTURE utilities.

Network Print Services operates as a queue service process to redirect output from an OpenVMS print queue to a NetWare print queue. This allows access to a wide variety of printers, such as color, PostScript, or laser, that may not be available in the DEC environment. The user simply issues standard print commands from within their applications, or they can use the familiar OpenVMS DCL print command. The print job is then redirected to the NetWare queue—totally transparent to the user.

In summary, the Leverage Host Services provides a 100% software solution for seamless information, resource sharing, and enhanced productivity between two leading computing platforms.

10.11 Data Interface Systems DI3270 Gateway

Data Interface Systems Corporation of Austin, Texas, is a manufacturer of gateways between IBM mainframes and LANs. Before looking at the DI3270 product in detail, let's consider an evaluation checklist developed by DI for 3270 LAN gateways.

1. Verify compatibility of the 3270 terminal with the mainframe application.

2. Evaluate the various protocol, line speed, and attachment methods, and select the options that fit the user requirements.

3. Verify compatibility with the LAN operating system.

4. Determine the gateway capacities for attached devices (terminals and/or printers).

5. Understand the gateway pricing structure, which may be based upon a fixed rate for the gateway (with unlimited workstations), or a charge for the gateway and an additional charge for each workstation.

6. Consider whether a requirement for multiple gateways (to multiple hosts) exists.

7. Study the hardware/software mix of the gateway. Hardware-intensive systems contain on-board processors and buffers, but are less flexible when upgrading.

8. Evaluate the gateway performance with a test system prior to making a purchase commitment.

9. Determine how the gateway handles disconnections from the mainframe or a cluster controller. The ease of recovery from failures should be a key factor for consideration.

10. Consider the printing capabilities, such as spooling functions and where, physically, the printers will be placed.

11. Evaluate DOS "hot-key" support, considering performance and processing concurrency.

12. Determine the flexibility for remapping the 3270 keyboard to the workstation.

13. What file transfer utility does the gateway support, and is it compatible with the mainframe utility?

14. Define any Application Program Interfaces required, and determine if the gateway supports those APIs.

15. Look for user-related requirements, such as status line layout, configuration/reconfiguration options, and management tools.

16. Consider any requirement for foreign-language support, such as with an emulated printer.

17. Ask previous users for their experience (good and bad) with the gateway. Consider installation, configuration, and vendor support.

18. Consider the vendors' support for future enhancements to SNA/SAA. Do they have a good track record of keeping up with recently announced products?

Given the above evaluation criteria, consider the various DI3270 gateway alternatives shown in Figure 10-11. Mainframe connections are possible using several different emulations: a remote 3174 or 3274 controller connected with a dial-up or leased line (Figure 10-11a); coaxial cable attachment to a 3174/3274 emulating a 3299 multiplexer (Figure 10-11b); or token ring attachment to a 3174 or front-end processor (Figure 10-11c). Protocols available include SNA/SDLC, SNA/Coax DLC, SNA/802.2, remote BSC (Bisynchronous Communications), and coax non-SNA.

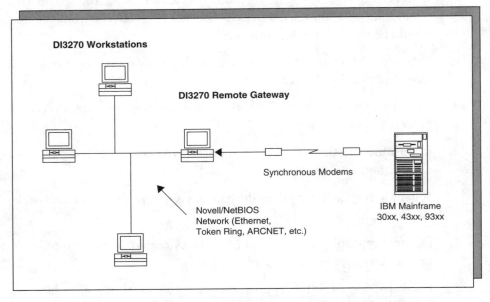

Figure 10-11a. 3270 remote gateway connections *(Courtesy of Data Interface Systems)*

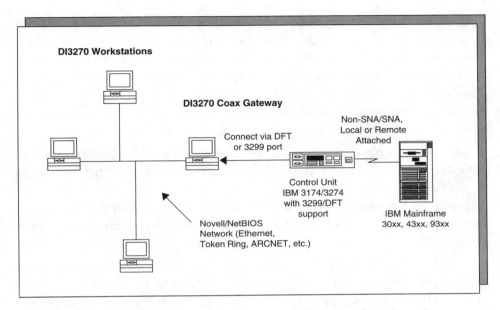

Figure 10-11b. 3270 coax gateway connections *(Courtesy of Data Interface Systems)*

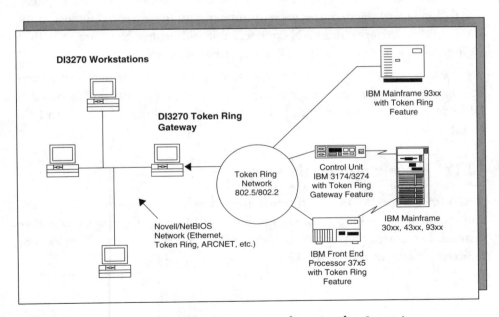

Figure 10-11c. 3270 802.2 LLC connections *(Courtesy of Data Interface Systems)*

Up to 253 sessions are supported via SNA/SDLC, 802.2 LLC (Logical Link Control), and X.25/QLLC (Qualified Logical Link Control); 32 per Bisync and non-SNA coax gateway; and 40 per SNA coax gateway (emulating a 3299 coax multiplexer). Each DOS workstation supports up to four concurrent host sessions plus one DOS session. Each DI3270 workstation operating in the Windows environment supports an unlimited number of sessions (though gateway capacity and memory will impose a limit based upon available resources).

A number of physical connection alternatives are available depending upon the gateway attachment (e.g. controller, remote dial-up, or FEP) that is selected. In all cases, however, additional hardware is required within the gateway workstation. Data Interface supports a number of SNA/SDLC communications boards that work with their software. This choice of the accompanying hardware depends upon the protocol and transmission speed required.

For LAN connections, two alternatives are available. The 802.2 LLC gateway supports direct LAN connection to the mainframe via token ring or Ethernet. In this case, the gateway, mainframe, and workstations are all on the same LAN. For connection to more than one LAN (such as if the mainframe has a token ring connection and the LAN is Ethernet), two adapters are required: one to connect to the mainframe environment, and the other to connect to the LAN. In this scenario, the LAN connection could be any NetWare, NetBIOS (Windows NT or OS/2), or TCP/IP compatible network.

What sets Data Interface Systems' products apart is the depth of understanding that they bring to the marketplace. A user gets a clear impression that DI understands the advantages (and pitfalls) of attaching a LAN to an IBM mainframe.

10.12 Micro-Integration Gateways

Micro-Integration (MI) Corp. of Frostburg, Maryland, specializes in both local and remote client solutions for connecting to IBM AS/400 and S/3X midrange systems. In the area of gateway solutions, MI offers packages for either local or remote connections (Figure 10-12).

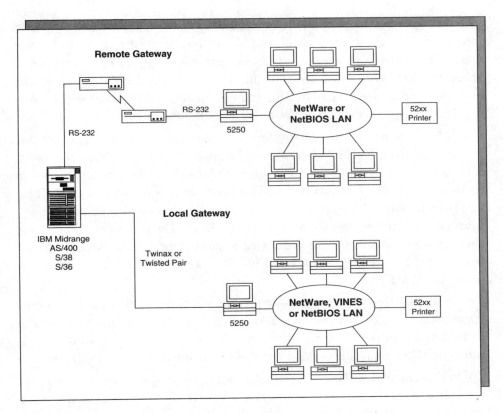

Figure 10-12. 5250 gateway connections *(Courtesy of Micro-Integration Corp.)*

5250 Local Gateway for Windows allows each PC user on the LAN to choose either the Windows or DOS operating system. The kit comes complete with Windows-based and DOS-based workstation software, so the operating system choice is flexible. There can even be a mixture of operating systems on a single LAN, allowing complete freedom to choose either operating system.

The connection can be made using twinax cable or twisted pair via the built-in balun (RJ-11) jack. The product supports the following devices: 5251-11, 5291, 5292-1, 3180-2 (27 x 32 full or scrolled) and 3196 displays; plus the 5219, 5224-1, 5225, 5256, and 3812 printers.

5250 Local Gateway for Windows also offers native support for Novell's NetWare or Banyan VINES protocols, in addition to the NetBIOS interfaces. This increases the speed and flexibility for the users. Up to six gateway cards can be installed in a single server (or four in a MicroChannel machine), providing significant equipment cost savings. Another important feature—IBM PC Support/400 access for each workstation—allows all the users to use AS/400 functions like message, workstation, shared folders, and PC Organizer. The product also comes in a DOS-only version for sites not requiring Windows compatibility.

5250 Remote Gateway provides remote connections via synchronous modems between NetBIOS-compatible LANs and IBM midrange processors. It comes in two versions: the 16-session (ASA card) version, which allows up to 16 simultaneous sessions per card and runs at speeds of up to 19.2 Kbps; and the 64-session (ICA card) version, which allows up to 64 simultaneous sessions per card and runs at speeds of up to 64 Kbps. The gateways eliminate the need for an expensive remote controller by emulating the following IBM controllers: 5251 model 12, 5294, and 5394. PC Support/400 on the workstation is also provided.

To summarize, MI offers full-featured products, for both local and remote environments, that allow PCs on a LAN to communicate through a gateway to an IBM midrange host. The products' abilities to easily integrate networking software with IBM applications make for a powerful internetworking solution.

In this chapter, we have studied gateways that provide Application Layer connectivity solutions. In most cases, third-party solutions provide the most creative and user-friendly solutions since they have been developed in direct response to marketplace needs. A listing of vendors supplying internetworking solutions is given in Appendix F. Another excellent source of gateway solutions is the Annual Buyer's Guides published by the major networking periodicals (references [10-14] and [10-15]).

10.13 References

[10-1]   Yori, Robert S. "Multivendor LANs," *LAN Computing* (October 1990): 33–37.

[10-2]   Marsh, Bob. "Token-Ring and Unix: The Odd Couple of the '90s." *Network Computing* (January 1993): 124–126.

[10-3]   Minoli, Dan. "The Distributed SNA Question—APPN or APPI?" *Network Computing* (February 1993): 126–132.

[10-4]   Hall, Eric. "Interoperability Assessment—Attachmate's Extra!" *Network Computing* (May 1993): 119–123.

[10-5]   Shulken, Susan and Tim Huntley. "Linking LANs and SNA Networks with APPC and APPN." *STACKS: The Network Journal* (December 1993): 41–46.

[10-6]   Routt, Thomas J. "APPN and TCP/IP: Plotting a Backbone Strategy." *Data Communications* (March 1994): 107–114.

[10-7]   Nemzow, Martin. "Plan for a Mainframe Link." *STACKS: The Network Journal* (April 1994): 37–45.

[10-8]   Tolly, Kevin, and David Newman. "Testing Unix-to-SNA Gateways." *Data Communications* (May 1994): 93–104.

[10-9]   Higgins, Kelly Jackson. "When Networking Worlds Collide." *Open Systems Today* (October 3, 1994): 52–57.

[10-10] Carr, Eric. "Global E-Mail Communications Through SMTP." *Network Computing* (October 15, 1994): 36–42.

[10-11] Sliter, Tom. "From Mainframe to Mainstream: SNA Integration." *STACKS: The Network Journal* (January 1995): 33–42.

[10-12] Fielder, David. "A Simple Desktop Links Unix and PC Users." *Open Systems Today* (January 9, 1995): 38.

[10-13] Haber, Lynn. "Client-Server Links Empower PC Users." *Open Systems Today* (January 9, 1995): HP1–HP6.

[10-14] "Annual Buyer's Guide." *LAN Magazine*, November 1994.

[10-15] "1995 Internetworking Product Guide." *Data Communications*, October 21, 1994.

11 Implementing the Internetwork

No reference on internetworking is complete without a discussion of internetwork implementation and management. An attempt has been made to address general "internetwork" requirements (whatever that means), so not all steps may be applicable to your case. If some steps don't apply, skip them and forge ahead. In order to calm the sleepless nights of the implementors, here is a 40-step plan for guidance. Refer to the flowchart (Figures 11-1a to 11-1h) as you study.

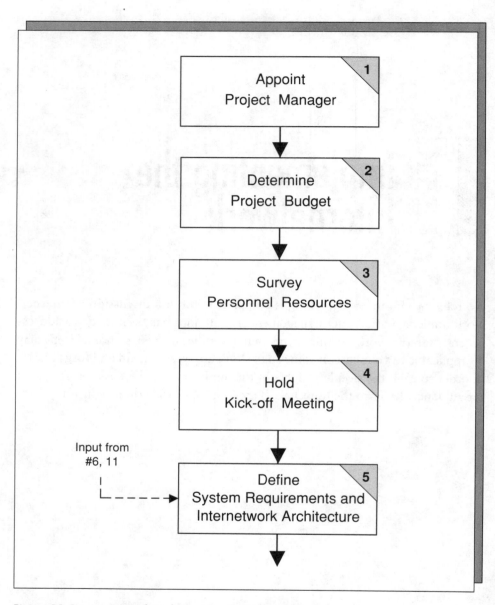

Figure 11-1a. Internetwork implementation flowchart

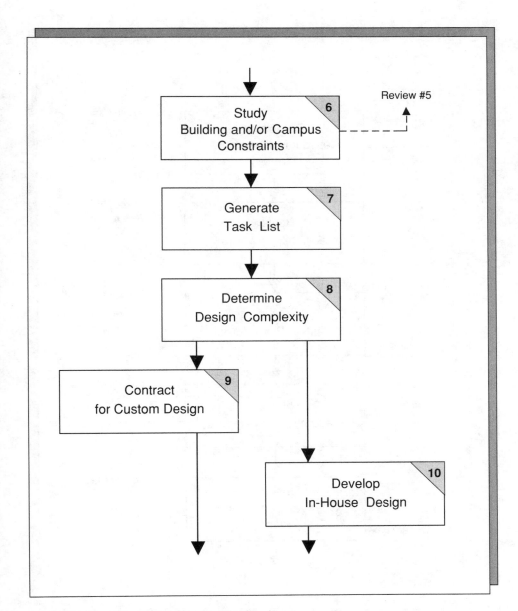

Figure 11-1b. Internetwork implementation flowchart

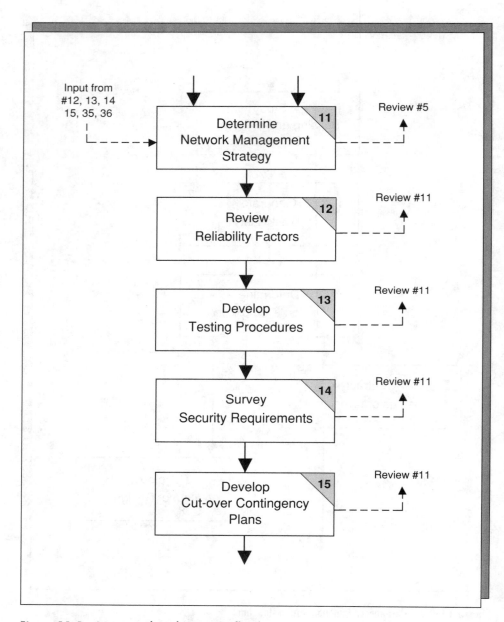

Figure 11-1c. Internetwork implementation flowchart

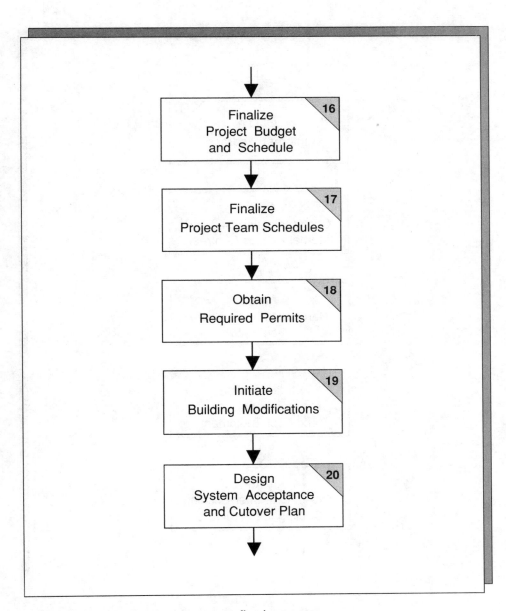

Figure 11-1d. Internetwork implementation flowchart

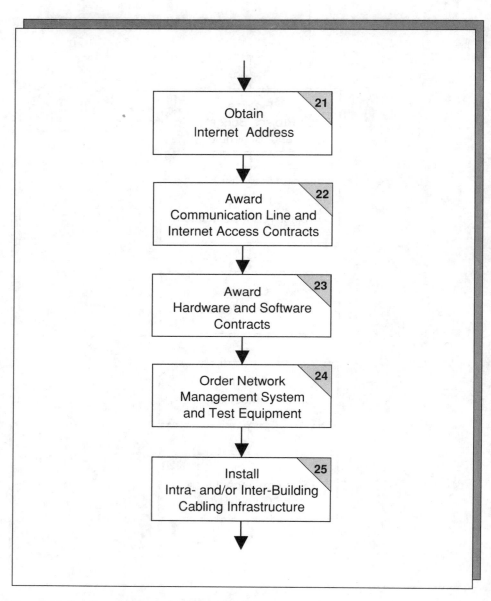

Figure 11-1e. Internetwork implementation flowchart

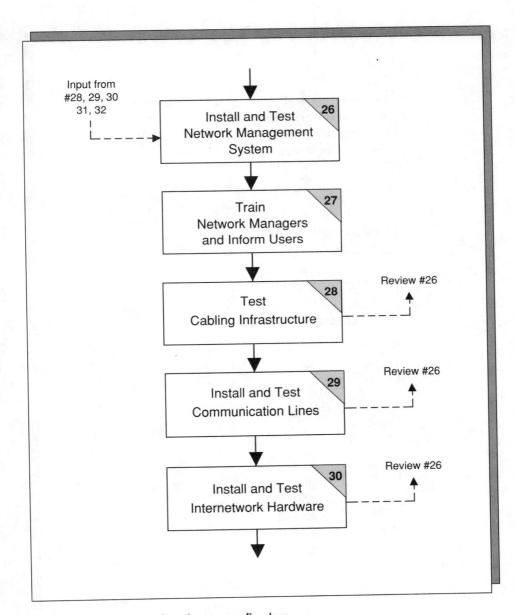

Figure 11-1f. Internetwork implementation flowchart

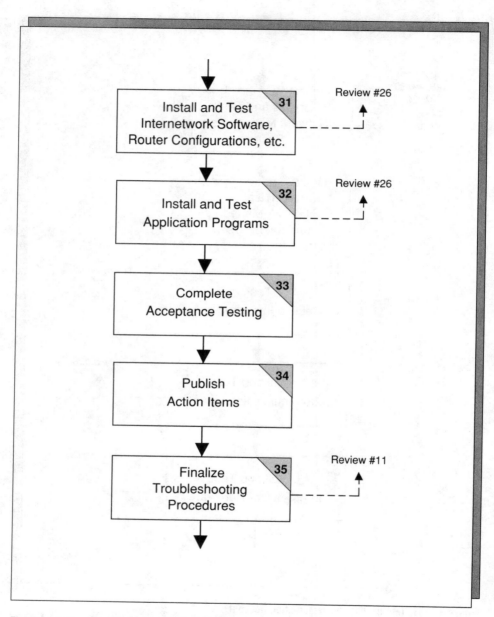

Figure 11-1g. Internetwork implementation flowchart

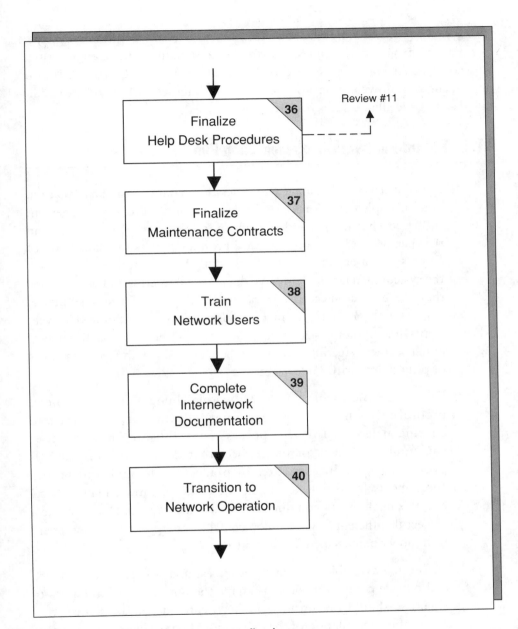

Figure 11-1h. Internetwork implementation flowchart

Note that while this flowchart is illustrated as a linear progression of steps, in reality no project goes from Step A to Step Z without some re-engineering. Some of these feedback paths are also illustrated on Figures 11-1a to 11-1h. An implementation flowchart, customized for your internetwork, may have additional steps or feedback paths required.

11.1 The Internetwork Implementation Plan

1. Appoint a system manager, internetwork contacts in each location, and an implementation committee, as required. Project-management theory teaches us that unless someone's feet are held to the fire and that person made responsible for a project's success, the likelihood of success is dramatically reduced. Beyond the technical qualifications, the system manager should have the personal interest and desire to see that the project succeeds. Don't forget that when responsibility is conveyed, the authority to make it happen must be authorized as well. Depending upon the size of the project, it may be advisable to appoint a management steering committee that can assist with resolving issues of project authority, budgets, etc.

2. Determine the available (or allowable) budget for the project, including such costs as personnel, equipment, cabling, and contingencies. Part of this process is establishing how the user community will pay for the services that the network provides. If procedures are not already in place to bill back individual departments for their share of the network operation, maintenance, etc., this might be a good time to consider such a plan. Don't initiate a project if sufficient funds are not available, and if a clear commitment from upper management is not evident.

3. Survey the available personnel resources, and decide if you need to add outside contractors or consultants to your team. Several areas of expertise should be considered. Electrical codes and practices that might affect installation of the cable should be reviewed by an expert. Do not make a mistake (such as installing the wrong type of twisted pair cable) that could affect the strategic direction of your company

for years to come. Other areas to consider include telecommunications facility capacity planning and other growth projections for your industry type. The design may be more than you want to tackle technically; engineering assistance is available for cabling infrastructure design, traffic studies, protocol optimization, and other specialties. Also determine what type of a design review process will be used for this project, to assure a cohesive and integrated approach to all the various elements.

4. Hold a project kick-off meeting, assign responsibilities, and develop a project schedule. Some cleverness and innovation can go a long way here—remember that all team members need a "buy-in" since their contribution to this project may be only one of their responsibilities. Do what you can to get all members focused and pulling in the same direction. Initiate an action-item database that describes open issues, the responsible parties, due dates, etc. Circulate this database information on a periodic basis to all team members, the steering committee, and other relevant managers.

5. Survey key personnel for their input about the system's requirements and internetwork architecture. It is impossible to define all aspects of the design without a written functional requirements document. The plan will also be used by vendors bidding on the project in order to define how their products fit into the complete internetwork. Circulate the functional-requirements document to upper management for approval, and to all project team members for review. Consider additional input from steps 6 and 11.

6. Consult the building owner, other tenants, and municipal authorities for any constraints that might affect the system's installation. Surprises such as fire walls that went unnoticed or unknown conduit runs are not any fun to deal with. Take a walking tour of the building facility and/or campus, and be on the lookout for anything that might need special attention. Provide feedback to step 5.

7. Use the requirements document and building survey to generate a complete list of required tasks. (Project Managers refer to this as a work-breakdown structure.) If the project is large enough to so

warrant, use a PC-based project management tool to generate a schedule and identify the critical path. Distribute the schedule to all team members.

8. Determine the complexity of the internetwork design, as influenced by factors such as the number of locations to connect, the number of workstations and servers per location, LAN and routing protocols to be supported, broadband technologies to explore, etc. Proceed with Steps 9 or 10 as appropriate, and expect that several iterations of these three steps (8, 9, and 10) may be required.

9. Solicit bids for the hardware, software, communication facilities, and cabling infrastructure designs. In many cases, vendors will be willing (or eager) to provide a design without charge. Make sure that an impartial third party is available to lend a measure of objectivity to vendor-generated proposals.

10. Design the internetwork yourself, and draw a complete schematic of the system. Use the guidelines in Section 2.1 for the LAN to LAN portions, and the guidelines in Section 6.1 for the LAN to WAN portions. Beware of single-vendor or other sole-source solutions. Resist the urge to be a field trial or beta test site for a new product or system unless a fallback plan (i.e. "plan B") is clearly feasible.

11. A clear network management strategy should be determined in conjunction with the design of the internetwork architecture. This strategy should address the network management protocol to be used, such as the Simple Network Management Protocol (SNMP); the network management platform to be implemented, such as Hewlett-Packard's OpenView, IBM's NetView, or SunConnect's SunNet Manager; and any device-specific management applications required, such as those to support wiring hubs or routers. Anticipate that input from steps 12, 13, 14, 15, 35, and 36 may be forthcoming, and then provide feedback to the system requirements (step 5).

12. Make a review of the internetwork reliability factors. Also consider the effects and costs that downtime would have on the internetwork. For critical components and circuits, consider stocking spare parts

on-site yourself, or adding additional hot-standby or dial-backup lines. Provide feedback to step 11.

13. Develop system testing procedures for all hardware and software components, as well as the transmission facilities. Identify all vendor-specific areas of responsibility—such as testing and maintenance—defined in the contracts and warranties, and develop a list of all vendor support contacts. Make sure that components are physically located so that test equipment can be used in close proximity. Assure that adequate power and a telephone line are available close to critical components such as servers and routers, and that a fax machine is readily accessible. It is also helpful to compile a list of required troubleshooting tools. Consider hand tools, meters, interface testers, cable testers, and protocol analyzers. See reference [11-1], Chapter 3, for guidance in making your choices. Provide feedback to step 11.

14. Consider the security of the internetwork. Where remote (dial-in) access is involved, look at barrier codes, passwords, and other methods of authenticating network access. Putting yourself in the shoes of a potential hacker, determine the degree of difficulty involved in infiltrating the internetwork, and build appropriate safeguards into the design. Provide feedback to step 11.

15. Develop a contingency plan if the new system is replacing an existing system. Determine if a flash cutover or phased cutover is more appropriate, based upon the "mission critical" nature of the project. Require that any installation vendors develop methods and procedures that support the sequencing required for a successful cutover. Provide feedback to step 11.

16. Finalize the project budget and schedule, allowing for contingencies. Obtain management approval before proceeding.

17. Now that the project is a go, develop a schedule for periodic project team meetings, and begin publishing and distributing schedules and meeting minutes to all affected organizations.

18. Obtain building permits, as required, for all installation locations.

19. Initiate major building additions, such as computer room modifications, required to accommodate the new system. Make a survey of all equipment and wiring closets to ensure that adequate power is readily available.

20. Develop system-acceptance and cutover plans that will thoroughly test all cabling, communication facilities, hardware and software modules. This plan may take some time to develop, and will require a thorough understanding of the internetwork hardware and software operation and configuration, plus the various phases in which the internetwork will be installed. Good source information for the acceptance plan portion of this task is often found in the installation guides for the components that are part of the entire system. Another valuable technique is to review the functional requirements document, and to outline the steps required to verify the individual requirements. For example: "connect to a remote IBM host via a Proteon router. Establish a TELNET session emulating a DEC VT220 terminal." Ask for vendor and user input to these plans, to assure that all internetwork functions are covered.

21. Obtain an internet address or addresses from the central authority in your country, such as the Internet Assigned Numbers Authority (IANA) in the United States (see reference [7-6]). Distribute these addresses to all hardware and software vendors, as well as to the project team.

22. Award contracts for communication facilities from LEC, IXC, or PDN vendors. If Internet access is being added for the first time, survey the available vendors, and begin the process to find one that meets your needs. Coordinate cutover dates for these transmission facilities to correspond with hardware installation for end-to-end testing.

23. Award contracts for hardware and software components. Obtain delivery dates from vendors to include in the project schedule. Obtain commitments from vendors for training personnel on the operation of the various components.

24. Award contracts for the network management system and its components, and order test equipment from the list developed in item 13.

25. Begin installation of new wiring or cabling systems needed to support the internetwork, both for intra-building and inter-building applications. Allow for plenty of growth—a factor of two to three times the initial requirement is often used for sizing twisted pair cables to avoid premature obsolescence.

26. Install and test the network management system, so that the various internetwork components can be tested as they are brought on-line. Anticipate feedback from steps 28, 29, 30, 31, and 32 as the various internetwork components and systems are brought on-line and re-tested with the network management system.

27. Schedule training classes on the installation and maintenance of all new hardware, software, and network management systems. For most projects, there is an interval between the time the equipment is ordered and the time when it is to be installed. Take advantage of this interim period, educating yourself on the intricacies of the challenges ahead. Also consider brown-bag lunch meetings to keep personnel who may be affected (but not directly involved in the project) informed of the progress. Since installation invariably creates workplace disruption, help those who will be affected to understand how the internetwork will improve their voice, data, and/or image communication.

28. Thoroughly test the newly-installed cable plant prior to installing any other components. Provide feedback to step 26.

29. Install and test all communication lines. Do not take noise or error rate measurements during evenings or weekends, as potential problem sources may not be operating during those hours. Provide feedback to step 26.

30. Install hardware systems, and test them as stand-alone devices. Also install redundant systems such as powerful-transfer or uninterruptible power supplies (UPSs) that are supporting the internetwork. Provide feedback to step 26.

31. Install internetwork software modules, such as operating systems, TCP/IP drivers, router software, etc., paying very close attention to details such as Internet addresses, routing protocol configurations, and other parameters. Where possible, install and test the various modules one at a time, to minimize any interaction between subsystems. Provide feedback to step 26.

32. Install all application programs such as SMTP or FTP modules, and test them as a stand-alone device on that hardware platform. Provide feedback to step 26.

33. Bring out the system-acceptance plan, and start the testing process. Be sure to allow plenty of time for this step, as the integration of components from multiple vendors into a single internetwork may identify problems that were not anticipated. Should problems arise, schedule a round-table session with all vendors, and avoid placing blame or finger-pointing. Most vendors are eager to help resolve difficult problems when a cooperative—not confrontational—atmosphere is presented.

34. Develop a list of unresolved issues, define the responsible parties and due dates, and publish the list as high-priority action items in the project team meeting minutes. This list should also be added to the database discussed in item 4.

35. Finalize the troubleshooting procedures for all components of the internetwork. A model for fault-isolation flowcharts is given in Chapter 10 of reference [11-1], and many vendors' technical documents also provide valuable information. The time to learn how to use your new test equipment is now, when life is (relatively) calm. Don't wait until a failure forces you into troubleshooting mode—prepare now. Provide feedback to step 11.

36. Finalize the problem-reporting procedure for the internetwork. This may consist of a centralized help desk, or contacts at each geographic location. Make sure that the help desk personnel know who they can call for additional assistance. Consider establishing a user's group for resolution of procedural or administrative complaints. Integrate these procedures into your overall network management architecture. Provide feedback to step 11.

37. Finalize all maintenance contracts, if used, and develop clear procedures for interaction between the help desk and maintenance providers.

38. Train all users of the internetwork, based upon their need for information. Consider separate tutorials for clerical, professional, and executive staffs. Provide notes or quick reference guides to minimize calls to the help desk.

39. Complete all internetwork documentation, including system schematic, cable plant, equipment locations, internet addresses, and any user-specific issues such as account codes or passwords. Chapter 2 of reference [11-1] provides some guidance.

40. Transition the project from the implementation phase to the operation phase. Review the budget and allocate any excess funds for a project team party. Many people have contributed to the success of this project—make sure that they all are properly recognized.

11.2 A Final Word

As you would undoubtedly agree, a number of issues concerning internetwork design and implementation are never learned from a text. Painful as it sometimes is, experience is often the best teacher. While experiencing the pain, however, a good sense of humor is essential. In closing, I present RFC 968 (reference [11-2]), written by Vincent Cerf, one of the most experienced "internetworkers." May his words be remembered during those frustrating moments.

"'Twas the Night Before Start-up"

'Twas the night before start-up and all through the net,
*   not a packet was moving; no bit nor octet.*
The engineers rattled their cards in despair,
*   hoping a bad chip would blow with a flare.*
The salesmen were nestled all snug in their beds,
*   while visions of data nets danced in their heads.*
And I with my datascope tracings and dumps
*   prepared for some pretty bad bruises and lumps.*

When out in the hall there arose such a clatter,
  I sprang from my desk to see what was the matter.
There stood at the threshold with PC in tow,
  An ARPANET hacker, all ready to go.
I could see from the creases that covered his brow,
  he'd conquer the crisis confronting him now.
More rapid than eagles, he checked each alarm
  and scrutinized each for its potential harm.

On LAPB, on OSI, X.25! TCP, SNA, V.35!

His eyes were afire with the strength of his gaze;
  no bug could hide long; not for hours or days.
A wink of his eye and twitch of his head,
  soon gave me to know I had little to dread.
He spoke not a word, but went straight to his work,
  fixing a net that had gone plumb berserk;
And laying a finger on one suspect line,
  he entered a patch and the net came up fine!
The packet flowed neatly and protocols matched;
  he hosts interfaced and shift-registers latched.
He tested the system from Gateway to PAD;
  not one bit was dropped; no checksum was bad.
At last he was finished and wearily sighed
  and turned to explain why the system had died.
I twisted my fingers and counted to ten;
  an off-by-one index had done it again...

11.3 References

[11-1] Miller, Mark A. *LAN Troubleshooting Handbook*, 2nd edition. New York, NY: M&T Books, Inc., 1993.

[11-2] Cerf, Vincent. *'Twas the Night Before Startup.* RFC 968, December 1985.

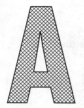# Addresses of Standards Organizations

ATIS Publications
Alliance for Telecommunications
    Industry Solutions
1200 G St. N.W., Suite 500
Washington, DC 20005
(202) 628-6380

AT&T Publications
AT&T Technologies Commercial Sales
P.O. Box 19901
Indianapolis, IN 46219
(317) 322-6557 or (800) 432-6600

BELLCORE Standards
Bell Communications Research
Information Management Services
8 Corporate Pl., Suite 3A-184
Piscataway, NJ 08854-4196
(908) 699-5800 or
    (800) 521-2673

CSA Standards
Canadian Standards Association
178 Rexdale Boulevard
Rexdale, ON M9W 1R3 Canada
(416) 747-4363

ECMA Standards
European Computer Manufacturers
    Association
114, Rue de rhone CH-1204
Geneva, Switzerland
41 22 735-3634

EIA Standards
Electronic Industries Association
2500 Wilsom Blvd.
Arlington, VA 22201
(202) 457-4900

IEEE Standards
Institute of Electrical and Electronics
    Engineers
445 Hoes Lane
P.O. Box 1331
Piscataway, NJ 08855-1331
(908) 981-1393 or
    (800) 678-4333

ISO and ANSI Standards
American National Standards
    Institute
11 W. 42nd St., 13th Floor
New York, NY 10036
(212) 642-4900

ISO Standards
International Organization for
    Standardization
1, Rue de Varembe
CH-1211
Geneva 20, Switzerland
41 22 749-0111
Fax: 41 22 730-5853

**ITU-T (CCITT) Recommendations
    and Federal Information
    Processing Standards (FIPS)**
U.S. Department of Commerce
National Technical Information
    Service
5285 Port Royal Rd.
Springfield, VA 22161
(703) 487-4650

Military Standards Sales
Naval Publications and Forms Center
Commanding Officer
NPFC 43
5801 Tabor Ave.
Philadelphia, PA 19120
(215) 697-3321

**National Institute of Standards and
    Technology**
Technology Building 225, Room B-64
Gaithersburg, MD 20899
(301) 975-2816

 # Broadband Technology Forums

ATM Forum Worldwide Headquarters
303 Vintage Park Dr.
Foster City, CA 94404
(415) 578-6860
Fax: (415) 525-0182
Email: info@atmforum.com
Faxback: (415) 688-4318
WWW: http://www.atmforum.com

ATM Forum European Office
10, Rue Thierry Le Luron
92593 Levallois-Perret Cedex France
33 1 46 39 56 56
Fax: 33 1 46 39 56 99

Frame Relay Forum North American Office
303 Vintage Park Dr.
Foster City, CA 94404-1138
(415) 578-6980
Fax: (415) 525-0182
Email: frf@interop.com
Faxback: (415) 688-4317
FTP: ftp://frame-relay.indiana.edu
directory /pub/frame-relay
WWW: http://frame-relay.indiana.edu

Frame Relay Forum Pacific Office
c/o Interlink Communications
14 Aquatic Dr., Unit #4
Frenchs Forest, NSW 2086 Australia
61 2 975 2577
Fax: 61 2 452 5397

Frame Relay Forum European Office
c/o OST, BP 158
Z1 Sud Est rue du bas Village
35510 Cesson Sevigne cedex, France
33 99 51 76 55
Fax: 33 99 41 71 75

Frame Relay Forum Japanese Office
c/o FPT
Nisso No. 22 Bldg., 5th Floor
1-11-10, Azabudai
Minato-ku Tokyo, 106 Japan
81 3 3583 5811
Fax: 81 3 3583 5813

SMDS Interest Group
303 Vintage Park Dr.
Foster City, CA 94404
(415) 578-6979
Fax: (415) 525-0182
Email: sig@interop.com
Faxback: (415) 688-4314
FTP: ftp://ftp.acc.com
directory /pub/smds

C Obtaining Internet Information

Much of the administration functions for the Internet are handled by the Inter-NIC. Directory and Database Services are handled by AT&T, while registration services are handled by Network Solutions, Inc. Addresses for these organizations are as follows:

Directory and Database Services:

AT&T
(800) 862-0677 or (908) 668-6587
Fax: (908) 668-3763
Email: admin@ds.internic.net

Registration Services:

Network Solutions, Inc.
Attn.: InterNIC Registration Services
505 Huntmar Park Dr.
Herndon, VA 22070
(703) 742-4777
Email: admin@rs.internic.net

Obtaining RFCs

RFCs may be obtained online via the Internet. To obtain an RFC online, use FTP to log in to the desired host (see below), with name = **anonymous** and password = **guest**. The RFCs are located in a designated subdirectory (see below), filename **rfcnnnn.txt** or **rfcnnnn.ps**. The nnnn represents the RFC number, e.g. RFC1175. Both ASCII (**txt** suffix) and PostScript (**ps** suffix) files are available. FYI documents may be obtained in a similar manner. The filenames are **fyinn.txt** or **fyinn.ps**.

The primary repositories of RFCs include:

- **DS.INTERNIC.NET** (directory **/ftp/rfc**, filename **rfcnnnn.txt** or **rfcnnnn.ps**)

- **NIS.NSF.NET** (directory **internet/documents/rfc**, filename **rfcnnnn.txt**)

- **NISC.SRI.COM** (directory **rfc**, filename **RFCnnnn.TXT.v** where "v" is the version number of the RFC)

- **VENERA.ISI.EDU** (directory **in-notes**, filename **rfcnnnn.txt**)

Note that some systems require leading zeros in the RFC number. In other words, if rfc868.txt does not work, try rfc0868.txt.

A second method of obtaining RFCs is to use electronic mail. The following is an excerpt from the HELP file, obtained via the Internet using this method.

This automated mail service is provided by the DDN Network Information Center. It allows access to NIC documents and information via ordinary electronic mail. This is especially useful for people who do not have access to the NIC via a direct Internet link, such as BITNET, CSNET and UUCP sites.

To use the mail service, send a mail message to **SERVICE@NIC.DDN.MIL**. In the SUBJECT field, request the type of service you wish followed by any needed arguments. The message body is normally ignored; however, if the SUBJECT field is empty, the first line of the message body will be used as the request. Large files will be broken into smaller separate messages. However, a few files are too large to be sent through the mail system. Requests are processed automatically once a day.

The following services are currently available:

HELP	This message; a list of current services.
HOST xxx	Returns information about host xxx.
WHOIS xxx	Used to get more details about a host.
IEN nnn	nnn is the IEN number or the word INDEX.
IETF xxx	xxx is a file name
INDEX	Returns the master list of available index files.
INTERNET-DRAFTS xxx	xxx is a file name
NETINFO xxx	xxx is a file name or the word INDEX.
RFC nnn	nnn is the RFC number or the word INDEX.
RFC nnn.PS	to retrieve an available Postscript RFC. Check RFC INDEX for form of RFC.
FYI nnn	nnn is the FYI number or the word INDEX.
FYI nnn.PS	to retrieve postscript versions of FYI files.
SEND xxx	xxx is a fully specified file name.
WHOIS xxx	Returns information about xxx from the WHOIS service. Use "WHOIS HELP" for information on how to use WHOIS.

Example SUBJECT lines:

HELP

RFC 822

RFC INDEX

RFC 1119.PS

FYI 1

IETF 1IETF-DESCRIPTION.TXT

INTERNET-DRAFTS 1ID-ABSTRACTS.TXT

NETINFO DOMAIN-TEMPLATE.TXT

SEND RFC: RFC-BY-AUTHOR.TXT

SEND IETF/1WG-SUMMARY.TXT

SEND INTERNET-DRAFTS/DRAFT-IETF-NETDATA-NETDATA-0.TXT

HOST DIIS

WHOIS KOSTERS, MARK

Send comments or suggestions to **SUGGESTIONS@NIC.DDN.MIL**. Send questions and bug reports to **BUG-SERVICE@NIC.DDN.MIL**.

Note that a space is required between the document type and the document number. In other words, RFC 1187 will work, RFC1187 will not.

The RFC-Info Service

A new service to assist users with Internet information was announced in the March 1992 issue of *ConneXions, the Interoperability Report*. Following is the text detailing the new service, which was obtained by using "Help:Help", described below.

RFC-Info is an email based service to help in locating and retrieval of RFCs and FYIs. Users can ask for "lists" of all RFCs and FYIs having certain attributes ("filters") such as their ID, keywords, title, author, issuing organization, and date. Once an RFC is uniquely identified (e.g., by its RFC number) it may also be retrieved.

To use the service send email to **RFC-INFO@ISI.EDU** with your requests in the body of the message. Feel free to put anything in the SUBJECT, the system ignores it. (All is case independent, obviously.)

To get started you may send a message to **RFC-INFO@ISI.EDU** with requests such as in the following examples (without the explanation between []):

Help: Help   [to get this information]

List: FYI   [list the FYI notes]

List: RFC keywords: window	[list RFCs with window as keyword or in title]
List: FYI Keywords: window	[list FYIs about windows]
List: * Keywords: window	[list both RFCs and FYIs about windows]
List: RFC title: ARPA*NET	[list RFCs about ARPANET, ARPA NETWORK, etc.]

List: RFC
   Organization: MITRE
   Dated-after: Jul-01-1991
   Dated-before: Aug-31-1991
	[list RFCs issued by MITRE, dated 7+8/1991]

List: RFC Obsoletes: RFC0010	[list RFCs obsoleting a given RFC]
List: RFC Author: Bracken*	[list RFCs by authors starting with "Bracken"] [* is a wild card that matches everything]

List: RFC
   Authors: J. Postel
   Authors: R. Gillman
	[list RFCs by both Postel and Gillman]
	 [note, the "filters" are ANDed]

List: RFC Authors: Crocker	[list RFCs by any Crocker]
List: RFC Authors: S.D. Crocker	[list only RFCs by S.D. Crocker]
List: RFC Authors: D. Crocker	[list only RFCs by D. Crocker]
Retrieve: RFC Doc-ID: RFC0822	[retrieve RFC-822] [note, always 4 digits in RFC#]
Help: Manual	[to retrieve the long user manual, 30+ pages]
Help: List	[how to use the LIST request]

Help: Retrieve	[how to use the RETRIEVE request]
Help: Topics	[list topics for which help is available]
Help: Dates	["Dates" is such a topic]
List: keywords	[list the keywords in use]
List: organizations	[list the organizations known to the system]

Please try using this service. Report problems to **RFC-MANAGER@ISI.EDU**

A useful way to test this service is to retrieve the file "Where and how to get new RFCs". Place the following in the message body:

Help: ways_to_get_rfcs

Internet Mailing Lists

A number of mailing lists are maintained on the Internet for the purposes of solic-iting information and discussions on specific subjects. In addition, a number of the Internet Engineering Task Force (IETF) working groups maintain a list for the exchange of information that is specific to that group.

For example, the IETF maintains two lists: the IETF General Discussion list and the IETF Announcement list. To join the IETF Announcement list, send a request to: <ietf-announce-request@cnri.reston.va.us>. To join the IETF General Discussion, send a request to: <ietf-request@cnri.reston.va.us>.

A number of other mailing lists are available. To join a mailing list, send a message to the associated request list: <listname>-request@<listhost> (see the example for the IETF lists given above). In the table below are some mailing lists and their email addresses:

Mailing List Subject	Email Address
ATM General Discussion	atm@hpl.hp.com
Frame Relay General Discussion	frftc@acc.com
Remote Monitoring Working Group	rmonmib@jarthur.claremont.edu
SMDS General Discussion	smdstc@nsco.network.com
SNMP General Discussion	snmp@psi.com

D Obtaining ITU Documents

Documents published by the International Telecommunications Union are currently available online. The following information was excerpted from the ITU-4313 and ITU-5971 documents, which can be retrieved using the instructions given below.

From ITUDOC.ITUDOC@itu.ch Tue Mar 21 09:19:04 1995
Date: Tue, 21 Mar 1995 12:03:31 +0100 (CET)
From: ITU Document Mail Server +41 22 730 5554
<ITUDOC.ITUDOC@itu.ch>
To: "Boomer Miller" <boomer@diginet.com>
Subject: re: GET ITU-4313 (ITUDOC Concise Access Guide (Gopher,
Telnet, X.25, Dial-up, Email))

********* WELCOME TO ITU'S DOCUMENT MAIL SERVER *********
This service is provided by the International Telecommunication
Union (ITU) in Geneva, Switzerland and is part of its Telecom
Information Exchange Services (TIES) project.

For help with this or other TIES interfaces (e.g., Gopher), send
the line HELP in the message body to this address (itudoc@itu.ch).

Include the line GET ITU-5971 for a list of available Road Map & Index files.

NEWS FLASH: For concise info on available interfaces, send the command GET ITU-4313

REPLY TO => GET ITU-4313

Replied on March 21, 1995 at 1:01 PM local time, Geneva.

------- Attributes of Attachment -------
UPI: ITU-4313
English Title: ITUDOC Concise Access Guide (Gopher, Telnet, X.25, Dial-up, Email)
Format: ASCII
Size: 3269 bytes
Last Modified Date: 1993-10-21 10:08:17 GMT
Language (E=English, F=French, S=Spanish): E
ITU Document Store Group(s):
/about/itudoc (About ITUDOC)

* * * * * * * * * * * * * * * * * * *END COVER MESSAGE* *
ACCESS METHODS TO ITUDOC VIA GOPHER, TELNET, X.25, DIAL-UP AND EMAIL
International Telecommunication Union
Information Services Department
Place des Nations
1211 Geneva 20
Switzerland

TEL: +41 22 730 5554
FAX: +41 22 730 5337
RFC822: helpdesk@itu.ch
X.400: S=helpdesk;A=arcom;P=itu;C=ch
INTERACTIVE ACCESS TO ITUDOC
Interactive access to ITUDOC is available as one of ITU's 'Open

Services' available in TIES (Telecom Information Exchange Services). Connectivity to TIES is possible via:

1. GOPHER CLIENT

   Pointer to the ITU Gopher Server is

   Name=International Telecommunication Union (ITU)
   Host=info.itu.ch
   Port=70

2. TELNET

   Telnet: ties.itu.ch or info.itu.ch (login name 'gopher')

3. X.25

   Call the X.25 DTE address, on TELEPAC, the Swiss PSPDN

   #228468111112

   where # is local prefix for international routing, login name 'gopher'

4. DIAL-UP

   +41 22 733 7575 (Swiss telephone number, login name 'gopher')

Supported modem protocols include ITU-T (CCITT) V.21, V.22, V.22bis, V.32, V.42, V.42bis Recommendations, Bell212A and MNP 2, 3, 4, 5. Basic settings should be no parity, 8 data bits (necessary for on-line reading of multilingual material), speed 300 to 9,600 bps.

For downloading documents/files, several file transfer methods are supported (e.g., Kermit, XModem, Text, email).

EMAIL ACCESS TO ITUDOC
For help on the ITUDOC electronic mail interface, send a message
with the line HELP in it to:

itudoc@itu.ch

The mail server will return to you a help document explaining all
valid commands.

Road Map and Index files describe the hierarchy of ITUDOC groups
and list available documents. Road Map and Index files are updated
every two weeks. The files listed below can be retrieved by sending
email to:

itudoc@itu.ch

with

GET <UPI>

in the message body.

UPIs (Unique Permanent Identifier) for key ITUDOC index files are
listed below:
UPI Title

UPI	Title
ITU-1800	Road Map and Index for the About ITUDOC Group
ITU-1700	Road Map and Index for the ITU General Secretariat Group
ITU-1300	Road Map and Index for the ITU Development Sector Group
ITU-1200	Road Map and Index for the ITU Radiocommunication Sector Group
ITU-1100	Road Map and Index for the ITU Telecommunication Standardization Sector Group
ITU-1500	Road Map and Index for the Special Interest Groups Group
ITU-1400	Road Map and Index for the Telecom Information Exchange Services - TIES Group

ITU-1600   Road Map and Index for the complete ITU Document Store
            (Please Note: very large)
ITU-1900   Road Map and Index for the United Nations UN/EDIFACT
            Standards Database (EDICORE) Group

For example:

To: itudoc@itu.ch
FROM: (NAME)
SUBJECT: (IGNORED)

GET ITU-1100
----

will retrieve the Road Map and Index for the ITU Telecommunication
Standardization Group.

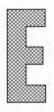 # Selected Carriers Providing Private Line, Public Data Network, and Broadband Services

Ameritech Corp.
2000 W. Ameritech Center Dr.
Hoffman Estates, IL 60196
(708) 248-2000

AT&T
32 Ave. of the Americas
New York, NY 10013
(212) 387-5400

Bell Atlantic Corp.
540 Broad St.
Newark, NJ 07102
(201) 649-9900

Bellsouth Corp.
1155 Peachtree St. N.E.
Atlanta, GA 30309
(404) 249-2000

Cable & Wireless Inc.
1919 Gallows Rd.
Vienna, VA 22182
(703) 790-5300

CERFnet
P.O. Box 85608
San Diego, CA 92121
(800) 876-2373

Compuserve Inc.
5000 Arlington Center Blvd.
Columbus, OH 43220
(614) 457-8600

EMI Communications Corp.
5015 Campuswood Dr.
E. Syracuse, NY 13057
(315) 433-0022

GTE Corp.
600 Hidden Ridge
Irving, TX 75038
(214) 718-5000

Infonet Inc.
2100 E. Grand Ave.
El Segundo, CA 90245
(310) 335-2600

MCI Communications Corp.
1801 Pennsylvania Ave., N.W.
Washington DC 20006
(202) 872-1600

Nynex Corp.
1113 Westchester Ave.
White Plains, NY 10604
(914) 644-7600

Pacific Bell
140 New Montgomery St.
San Francisco, CA 94105
(415) 542-9000

Packets
3079 Kilgore Rd.
Rancho Cordova, CA 95670
(916) 635-9300

PacNet, Inc.
7525 S.E. 24th St.
Mercer Island, WA 98040
(206) 232-9900

Southern New England Telephone Co.
227 Church St.
New Haven, CT 06510
(203) 771-5200

Southwestern Bell Corp.
One Bell Center
St. Louis, MO 63101
(314) 235-0299

Sprint International
12524 Sunrise Valley Dr.
Reston, VA 22091
(703) 689-6000

US West Inc.
7800 E. Orchard Rd.
Englewood, CO 80111
(303) 793-6500

UNISPAN
5015 Campuswood Dr.
E. Syracuse, NY 13057
(315) 433-0022

WilTel
One Williams Center
Tulsa, OK 74172
(918) 588-3210

 # Selected
Internetworking Vendors

About Software Corporation (ASC)
10601 S. De Anza Blvd.
Suite 105
Cupertino, CA 95014
(408) 725-4242
(800) 557-6389
Fax: (408) 725-4243

Accent Technology
20 Trafalgar Square
Nashua, NH 03063
(603) 886-1570
Fax: (603) 598-8268

ACE/North Hills
7934 Nieman Rd.
Lenexa, KS 66214
(913) 888-4999
(800) 998-4223
Fax: (913) 888-4103

ACS Telecom
25825 Eshelman Ave.
Lomita, CA 90717
(310) 325-3055
(800) 325-0425
Fax: (310) 325-3059

ACSYS Inc.
20 Burlington Mall Rd.
Suite 400
Burlington, MA 01830
(617) 275-4455
(800) 462-2797

ACT Networks Inc.
188 Camino Ruiz
Camarillo, CA 93012
(805) 388-2474
Fax: (805) 388-3504

Adax Inc.
614 Bancroft Way
Berkeley, CA 94710
(510) 548-7047
Fax: (510) 548-5526

ADC Fibermux
21415 Plummer St
Chatsworth, CA 91311
(818) 709-6000
(800) 342-3768
Fax: (818) 709-1556

ADC Kentrox
P.O. Box 10704
Portland, OR 97210
(503) 643-1681
(800) 733-5511
Fax: (503) 641-3341

ADI Systems
2115 Ringwood Ave.
San Jose, CA 95131
(408) 944-0100
(800) 228-0530
Fax: (408) 944-0300

Adtech Inc.
3465 Waialae Ave.
Suite 200
Honolulu, HI 96816
(808) 734-3300
(800) 348-0084
Fax: (808) 734-7100

Addtron Technology
47968 Fremont Blvd.
Fremont, CA 94538
(510) 770-0120
(800) 998-4638
Fax: (510) 770-0171

Adtran Inc.
901 Explorer Blvd.
Huntsville, AL 35806
(205) 971-8000
(800) 827-0807

**Advanced Computer Com-
munications (ACC)**
10261 Bubb Rd.
Cupertino, CA 95014
(408) 366-9600
(800) 444-7854
Fax: (408) 446-5234

**Advanced Digital Informa-
tion (ADIC)**
14737 N.E. 87th St.
Redmond, WA 98073
(206) 881-8004
(800) 366-1233
Fax: (206) 881-2296

Advanced Logic Research
9401 Jeronimo
Irvine, CA 92718
(714) 581-6770
(800) 444-4257
Fax: (714) 581-9240

Advantis
231 N. Martingdale Rd.
Schaumburg, IL 60173
(800) 888-4103
Fax: (813) 878-4212

Aerocomm
13228 W. 99th St.
Lenexa, KS 66215
(913) 492-2320
(800) 492-2320
Fax: (913) 492-1243

A 'n' D Cable Products
5100-1B Clayton Rd., #302
Concord, CA 94521
(510) 672-3005
(800) 394-3008
Fax: (510) 672-0317

AGE Logic Inc.
9985 Pacific Heights Blvd.
San Diego, CA 92121
(619) 455-8600

AG Group Inc.
2540 Camino Diablo, Ste. 200
Walnut Creek, CA 94596
(510) 937-7900
(800) 466-2447
Fax: (510) 937-2479

Agile Networks Inc.
200 Baker Ave.
Concord, MA 01742
(508) 287-0700
(800) 286-9526
Fax: (508) 287-0606

**Applitek Corporation/LAN
City**
100 Brickstone Square
Andover, MA 01810
(508) 475-4050
(800) 526-2489
Fax: (508) 475-0550

APT Communications, Inc.
9607 Dr. Perry Rd.
Ijamsville, MD 21754
(301) 831-1182
(800) 842-0626
Fax: (301) 874-5255

A la Mode
1015 Waterwood Pkwy.,
Bldg. F
Edmond, OK 73034
(405) 359-6587
(800) 252-6633
Fax: (405) 359-8612

Alantec
70 Plumeria Dr.
San Jose, CA 95134
(408) 955-9000
(800) 252-6832
Fax: (408) 955-9500

Alcatel Network Systems
2912 Wake Forest Rd.
Raleigh, NC 27609
(919) 850-6000
(800) 767-2043
Fax: (919) 850-6171

Alcatel Data Networks
12502 Sunrise Valley Dr.
Reston, VA 22096
(703) 689-7400
Fax: (703) 689-5652

Alcatel Canada Wire
250 Ferrand Dr.
Don Mills, ON M3C 3J4
Canada
(416) 424-5091
(800) 561-2225
Fax: (416) 424-5226

Alfa Inc.
110 Breeds Hill Rd., Suite 9
Hyannis, MA 02601
(508) 790-6901
Fax: (508) 790-6903

Alfa Inc.
325 E. North Ave., Suite 1A
Westfield, NJ 07090
(908) 789-2068
Fax: (908) 789-2403

Allen Systems Group
750 11th St. S.
Naples, FL 33940
(813) 263-8447
(800) 932-5536
Fax: (813) 263-1952

Alpha Technologies
3767 Alpha Way
Bellingham, WA 98226
(360) 647-2360
(800) 322-5742
Fax: (360) 671-4936

Alps Electric
3553 N. First St.
San Jose, CA 95134
(408) 432-6000
(800) 825-2577
Fax: (408) 432-6035

Alta Research
600 S. Federal Hwy.
Deerfield Beach, FL 33441
(305) 428-8535
(800) 423-8535
Fax: (305) 428-8678

**Alta Group of Cadence
Design Systems**
919 E. Hillsdale Blvd.
Foster City, CA 94404
(415) 574-5800
Fax: (415) 358-3601

Alternet
3060 Williams Dr.
Suite 601
Fairfax, VA 22031
(703) 206-5600
Fax: (703) 205-5601

Amber Wave Systems
403 Massachusetts Ave.
Suite 202
Acton, MA 01720
(508) 266-2852
Fax: (266-1159

American Data
2662 Holcomb Bridge Rd.,
Suite 340
Alpharetta, GA 30202
(404) 998-5554
(800) 783-9799
Fax: (404) 998-6226

American Hytech
565 William Pitt Way
Pittsburg, PA 15238
(412) 826-3333
(800) 297-4878
Fax: (412) 826-3335

**American Mobile Satellite
Corp.**
10802 Parkridge Blvd.
Reston, VA 22091
(703) 758-6000
(800) 752-2672
Fax: (703) 758-6111

**Analog & Digital
Peripherals Inc. (ADPI)**
251 S. Mulberry
Troy, OH 45373
(513) 339-2241
(800) 758-1041
Fax: (513) 339-0070

Anco Technology
140 N. Palm St
Brea, CA 92621
(714) 992-9000
(800) 545-2626
Fax: (714) 992-1672

Ancor Communications
6130 Blue Circle Dr.
Minnetonka, MN 55343
(612) 932-4000
Fax: (612) 932-4037

Andrew Corporation
10500 W. 153rd St.
Orland Park, IL 60462
(708) 349-3300
(800) 328-2696
Fax: (708) 3495673

Annexus Data Systems
10559 Lansford Lane
San Diego, CA 92126
(619) 530-0019
Fax: (619) 530-0096

Anet Systems
1460 S.W. 3rd St.
Pompano Beach, FL 33069
(305) 784-9431
Fax: (305) 784-0904

ANS
1875 Campus Commons Dr.
Suite 220
Reston, VA 22091
(703) 758-7700
(800) 456-8267
Fax: (703) 758-7717

ANS Co+re Systems Inc.
100 Clearbrook Rd.
Elmsford, NY 10523
(914) 789-5300
(800) 962-7222
Fax: (914) 789-5310

Answer Software
20045 Stevens Creek Blvd.
Cupertino, CA 95014
(408) 253-7515
Fax: (408) 253-8430

Answer Systems
2 N. Second St., Suite 1000
San Jose, CA 95113
(408) 280-5110
(800) 677-2679
Fax: (408) 280-1004

AnswerSet
5335 S.W. Meadows Rd.
Suite 450
Lake Oswego, OR 97035
(503) 598-4500
Fax: (503) 598-4515

Apertus Technologies
7275 Flying Cloud Dr.
Eden Prairie, MN 55344
(612) 828-0300
(800) 876-7671
Fax: (612) 828-0454

Apex PC Solutions
4580 150th Ave. N.E.
Redmond, WA 98052
(206) 861-5858
(800) 861-5858
Fax: (206) 861-5757

451

Apsylog Inc.
1900 Embarcadero Rd.
Palo Alto, CA 94303
(415) 812-7700
Fax: (415) 812-7707

Alisa Systems, Inc.
221 E. Walnut, Suite 175
Pasadena, CA 91101
(818) 792-9474
(800) 992-5472
Fax: (818) 792-4068

Allied Telesis, Inc.
575 E. Middlefield Rd.
Mountain View, CA 94043
(415) 964-2771
(800) 424-4282
Fax: (415) 964-0944

American Power
    Conversion Corp.
132 Fairgrounds Rd.
West Kingston, RI 02892
(401) 789-5735
(800) 800-4272
Fax: (401) 789-3710

AMP
P.O. Box 3608
Harrisburg, PA 17105
(717) 564-0100
(800) 522-6752
Fax: (717) 986-7575

Anixter Brothers, Inc.
6602 Owens Dr., Suite 300
Pleasanton, CA 94588
(510) 463-1223
Fax: (510) 463-1255

Apple Computer, Inc.
20525 Mariani Ave.
Cupertino, CA 95014
(408) 996-1010
(800) 767-2775
Fax: (408) 974-6726

Applied Computing Devices
100 S. Campus Dr.
Terre Haute, IN 47802
(812) 232 6051
Fax: (812) 231 5280

APT Communications, Inc.
9607 Dr. Perry Rd.
Ijamsville, MD 21754
(301) 831-1182
(800) 842-0626
Fax: (301) 874-5255

Arcada Software
37 Skyline Dr., Suite 1101
Lake Mary, FL 32746
(407) 262-8000
(800) 327-2232
Fax: (407) 262-8116

Arco Computer Products
2750 N. 29th Ave., Ste. 316
Hollywood, FL 33020
(305) 925-2688
(800) 458-1666
Fax: (305) 925-2889

Arctos Systems
300 March Rd., Suite 304
Kanata, ON K2K 2E2
Canada
(613) 591-3084
Fax: (613) 591-1806

Arnet
618 Grassmere Park Dr.
Suite 6
Nashville, TN 37211
(615) 834-8000
(800) 366-8844
Fax: (615) 834-5399

Artisoft
2202 N. Forbes Blvd.
Tucson, AZ 85745
(602) 670-7100
(800) 233-5564
Fax: (602) 670-7101

Asante Technologies
404 Tasman Dr.
Sunnyvale, CA 94089
(408) 752-8388
(800) 662-9686
Fax: (408) 734-4864

Ascend Communications
1275 Harbor Bay Pkwy.
Alameda, CA 94502
(510) 769-6001
(800) 621-9578
Fax: (510) 814-2300

Ascom Timeplex Inc.
400 Chestnut Ridge Rd.
Woodcliff Lake, NJ 07675
(201) 391-1111
(800) 776-2677
Fax: (201) 573-6470

ASP Computer Products
160 San Gabriel Dr.
Sunnyvale, CA 94086
(408) 746-2965
(800) 445-6190
Fax: (408) 746-2803

AST Research
16215 Alton Pkwy.
Irvine, CA 92718
(714) 727-4141
(800) 876-4278
Fax: (800) 926-1278

Astarte Fiber Networks
2555 55th St., Suite 100
Boulder, CO 80301
(303) 443-8778
(800) 872-8777
Fax: (303) 449-2975

AT&T Global Information
    Solutions
1700 S. Patterson Blvd.
Dayton, OH 45479
(513) 445-5000

452

Attachmate Canada
3738 N. Fraser Way
Unit 101
Burnaby, BC V5J 5G1
   Canada
(604) 431-0727
(800) 663-8702
Fax: (604) 431-0818

AT&T Computer Systems
Gatehall Dr.
Parsippany, NJ 07054
(201) 397-4800
Fax: (201) 397-4918

Attachmate Corp.
3617 131st Ave. S.E.
Bellevue, WA 98006
(206) 644-4010
(800) 426-6283
Fax: (206) 747-9924

Augmentix
9351 Grant St., Suite 430
Thornton, CO 80229
(303) 431-8991
(800) 232-4687
Fax: (303) 451-1908

Auspex Systems Inc.
2952 Bunker Hill Lane
Santa Clara, CA 95054
(408) 492-0900
Fax: (408) 492-0909

Automated Programming
   Technologies
30100 Telegraph, Suite 402
Bingham Farms, MI 48025
(810) 540-9877
Fax: (810) 540-0403

Autotrol Technology
12500 N. Washington
Denver, CO 80241
(303) 452-4919
(800) 233 2882
Fax: (303) 252 2249

Avalan Technology
P.O. Box 6888
Holliston, MA 01746
(508) 429-6482
(800) 441-2281
Fax: (508) 429-3179

Avanti Technology
13492 Research Blvd.
Suite 120–271
Austin, TX 78750
(512) 335-1168
(800) 638-1168
Fax: (512) 335-7838

Avatar
65 South St.
Hopkinton, MA 01748
(508) 435-3000
(800) 282-3270
Fax: (508) 435-2470

Axon Networks
199 Wells Ave.
Newton, MA 02159
(617) 630-9600
Fax: (617) 630-9604

Aydin Computer &
   Monitor Systems
700 Dresher Rd.
Horsham, PA 19044
(215) 657-8600
Fax: (215) 657-5470

Azure Technologies
63 South St.
Hopkinton, MA 01748
(508) 435-3800
(800) 233-3800
Fax: (508) 435-0448

Banyan Systems, Inc.
115 Flanders Rd., Suite 5
Westboro, MA 01581
(508) 898-1000
(800) 828-2404
Fax: (508) 836-1810

Baranof Software
85 School St.
Watertown, MA 02172
(617) 926-6626
(800) 462-4565
Fax: (617) 926-6636

Barr Systems
4131 N.W. 28th Lane
Gainesville, FL 32606
(904) 371-3050
(800) 227-7797
Fax: (904) 491-3141

Baseline Software
P.O. Box 1219
Sausalito, CA 94966
(415) 332-7763
(800) 829-9955
Fax: (415) 332-8032

Bay Technical Associates
200 N. 2nd St.
Bay St. Louis, MS 39520
(601) 467-8231
(800) 523-2702
Fax: (601) 467-4551

Bay Networks
4401 Great America Pkwy.
P.O. Box 58185
Santa Clara, CA 95052
(408) 988-2400
Fax: (408) 988-5525

Bay Networks
2 Federal St.
Billerica, MA 01821
(508) 670-8888
(800) 222-7611
Fax: (508) 436-3658

BBN Communications Corp.
150 Cambridge Park Dr.
Cambridge, MA 02140
(617) 873-2000
Fax: (617) 873-2509

Beame & Whiteside Software
706 Hillsborough St.
Raleigh, NC 27603
(919) 831-8989
(800) 463-6637
Fax: (919) 831-8990

Bear Computer Systems Inc.
9584 Topanga Canyon Blvd.
Chatsworth CA 91311
(818) 341-0403
(800) 255 0662
Fax: (818) 341-1831

Bell Atlantic Software Systems
14 Washington Rd., Bldg. 2
Princeton Junction, NJ 08550
(609) 936-2900
Fax: (609) 936-2859

Bendata
1125 Kelly Johnson Blvd.
Suite 100
Colorado Springs, CO 80920
(719) 531-5007
(800) 776-7889
Fax: (719) 536-9623

Best Power Technology
P.O. Box 280
Necedah, WI 54646
(608) 565-7200
(800) 356-5794
Fax: (608) 565-2221

BGL Technology Corp.
451 Constitution Ave.
Camarillo, CA 93012
(805) 987-7305
Fax: (805) 987-7346

Biscom
321 Billerica Rd.
Chelmsford, MA 01824
(508) 250-1800
(800) 477-2472
Fax: (508) 250-4449

Black Box Corporation
1000 Park Dr.
Pittsburgh, PA 15241
(412) 746-5500
Fax: (412) 746-0746

Blast, Inc.
49 Salisbury St. W
Pittsboro, NC 27312
(919) 542-3007
(800) 242-5278
Fax: (919) 542-0161

Blue Lance
1700 W. Loop S.
Suite 1100
Houston, TX 77027
(713) 680-1187
Fax: (713) 622-1370

Blue Ocean Software
15310 Amberly Dr.
Suite 250
Tampa, FL 33647
(813) 977-4553
Fax: (813) 979-4447

Boca Research
6413 Congress Ave.
Boca Raton, FL 33487
(407) 997-6227
Fax: (407) 997-0918

Bravo Communications
1310 Tully Rd., Suite 107
San Jose, CA 95122
(408) 297-8700
(800) 366-0297
Fax: (408) 297-8701

BRIO Technology Inc.
444 Castro St., Suite 700
Mountain View, CA 94041
(415) 961-4110
(800) 486-2746
Fax: (415) 961-4572

Brixton Systems
185 Alewise Pkwy.
Cambridge, MA 02138
(617) 661-6262
(800) 274-9866
Fax: (617) 547-9820

Bull HN Information Systems
Technology Park
2 Wall St.
Billerica, MA 01821
(508) 294-6000
Fax: (508) 294-6440

Business Objects
20813 Stevens Creek Blvd.
Suite 100
Cupertino, CA 95014
(408) 973-9300
(800) 705-1515
Fax: (408) 973-1057

Bytex
4 Technology Dr.
Westborough MA 01581
(508) 366-8000
(800) 227-1145
Fax: (508) 366-7977

Cable Techniques
8910 Activity Rd., Suite H
San Diego, CA 92126
(619) 695-3533
Fax: (619) 695-9310

Cabletron Systems, Inc.
35 Industrial Way
Rochester, NH 03867-0505
(603) 332-9400
Fax: (603) 337-2211

CACI Products
3344 N. Torey Pines Ct.
La Jolla, CA 92037
(619) 457-9681
Fax: (619) 457-1184

Cactus Computer, Inc.
1120 Metrocrest Dr.
Suite 103
Carrollton, TX 75006
(214) 416-0525
Fax: (214) 416-7151

Cadence Design Systems
919 E. Hillsdale Blvd.
Suite 300
Foster City, CA 94404
(415) 574-5800
Fax: (415) 358-3601

CalComp
2411 W. LaPalma Ave.
Anaheim, CA 92801
(714) 821-2000
Fax: (714) 821-2404

Calculus
1761 W. Hillsboro Blvd.
Deerfield Beach, FL 33442
(305) 481-2334
Fax: (305) 481-1866

California Microwave
985 Almanor Ave.
Sunnyvale, CA 94086
(408) 732-4000
(800) 831-3104
Fax: (408) 732-4244

Cameo Communications
71 Spitbrook Rd.
Nashua, NH 03060
(603) 888-8869
(800) 438-4827
Fax: (603) 888-8906

Campbell Services
21700 Northwestern Hwy.
Suite 1070
Southfield, MI 48075
(810) 559-5955
(800) 345-6747
Fax: (810) 559-1034

Canary Communications
1851 Zanker Rd.
San Jose, CA 95112
(408) 453-9201
(800) 883-9201
Fax: (408) 453-0940

Canoga Perkins
21012 Lassen St.
Chatsworth, CA 91311
(818) 718-6300
Fax: (818) 718-6312

Cascade Communications
5 Carlisle Rd.
Westford, MA 01886
(508) 692-2600
(800) 342-5926
Fax: (508) 692-9214

Castelle
3255-3 Scott Blvd.
Santa Clara, CA 95054
(408) 496-0474
(800) 289-7555
Fax: (408) 492-1964

Castle Rock Computing
20863 Stevens Creek Blvd.
Suite 530
Cupertino, CA 95014
(408) 867-6492
(800) 331-7667
Fax: (408) 432-0892

Cayman Systems, Inc.
400 Unicorn Park Dr.
Suite 3
Woburn, MA 01801
(617) 932-1100
(800) 473-4776
Fax: (617) 932-0853

CBT Systems USA
400 Oyster Point Blvd.
Suite 401
South San Francisco, CA 94080
(415) 737-9050
(800) 929-9050
Fax: (415) 737-0377

CE Software
1801 Industrial Circle
West Des Moines, IA 50265
(515) 221-1801
(800) 523-7638
Fax: (515) 221-1806

CEC
208 E.51st St., Suite 400
New York, NY 10022
(800) 477-0791
Fax: (718) 885-3101

CeLan Technology
2323 Calle del Mundo
Santa Clara, CA 95054
(408) 988-8288
(800) 272-3526
Fax: (408)988-8289

Central Point
15220 N.W. Greenbrier Pkwy.
Beaverton, OR 97006
(503) 690-8088
(800) 305-0936
Fax: (503) 690-8083

Champlain Cable
12 Hercules Dr.
Colchester, VT 05446
(802) 655-2121
(800) 451-5162
Fax: (802)654-4224

Chatsworth Products
20700 Plummer St.
Chatsworth, CA 91311
(818) 882-8595
Fax: (818) 773-6972

CBIS, Inc.
5875 Peachtree Industrial Blvd.
Norcross, GA 30092
(404) 446-1332
(800) 835-3375
Fax: (404) 446-9164

Cheyenne Software Inc.
55 Bryant Ave.
Roslyn, NY 11576
(516) 484-5110
(800) 243-9462
Fax: (516) 484-3446

**CHI/COR Information
    Management**
300 S.Wacker Dr.
Chicago, IL 60606
(312) 322-0150
(800) 448-8777
Fax: (312) 322-0161

Chipcom Corporation
118 Turnpike Rd.
Southborough, MA 01772
(508) 460-8900
(800) 228-9930
Fax: (508) 460-8950

CIE America
2701 Dow Ave.
Tustin, CA 92680
(714) 573-2942
(800) 877-1421
Fax: (714) 757-4488

Ciprico
2800 Campus Dr., Suite 60
Plymouth, MN 55441
(612) 551-4000
(800) 727-4669
Fax: (612) 551-4002

Circuit Masters
10014 Kent Town
Sugarland, TX 77478
(713) 242-9353
Fax: (713) 242-4632

Cisco Systems Inc.
1525 O'Brien Dr.
Menlo Park, CA 94025
(415) 326-1941
(800) 553-6387
Fax: (415) 326-1989

Citrix Systems
210 University Dr.,
Suite 700
Coral Springs, FL 33071
(305) 755-0559
(800) 437-7503
Fax: (305) 341-6880

Claflin & Clayton, Inc.
203 S.W. Cutoff
Northboro, MA 01532
(508) 393-7979
Fax(508) 393-8788

Clary Corporation
1960 S. Walker Ave.
Monrovia, CA 91016
(818) 359-4486
(800) 442-5279
Fax: (818) 305-0254

Clearpoint Research Corp.
227 South St.
Hopkinton, MA 01748
(508) 435-2000
Fax: (508) 435-7530

Clovis
25 Porter Rd.
Littleton, MA 01460
(508) 486-4367
(800) 959-2556
Fax: (508) 486-3755

**CMC/Rockwell
    International**
7402 Hollister Ave.
Santa Barbara, CA 93117
(805) 968-4262
(800) 262-8023
Fax: (805) 968-6478

.CNet Technology
2199 Zanker Rd.
San Jose, CA 95131
(408) 954-8000
(800) 486-2638
Fax: (408) 954-8866

Codenoll Technology
1086 N. Broadway
Yonkers, NY 10701
(914) 965-6300
(800) 966-1512
Fax: (914) 965-9811

Codex/Motorola
20 Cabot Blvd.
Mansfield, MA 02048
(508) 261-4000
Fax: (508) 261-7105

Cogent Data Technologies
15375 S.E. 30th Pl.
Suite 310
Bellevue, WA 98007
(206) 603-0333
(800) 426-4368
Fax: (206) 603-9223

**Colorado Memory Systems
    Div of Hewlett Packard**
800 S. Taft Ave.
Loveland, CO 80537
(303) 635-1500
(800) 845-7905
Fax: (303) 667-0997

Colorbus
1821 McDurmott W.
Irvine, CA 92714
(714) 852-1850
(800) 742-2695
Fax: (714) 852-1909

Combinet
333 W. El Camino Real
Suite 240
Sunnyvale, CA 94087
(408) 522-9020
Fax: (408) 732-5479

Communication Cabling Systems
10202 Douglas
Des Moines, IA 50322
(512) 278-0111
(800) 515-9595
Fax: (515) 278-9424

Comlink, Inc.
44790 S. Grimmer Blvd.
Suite 207
Fremont, CA 94538
(510) 490-4690
(800) 433-3892
Fax: (415) 490-4664

Commvision
510 Logue Ave.
Mountain View, CA 94043
(415) 254-5720
(800) 832-6526
Fax: (415)254-9320

Compatible Systems
4730 Walnut St., Suite 102
Boulder, CO 80301
(303) 444-9532
(800) 356-0283
Fax: (303) 444-9595

COMPAQ Computer
2055 SH 249
Houston, TX 77070
(713) 374-0484
(800) 652-6672
Fax: (713) 374-4583

Compex
4051 E. La Palma
Anaheim, CA 92807
(714) 630-7302
(800) 279-8891
Fax: (714) 630-6521

Compulink Management Center
370 S. Crenshaw Blvd.
Suite E106
Torrance, CA 90503
(310) 212-5465
Fax: (310) 212-5064

Computer Associates
1 Computer Associates Plaza
Islandia, NY 11788
(516) 342-5224
(800) 225-5224
Fax: (516) 342-5329

Computer Knacks
621 Shrewsbury Ave.
Shrewsbury, NJ 07702
(908) 530-0262
(800) 551-1433
Fax: (908)741-0972

Computer Mail Services
20300 Civic Center Dr.
Suite 300
Southfield, MI 48076
(810) 352-6700
(800) 883-2674
Fax: (810) 352-8387

Computer Modules
2350 Walsh Ave.
Santa Clara, CA 95051
(408) 496-1881
Fax: (408) 496-1886

Computer Network Technology
6500 Wedgwood Rd.
Maple Grove, MN 55311
(612) 550-8000
(800) 638-8324
Fax: (612) 550-8800

Computer Power
124 W. Main St
High Bridge, NJ 08829
(908) 638-8000
(800) 526-5088
Fax: (908) 638-4931

Computer System Products
14305 N. 21st Ave.
Plymouth, MN 55447
(612) 476-6866
(800) 422-2537
Fax: (612) 475-8457

Comtrol
P.O. Box 64750
St. Paul, MN 55164
(612) 631-7654
(800) 926-6876
Fax: (612) 631-8117

Concord Communications Inc.
33 Boston Post Rd. W.
Marlborough, MA 01752
(508) 460-4646
Fax: (508) 481-9772

Concurrent Computer Corp.
One Robbins Rd.
Westford, MA 01886-4152
(508) 692-6200
Fax: (508) 692-5057

Conner Periphals
450 Technology Park Dr.
Lake Mary, FL 32746
(407) 263-3500
(800) 526-6637
Fax: (407) 263-3555

Conner Presales Support
1650 Sunflower Ave.
Costa Mesa, CA 92626
(714) 641-1230
(800) 626-6637
Fax: (714) 641-2590

Contact East
335 Willow St.
N. Andover, MA 01845
(508) 682-2000
(800) 225-5334
Fax: (508) 688-7829

Contemporary Cybernetics
Group
Rock Landing Corporate Ctr.
11846 Rock Landing
Newport News, VA 23606
(804) 873-9000
Fax: (804) 873-8836

Control Data Systems
4201 N. Lexington Ave.
Arden Hills, MN 55126
(612) 482-6736
(800) 257-6736
Fax: (612) 482-2000

Core
7171 N. Federal Hwy.
Boca Raton, FL 33487
(407) 997-6044
(800) 688-9910
Fax: (407) 997-6009

Corning, Opto-Electronics
Group
35 W. Market St.
Corning, NY 14831
(607) 974-4476
(800) 525-2524
Fax: (607) 974-7522

Cougar Mountain Software
P.O. Box 6886
Boise, ID 83705
(208) 344-2540
(800) 358-3388
Fax: (208) 343-0267

Cray Communications Inc.
9020 Junction Dr.
Annapolis, MD 20701
(301) 317-7710
(800) 359-7710
Fax: (301) 317-7220

Cray Research, Inc.
655 Lone Oak Dr.
Egan, MN 55121
(612) 683-7100
(800) 284-2729
Fax: (612) 683-7199

CrossComm Corporation
450 Donald Lynch Blvd.
Marlborough MA 01752
(508) 481-4060
(800) 388-1200
Fax: (508) 490-5535

Crichlow Data Sciences
5925 Imperial Pkwy.
Suite 227
Mulberry, FL 33860
(813) 648-5444
(800) 678-4535
Fax: (813) 648-5546

Cross International
854 Walnut St., Suite B
Boulder, CO 80302
(303) 440-7313
Fax: (303) 442-2616

Crystal Point, Inc.
22232 17th Ave. S.E., #301
Bothell, WA 98021
(206) 487-3656
(800) 982-0628
Fax: (206) 487-3773

Cubix
2800 Lockheed Way
Carson City, NV 89706
(702) 883-7611
(800) 829-0554
Fax: (702) 882-2407

CXR/Digilog
2360 Maryland Rd.
Willow Grove, PA 19090
(215) 830-9400
(800) 344-4564
Fax: (215) 830-9444

CyberCorp.
P.O. Drawer 1988
Kennesaw, GA 30144
(404) 424-6240
Fax: (404) 424-8995

CyberSafe
2443 152nd Ave. N.E.
Redmond, WA 98052
(206) 883-8721
Fax: (206) 883-6951

Cybex
4912 Research Dr.
Huntsville, AL 35805
(205) 430-4000
Fax: (205) 430-4030

Cyclades
44140 Old Warm Springs
Blvd.
Fremont, CA 94538
(510) 770-9727
(800) 347-6601
Fax: (510) 770-0355

Cylink
910 Hermosa Ct.
Sunnyvale, CA 94086
(408) 735-5800
(800) 533-3958
Fax: (408) 735-6643

Cyma Systems
1400 E.Southern Ave.
Suite 800
Tempe, AZ 85282
(602) 831-2607
(800) 292-2962
Fax: (602) 345-5703

D & G Infosystems
148 Patterson Ave.
Hempstead, NY 11550
(516) 538-1240
(800) 430-4583
Fax: (516) 538-1077

D-Link Systems
5 Musick
Irvine, CA 92718
(714) 455-1688
(800) 326-1688
Fax: (714) 455-2521

Dalcon Computer Services
1321 Murfreesboro Rd.
Nashville, TN 37217
(615) 366-4300
Fax: (615) 367-6055

Danpex
1342 Ridder Park Dr.
San Jose, CA 95131
(408) 437-7557
(800) 452-1551
Fax: (408) 437-7559

Data Access
14000 S.W. 119th Ave.
Miami, FL 33186
(305) 238-0012
(800) 451-3539
Fax: (305) 238-0017

Datability, Inc.
One Palmer Terr.
Carlstadt, NJ 07072
(201) 438-2400
Fax: (201) 438-8060

Data General Corporation
4400 Computer Dr.
Westboro, MA 01580
(508) 366-8911
(800) 328-2436
Fax: (508) 366-1744

Data Interface Systems Corporation
11130 Jollyville Rd.
Suite 300
Austin, TX 78759
(512) 346-5641
(800) 351-4244
Fax: (512) 346-4035

Datapoint
8400 Datapoint Dr.
San Antonio, TX 78229
(210) 593-7850
(800) 334-9968
Fax: (210) 593-7518

Datastorm Technologies
3212 Lemone Industrial Blvd.
Columbia, MO 65201
(314) 443-3282
Fax: (314) 875-0595

David Systems Inc.
615 Tasman Dr.
Sunnyvale, CA 94088-3718
(408) 541-6000
(800) 762-7848
Fax: (408) 541-6985

DaVinci Systems
507 Airport Blvd., Suite 115
Morrisville, NC 27560
(919) 319-7000
(800) 328-4624
Fax: (919) 319-7088

Dayna Communications
849 W. Levoy Dr.
Salt Lake City, UT 84123
(801) 269-7200
(800) 531-0600
Fax: (801) 269-7363

Daystar Digital, Inc.
5556 Atlanta Hwy.
Flowery Branch, GA 30542
(404) 967-2077
(800) 962-2077
Fax: (404) 967-3018

DEI
230 N. Market Pl.
Escondido, CA 92029
(619) 743-8344
(800) 732-8344
Fax: (619) 743-5297

Delrina
6320 San Ignacio
San Jose, CA 95119
(408) 363-2345
(800) 268-6082
Fax: (408) 363-2340

Deltec NSSI
2727 Kurtz St.
San Diego, CA 92111
(619) 291-4211
(800) 854-2658
Fax: (619) 291-2973

Develcon
856 51st St. E.
Saskatoon, SK S7K 5C7
Canada
(306) 933-3300
(800) 667-9333
Fax: (306) 931-1370

Dickens Data Systems
1175 Northmeadow Pkwy.
Suite 150
Roswell, GA 30076
(404) 475-8860
(800) 448-6177
Fax: (404) 442-7525

DigiBoard
6400 Flying Cloud Dr.
Eden Prairie, MN 55344
(612) 943-9020
(800) 344-4273
Fax: (612) 943-5398

Digital Equipment Corporation
550 King St.
Littleton, MA 01460
(508) 486-5198
(800) 332-4636
Fax: (508) 486-5554

Digital Link
217 Humboldt Ct.
Sunnyvale, CA 94089
(408) 745-6200
(800) 441-1142
Fax: (408) 745-6250

Digital Ocean
11206 Thompson Ave.
Lenexa, KS 66219
(913) 888-3380
(800) 345-3474
Fax: (913) 888-3342

Digital Products
411 Waverley Oaks Rd.
Waltham, MA 02154
(617) 647-1234
(800) 243-2333
Fax: (617)647-4474

Digital Technology
2300 Edwin C. Moses Blvd.
Dayton, OH 45408
(513) 443-0412
(800) 852-1252
Fax: (513) 226-0511

Digitech Industries
55 Kenosia Ave.
Danbury, CT 06813
(203) 797-2676
Fax: (203) 797-2682

Distinct
12901 Saratoga Ave.
Suite 4
Saratoga, CA 95070
(408) 366-8933
Fax: (408) 366-0153

Diverse Logistics
2862 McGaw Ave.
Irvine, CA 92714
(714) 476-7171
(800) 345-6432
Fax: (714) 476-0633

DMA
1776 E. Jericho Turnpike
Huntington, NY 11743
(516) 462-0440
Fax: (516) 462-6652

Dynamic Software
109 S. Main St.
Greer, SC 29650-2020
(803) 877-1122
(800) 627-1218
Fax: (803) 879-2030

E-Comms
5720 144th St. N.W.
Gig Harbor, WA 98332
(206) 857-3399
(800) 247-1431
Fax: (206) 857-3444

Edimax Computer
3350 Scott Blvd., Bldg. 62
Santa Clara, CA 95054
(408) 496-1105
(800) 652-6776
Fax: (408) 980-1530

EFA
3040 Oakmead Village Dr.
Santa Clara, CA 95051
(408) 987-5400
(800) 800-3321
Fax: (408) 987-5415

EFI Electronics
2415 S. 2300 W.
Salt Lake City, UT 84119
(801) 977-9009
(800) 877-1174
Fax: (801) 977-0200

Eicon Technology Corp.
2196 32nd Ave.
Montreal, QUE H8T 3H7
  Canada
(514) 631-2592
(800) 676-9267
Fax: (514) 631-3092

Elan Software
17383 Sunset Blvd., Suite 101
Pacific Palisades, CA 90272
(310) 454-6800
(800) 654-3526
Fax: (310) 454-4848

Eliashim Microcomputers
4005 Wedgemere Dr.
Tampa, FL 33610
(813) 744-5177
(800) 477-5177
Fax: (813) 744-5197

Elisa Technology
4368 Enterprise St.
Fremont, CA 94538
(510) 651-5817
Fax: (510) 651-4834

ElseWare
101 Stewart St., Suite 700
Seattle, WA 98101
(206) 448-9600
(800) 357-3927
Fax: (206) 448-7220

Emerald Systems
15175 Innovation Dr.
San Diego, CA 92128
(619) 673-2161
(800) 767-2587
Fax: (619) 673-2288

Emerging Technologies Inc.
900 Walt Whitman Rd.
Melville, NY 11747
(516) 271-4525
Fax: (516) 271-4814

Emulex Corporation
3535 Harbor Blvd.
Costa Mesa, CA 92626
(714) 662-5600
(800) 854-7112
Fax: (714) 241-0792

Encore Computer Systems Division
6901 W. Sunrise Blvd.
Plantation, FL 33313
(305) 587-2900
(800) 726-2230
Fax: (305) 797-5793

Engage Communication
9053 Soquel Dr.
Aptos, CA 95003
(408) 688-1021
Fax: (408) 688-1421

Enterprise Solutions
2900 Townsgate Rd.
Suite 210
Westlake, CA 91361
(805) 449-4181
Fax: (805) 449-4186

EPE Technologies
1660 Scenic Ave.
Costa Mesa, CA 92626
(714) 557-1636
(800) 344-0570
Fax: (714) 434-7652

Epilogue Technology Corp.
11116 Desert Classic Lane
N.E.
Albuquerque NM 87111
(505) 271-9933
Fax: (505) 271-9798

Ergotron
1181 Trapp Rd.
St.Paul, MN 55121
(612) 452-8135
(800) 888-8452
Fax: (612)681-7715

Esker
1181 Chess Dr., Suite C
Foster City, CA 94404
(415) 341-9065
(800) 883-7537
Fax: (415) 341-6412

EtherCom
45990 Hotchkiss St.
Fremont, CA 95439
(510) 440-0242
Fax: (510) 659-8296

Equinox Systems
6851 W. Sunrise Blvd.
Plantation, FL 33313
(305) 791-5000
(800) 275-3500
Fax: (305) 746-9101

Essex Systems Inc.
One Central St.
Middleton MA 01949
(508) 750-6200
Fax: (508) 750-4699

Evergreen Systems
120 Landing Ct., Suite A
Novato, CA 94945
(415) 897-8888
Fax: (415) 897-6158

Exabyte
1685 38th St.
Boulder, CO 80301
(303) 442-4333
(800) 392-2983
Fax: (303) 447-7501

Excelltech
113 W. Third St.
Yankton, SD 57078
(605) 665-5811
Fax: (605) 665-8324

Exide Electronics Group
8521 Six Forks Rd.
Raleigh, NC 27615
(919) 872-3020
(800) 554-3448
Fax: (919) 870-3450

Express Systems
2101 Fourth Ave., Suite 303
Seattle, WA 98121
(206) 728-8300
(800) 321-4606
Fax: (206) 728-8301

Experdata
10301 Toledo Ave. S.
Bloomington, MN 55437
(612) 831-2122
Fax: (612) 835-0700

Extended Systems
5777 N. Meeker Ave.
Boise, ID 83704
(208) 322-7575
(800) 235-7576
Fax: (208) 377-1906

Farallon Computing Inc.
2470 Mariner Square Loop
Alameda, CA 94501
(510) 814-5100
Fax: (510) 814-5020

Fiber Instrument Sales
161 Clear Rd.
Oriskany, NY 13424
(315) 736-2206
(800) 445-2901
Fax: (315) 736-2285

FiberCom
3353 Orange Ave. N.E.
Roanoke, VA 24012
(703) 342-6700
(800) 537-6801
Fax: (703) 342-5961

Fibronics International
33 Riverside Dr.
Pembroke, MA 02359
(617) 826-0099
(800) 327-9526
Fax: (617) 826-7745

Firefox
2841 Junction Ave., Ste. 103
San Jose, CA 95134
(408) 321-8344
(800) 230-6090
Fax: (408) 321-8311

FEL Computing
10 Main St.
P.O. Box 72
Williamsville, VT 05362
(802) 348-7171
(800) 639-4110
Fax: (802) 348-7124

Fibermux Corporation
21415 Plummer St.
Chatsworth, CA 91311
(818) 709-6000
(800) 800-4624
Fax: (818) 709-1556

First Floor
444 Castro St., Suite 200
Mountain View, CA 94041
(415) 968-1101
(800) 639-6387
Fax: (415) 968-1193

**Fischer International
  Systems**
4073 Mercantile Ave.
Naples, FL 33942
(813) 643-1500
(800) 237-4510
Fax: (813) 643-3772

FlexiWare
1 Research Dr.
Shelton, CT 06484
(203) 925-3030
(800) 457-3361
Fax: (203) 925-3044

Fluke
6920 Seaway Blvd.
Everett, WA 98206
(800) 443-5853
Fax: (206) 347-6100

Fotec
529 Main St.
P.O. Box 246
Boston, MA 02129
(617) 241-7810
(800) 537-8254
Fax: (617) 241-8616

Four Seasons Software
2025 Lincoln Hwy.
Edison, NJ 08817
(908) 248-6667
(800) 949-0110
Fax: (908) 248-6675

Frederick Engineering Inc.
10200 Old Columbia Rd.
Columbia, MD 21046
(410) 290-9000
Fax: (410) 381-7180

**Frontier Software
  Development Inc.**
321 Billerica Rd.
Chelmsford, MA 01824
(508) 244-4000
Fax: (508) 244-4004

Frontier Technologies Inc.
10201 N. Port Washington Rd.
13 West
Mequon, WI 53092
(414) 241-4555
(800) 929-3054
Fax: (414) 241-7084

Frye Computer Systems
19 Temple Pl.
Boston, MA 02111
(617) 451-5400
(800) 234-3793
Fax: (617) 451-6711

FTP Software, Inc.
2 High St.
N. Andover, MA 01845
(508) 685-4000
(800) 282-4387
Fax: (508) 794-4488

Funk Software
222 Third St
Cambridge, MA 02142
(617) 497-6339
(800) 828-4146
Fax: (617) 547-1031

Futurus
3295 River Exchange
Suite 450
Norcross, GA 30092
(404) 242-7797
(800) 327-8296
Fax: (404) 242-7221

Galcom
211 Perry Pkwy., Unit 4
Gaithersburg, MD 20877
(301) 990-7100
(800) 966-4444
Fax: (301) 963-6383

Gandalf Data Inc.
130 Colonnade Rd. S.
Ottawa, ON K2E 7M4
Canada
(613) 723-6500
(800) 426-3253
Fax: (613) 226-1717

Ganson Engineering
18678 142nd Ave. N.E.
Woodinville, WA 98072
(206) 489-2090
Fax: (206) 489-2088

Garrett Communications
48531 Warm Spring Rd.
Fremont, CA 94539
(510) 438-9071
Fax: (510) 438-9072

GDT Softworks
4664 Lougheed Hwy., Suite
188
Burnaby, BC V5C 6B7
Canada
(604) 291-9121
(800) 663-6222
Fax: (604) 291-9689

General DataCom, Inc.
1579 Straits Turnpike
Middlebury, CT 06762
(203) 574-1118
Fax: (203) 758-8507

General Software
320 108th Ave N.E.
Suite 400
Bellevue, WA 98004
(206) 454-5755
Fax: (206) 454-5744

General Technology
415 Pineda Ct.
Melbourne, FL 32940
(407) 242-2733
(800) 274-2733
Fax: (407) 254-1407

Genicom
14800 Conference Center Dr.,
Ste. 400
Chantilly, VA 22021-3806
(703) 802-9200
(800) 443-6426
Fax: (703) 802-9093

GigaTrend
2234 Rutherford Rd.
Carlsbad, CA 92008
(619) 931-9122
(800) 743-4442
Fax: (619) 931-9959

Glasgal Communications
151 Veterans Dr.
Northvale, NJ 07647
(201) 768-8082
(800) 526-9261
Fax: (201) 768-2947

**Global Village
Communication**
1144 E. Arquez
Sunnyvale, CA 94086
(408) 523-1000
Fax: (408) 523-2407

Grafpoint Inc.
1485 Saratoga Ave.
San Jose, CA 95129
(408) 446-1919
(800) 426-2230
Fax: (408) 446-0666

Great Plains Software
1701 S.W. 38th St.
Fargo, ND 58103
(701) 281-0550
(800) 456-0025
Fax: (701) 281-3700

GTSI-Falcon
40100 Lafayette Center Dr.
Chantilly, VA 22021
(703) 631-3333
(800) 999-4874
Fax: (703) 222-5223

Gupta Technologies
1060 Marsh Rd.
Menlo Park, CA 94025
(415) 321-9500
(800) 876-3267
Fax: (415) 321-5471

Hadax Electronics
310 Philips Ave.
S.Hackensack, NJ 07606
(201) 807-1155
Fax: (201) 807-1782

**Hammersly Technology
Partners, Utopia Infor-
mation Systems Div.**
909 Montgomery St.
Suite 202
San Francisco, CA 94133
(415) 956-1300
(800) 786-4778
Fax: (415) 956-4260

**Harris Computer Systems
Division**
2101 W. Cypress Creek Rd.
Fort Lauderdale, FL 33309
(305) 974-1700
(800) 666-4544
Fax: (305) 977-5580

**Harris Corporation,
Dracon Div.**
809 Calle Plano
Camarillo, CA 93012
(805) 987-9511
(800) 437-2266
Fax: (805) 389-2467

**Hayes Microcomputer
Products, Inc.**
5953 Peachtree Industrial
Blvd.
Norcross, GA 30092
(404) 840-9200
Fax: (404) 447-0178

Helios Systems
1996 Lundy Ave.
San Jose, CA 95131
(408) 432-0292
(800) 366-2983
Fax: (408) 432-7323

**Hergo Ergonomic Supports
Systems**
321 5th Ave.
New York, NY 10016
(212) 684-4666
(800) 232-8737
Fax: (212) 684-3685

Hewlett-Packard Company
3000 Hanover St.
Palo Alto, CA 94304
(415) 857-1501
(800) 752-0900
Fax: (415) 857-5518

**Hewlett-Packard, Colorado
    Telecommunications Div.**
5070 Centennial Blvd.
Colorado Springs, CO 80919
(719) 531-4000
Fax: (719) 531-4505

**Hewlett-Packard Business
    Computing Systems**
19091 Pruneridge Ave.
Cupertino, CA 95014
(800) 752-0900
Fax: (408) 345-8609

High Caliber Systems
171 Madison Ave., 8th Floor
New York, NY 10016
(212) 684-5553
Fax: (212) 532-2362

Highland Technologies
7701 Greenbelt Rd.
Suite 505
Greenbelt, MD 20770
(301) 345-8200
Fax: (301) 345-8201

Hilgraeve
111 Conant Ave., Suite A
Monroe, MI 48161
(313) 243-0576
(800) 826-2760
Fax: (313) 243-0645

**Hitachi Computer Products
    (America)**
3101 Tasman Dr.
Santa Clara, CA 95054
(408) 986-9770
Fax: (408) 986-0449

HiTek Solutions
2361 Campus Dr., Suite 107
Irvine, CA 92715
(714) 474-8270
Fax: (714) 474-8272

Horizons Technology
3990 Ruffin Rd.
San Diego, CA 92123
(619) 292-8331
(800) 828-3808
Fax: (619) 292-7321

HT Communications
4480 Shopping Lane
Simi Valley, CA 93063
(805) 579-1700
Fax: (805) 522-5295

HT Research
1342 Bell Ave., Unit 3E
Tustin, CA 92680
(714) 566-9100
(800) 483-2677
Fax: (714) 566-9109

HTI Networks
532 Weddell Dr., Suite 1
Sunnyvale, CA 94089
(408) 745-0100
Fax: (408) 745-7711

Hughes LAN Systems Inc.
2200 Lawson Lane
Santa Clara, CA 95054
(408) 565-6000
Fax: (408) 565-6356

Hummingbird Communications
2900 John St., Unit 4
Markham, ON L3R 5G3
Canada
(905) 470-1203
Fax: (905) 470-1207

Hypercom
2851 W. Kathleen Rd.
Pheonix, AZ 85023
(602) 866-5399
(800) 577-5501
Fax: (602) 548-2166

I/O Concepts
2125 112th Ave. N.E.
Suite 303
Bellevue, WA 98004
(206) 450-0650
Fax: (206) 622-0058

IBM
Old Orchard Rd.
Armonk, NY 10504
(914) 765-1900
(800) 426-2468
Fax: (800) 232-9426

IC Engineering
P.O. Box 321
Owings Mills, MD 21117
(410) 363-8748

ICOT
3801 Zanker Rd.
San Jose, CA 95134
(408) 432-3138
(800) 762-3270
Fax: (408) 433-9466

IDEAssociates Inc.
29 Dunham Rd.
Billerica, MA 01821
(508) 663-6878
(800) 257-5027
Fax: (508) 663-8851

IMC Data Manager
1038-B Kiel Ct.
Sunnyvale, CA 94089
(408) 752-1100
(800) 537-5999
Fax: (408) 752-1110

IMC Networks
16931 Milliken Ave.
Irvine, CA 92714
(714) 724-1070
(800) 624-1070
Fax: (714) 724-1020

Impulse Technologies
25 Porter Rd.
Littleton, MA 01460
(508) 486-0001
(800) 800-2556
Fax: (508) 486-4108

Independence Technologies
42705 Lawrence Pl.
Fremont, CA 94538
(510) 438-2000
Fax: (510) 438-2034

Infinite Technologies
11433 Cronridge Dr.
Owings Mills, MD 21117
(410) 363-1097
(800) 678-1097
Fax: (410) 363-3779

Information Builders
1250 Broadway, 36th Floor
New York, NY 10001
(212) 736-4433
(800) 969-4636
Fax: (212) 268-7470

Informative Graphics
706 E. Bell Rd., Suite 207
Phoenix, AZ 85022
(602) 971-6061
(800) 398-7005
Fax: (602) 971-1714

Informix Software
4100 Bohannon Dr.
Menlo Park, CA 94025
(415) 926-6300
(800) 388-0366
Fax: (415) 926-6593

Information Presentation Technologies
555 Chorro St., Suite A
San Luis Obispo, CA 93405
(805) 541-3000
Fax: (805-541-3037

Innosoft International
1050 E. Garvey Ave. S.
Suite 250
West Covina, CA 91793
(818) 919-3600
(800) 552-5444
Fax: (818) 919-3614

InSoft
4718 Old Gettysburg Rd.
Suite 307
Mechanicsburg, PA 17055
(717) 730-9501
Fax: (717) 730-9504

Intel Corporation
2402 W. Beardsley Rd.
Phoenix, AZ 85027
(602) 869-4647
(800) 538-3373
Fax: (800) 525-3019

Intellicom
20415 Nordhoff St.
Chatsworth, CA 91311
(818) 407-3900
(800) 992-2882
Fax: (818) 882-2404

Intellipower
10-A Thomas St.
Irvine, CA 92718
(714) 587-0155
Fax: (714) 587-0230

InterActive
204 N. Main
Humboldt, SD 57035
(605) 363-5117
Fax: (605) 363-5102

InterConnections
14711 N.E. 29th Pl.
Bellevue, WA 98007
(206) 881-5773
(800) 950-5773
Fax: (206) 867-5022

Interlink Computer Sciences
47370 Fremont Blvd.
Fremont, CA 94538
(510) 657-9800
(800) 422-3711
Fax: (510) 657-9816

InterCon Systems Corp.
950 Herndon Pkwy.
Suite 420
Herndon, VA 22070
(703) 709-9890
(800)468-7266
Fax: (703) 709-5555

International Connectors & Cable
16918 Edwards Rd.
Cerritos, CA 90703
(310) 926-0734
(800) 333-7776
Fax: (310) 926-5290

International Data Sciences
501 Jefferson Blvd.
Warwick, RI 02886
(401) 737-9900
(800) 437-3282
Fax: (401) 737-9911

Interphase
13800 Senlac
Dallas, TX 75234
(214) 919-9000
(800) 327-8638
Fax: (214) 919-9200

Interprise Network Services
1999 Broadway, Suite 800
Denver, CO 80202
(800) 672-8520
Fax: (303) 965-9281

Intrak
9999 Business Park Ave.
San Diego, CA 92131
(619) 695-1900
(800) 233-7494
Fax: (619) 271-4989

In Vision Systems
317 S. Main St., Suite 310
Tulsa, OK 74103
(918) 584-7772
(800) 847-1662
Fax: (918) 584-7775

Ipswitch, Inc.
669 Main St.,Suite 6
Wakefield, MA 01880
(617) 246-1150
Fax: (617) 245-2975

IQ Technologies
13625 N.E. 126th Pl., Suite
400
Kirkland, WA 98034
(206) 823-2273
(800) 227-2817
Fax: (206) 821-3961

IRI Software
200 Fifth Ave.
Waltham, MA 02154
(617) 890-1100
(800) 765-7227
Fax: (617) 890-4660

ISICAD
1920 W. Corporate Way
Anaheim, CA 92803
(714) 533-8910
(800) 634-1223
Fax: (714) 533-8642

Itoshu Technology Inc.
2701 Dow Ave.
Tustin, CA 92681
(714) 573-2721
(800) 347-2484
Fax: (714) 757-4423

ITT Datacom
666 E. Dyer Rd.
Santa Ana, CA 92705
(714) 754-2259
(800) 328-2266
Fax: (714) 754-2098

ITV Communications
15310 Amberly Dr.
Suite 150
Tampa, FL 33647
(813) 975-0564
(800) 370-5760
Fax: (813) 972-5587

J & L Information Systems
9600 Topanga Canyon Blvd.
Chatsworth, CA 91311
(818) 709-1778
Fax: (818) 882-9134

James River Group
125 N. First St.
Minneapolis, MN 55401
(612) 339-2521

JetFax
1376 Willow Rd.
Menlo Park, CA 94025
(415) 324-0600
(800) 753-8329
Fax: (415) 326-6003

JSB
108 Whispering Pines Dr.,
Suite 115
Scotts Valley, CA 95066
(408) 438-8300
(800) 359-3408
Fax: (408) 438-8360

JYACC
116 John St.
New York, NY 10038
(212) 267-7722
Fax: (212) 608-6753

Kalpana
1154 E.Arques Ave.
Sunnyvale, CA 94086
(408) 749-1600
(800) 488-0775
Fax: (408)749-1690

Katron Technologies
7400 Harwin Dr., Suite 120
Houston TX 77036
(713) 266-3891
(800) 275-6387
Fax: (713) 266-3893

Keylogic
P.O. Box 278
Goffstown, NH 03045
(603) 472-4006
(800) 641-4066
Fax: (603) 497-3785

Kingston Technology
17600 Newhope St.
Fountain Valley, CA 92708
(714) 435-2600
(800) 835-6575
Fax: (714) 435-2699

Klever Computers
1841 Zonker Rd.
San Jose, CA 95112
(408) 467-0888
(800) 745-4660
Fax: (408) 467-0899

Kofax Image Products
3 Jenner St.
Irvine, CA 92718
(714) 727-1733
Fax: (714) 727-3144

Legent Corp.
1901 N. Naper Blvd.
Naperville, IL 60563
(708) 505-9555
Fax: (708) 505-9574

Lago Systems
151 Allbright Way
Los Gatos, CA 95030
(408) 376-2750
(800) 866-5246
Fax: (408) 374-2330

LAN Support Group
2425 Fountain View
Suite 390
Houston, TX 77057
(713) 789-0881
(800) 749-8439
Fax: (713) 977-9111

LANart
145 Rosemary St.
Needham, MA 02194
(617) 444-1994
(800) 292-1994
Fax: (617) 444-3692

LANcast
10 Northern Blvd., Unit 5
Amherst, NJ 03031
(603) 880-1833
(800) 952-6227
Fax: (603) 881-9888

Landings Technology
163 Water St.
Merrill Block, Unit A2
Exeter, NH 03833
(603) 772-4500
(800) 222-3734
Fax: (603) 772-0141

Lane Telecommunications
5 Marineview Plaza
Suite 206
Hoboken, NJ 07030
(201) 798-0006
Fax: (201) 798-0045

Lanera Corporation
516 Valley Way
Milpitas, CA 95035
(408) 956-8344
Fax: (408) 956-8343

Lannet
17942 Cowan Ave.
Irvine, CA 92714
(714) 752-6638
(800) 552-6638
Fax: (714) 752-6641

LANOptics
13748 Neutron Rd.
Dallas, TX 75244
(214) 392-0647
(800) 533-8439
Fax: (214) 385-0723

LANovation
1313 Fifth St. S.E.
Minneapolis, MN 55414
(612) 379-3805
(800) 747-4487
Fax: (612) 378-3818

LANQuest
2225 Qume Dr.
San Jose, CA 95131
(408) 894-1000
(800) 487-1000
Fax: (408) 894-1001

LANSource Technologies
221 Dufferin St., Suite 310A
Toronto, ON M6K 3J2
Canada
(416) 535-3555
(800) 677-2727
Fax: (416) 535-6225

LANSpeed Systems
100 N. Hope Ave., Suite 20
Santa Barbara, CA 93110
(805) 682-9981
Fax: (805) 569-0311

Lantec
3549 N. University Ave.
Suite 325
Provo, UT 84604
(801) 375-7050
(800) 352-6832
Fax: (801) 375-7043

Lantell Systems
16250 Ventura Blvd., Ste. 202
Encino, CA 91436
(818) 905-1262
(800) 526-8355
Fax: (818) 905-1292

Larscom
4600 Patrick Henry Dr.
Santa Clara, CA 95054
(408) 988-6600
Fax: (408) 986-8690

Laser Communications
380 Massachusetts Ave.
Acton, MA 01720
(508) 266-1500
(800) 266-1505
Fax: (508) 635-0806

LearnKey
1845 W. Sunset Blvd.
St. George, UT 84770
(801) 674-9733
(800) 937-3279
Fax: (801) 674-9734

LeeMah DataCom Security
3948 Trust Way
Hayward, CA 94545
(510) 786-0790
(800) 992-0020
Fax: (510) 786-1123

Legacy Storage Systems
43 Riviera Dr.
Markham, ON L3R 5J6
Canada
(905) 475-1077
Fax: (905) 475-1088

Legato Systems
3145 Porter Dr.
Palo Alto, CA 94304
(415) 812-6000
Fax: (415) 812-6032

Legent
411 108th Ave. N.E.
Suite 600
Bellevue, WA 98004
(206) 688-2000
(800) 377-5327
Fax: (206) 688-2050

Legent Corp.
1889 Preston White Dr.
Reston, VA 22091
(703) 476-5900
Fax: (703) 476-1918

Lexmark International
740 New Circle Rd.
Lexington, KY 40511
(606) 232-2000
(800) 358-5835

The Light Brigade
7639 S. 180th St.
Kent, WA 98032
(206) 251-1240
Fax: (206) 251-1245

Lightspeed Software
1800 19th St.
Bakersfield, CA 93301
(805) 324-4291
Fax: (805) 324-1437

Linkpro
17 Aurora
Irvine, CA 92715
(714) 854-3322
(800) 449-7962
Fax: (714) 854-3312

Linksys
16811A Millikan Ave.
Irvine, CA 92714
(800) 546-5797
Fax: (714) 261-8868

Ling Systems
P.O. Box 11040
Tucson, AZ 85734
(602) 741-6480
(800) 870-3185
Fax: (602) 741-6419

Livingston Enterprises, Inc.
6920 Koll Center Pkwy
Suite 220
Pleasanton, CA 94566
(510) 426-0770
(800) 458-9966
Fax: (510) 426-8951

Locus Computing
9800 La Cienega Blvd.
Inglewood, CA 90301
(310) 670-6500
(800) 955-6287
Fax: (310) 670-2980

Logicworks
1060 Rte.206
Princeton, NJ 08540
(609) 252-1177
(800) 783-7946
Fax: (609) 252-1175

Longshine Microsystem
10400-9 Pioneer Blvd.
Santa Fe Springs, CA 90670
(310) 903-0899
Fax: (310) 944-2201

Loral Command & Control
9970 Federal Dr.
Colorado Springs, CO 80921
(719) 594-1000
Fax: (719) 594-1305

Lotus Development
55 Cambridge Pkwy.
Cambridge, MA 02142
(617) 577-8500
Fax: (617) 693-0968

Luxcom Inc.
3249 Laurelview Ct.
Fremont, CA 94538
(510) 770-3300
(800) 322-5000
Fax: (510) 770-3399

M & T Technologies
1435 N.Hayden Rd.
Scottsdale, AZ 85257
(602) 994-5131
Fax: (602) 994-1336

Madge Networks, Inc.
2310 N. 1st St.
San Jose, CA 95131
(408) 955-0700
(800) 876-2343
Fax: (408) 955-0970

Madison Cable
125 Goddard Memorial Dr.
Worcester, MA 01603
(508) 752-2884
Fax: (508) 752-4230

Magna
199 S. Bascom Ave., Ste. 810
Campbell, CA 95008
(408) 879-7900
(800) 631-6400
Fax: (408) 879-7979

Make Systems
201 San Antonio Circle
Suite 225
Mountain View, CA 94040
(415) 941-9800
(800) 545-6253
Fax: (415) 941-5856

Markham Computer
1 S. Ocean Blvd., Suite 301
Boca Raton, FL 33432
(407) 394-3994
(800) 262-7542
Fax: (407) 394-3844

Matrox Electronics System
1055 St. Regis Blvd.
Dorval, PQ H9P 2T4
Canada
(514) 685-2630
(800) 361-4903
Fax: (514) 685-2853

McAfee
2770 Walsh Ave.
Santa Clara, CA 95051
(408) 988-3832
(800) 866-6585
Fax: (408) 970-9727

McData Corporation
310 Interlocken Pkwy.
Broomfield, CO 80021
(303) 460-9200
(800) 752-0388
Fax: (303) 465-4996

MCI Communications Corp.
8003 W. Park Dr.
McLean, VA 22102
(800) 888-0800
Fax: (703) 260-7099

Megahertz
605 N. 5600 W.
Salt Lake City, UT 84116
(801) 320-7000
(800) 527-8677
Fax: (801) 320-6022

Memotec Communications
1 High St.
N.Andover, MA 01845
(508) 681-0600
Fax: (508) 681-0660

Mergent International
70 Inwood Rd.
Rocky Hill, CT 06067
(203) 257-4223
(800) 688-3227
Fax: (203) 257-4245

Meridian Data
5615 Scotts Valley Dr.
Scotts Valley, CA 95066
(408) 438-3100
(800) 767-2537
Fax: (408) 438-6816

Mesa Graphics Inc.
P.O. Box 600
Los Alamos, NM 87544
(505) 672-1998

Metacomp
10989 Via Frontera
San Diego, CA 92127
(619) 674-5000
Fax: (619) 674-5005

Metricom
980 University Ave.
Los Gatos, CA 95030
(408) 399-8133
Fax: (408) 354-1024

Micom Systems, Inc.
4100 Los Angeles Ave.
Simi Valley, CA 93063
(805) 583-8600
(800) 642-6687
Fax: (805) 583-1997

Micro Computer Systems
2300 Valley View, Suite 800
Irving, TX 75062
(214) 659-1514
Fax: (214) 659-1624

Micro Data Base Systems
1305 Cumberland Ave.
West Lafayette, IN 47906
(317) 463-7200
(800) 445-6327
Fax: (317) 463-1234

Micro Design International
6985 University Blvd.
Winter Park, FL 32792
(407) 677-8333
(800) 228-0891
Fax: (407) 677-8365

Microcom, Inc.
500 River Ridge Dr.
Norwood, MA 02062-5028
(617) 551-1000
(800) 822-8224
Fax: (617) 551-1006

Micro Decisionware
3035 Center Green Dr.
Boulder, CO 80301
(303) 443-2706
(800) 423-8737
Fax: (303) 443-2797

Microdyne
3601 Eisenhower Ave.
Alexandria, VA 22304
(703) 329-3700
(800) 255-3967
Fax: (703) 329-3716

Micro House International
4900 Pearl E. Circle
Suite 101
Boulder, CO 80301
(303) 443-3388
(800) 926-8299
Fax: (303) 443-3323

Micro Integration
1 Science Park
Frostburg, MD 21532
(301) 689-0800
(800) 832-4526
Fax: (301) 689-0808

MicroNet Technology
80 Technology
Irvine, CA 92718
(714) 453-6100
Fax: (714) 453-6101

Microplex Systems
8525 Commerce Ct.
Burnaby, BC V5A 4N3
Canada
(604) 444-4232
(800) 665-7798
Fax: (604) 444-4239

Micropolis
21211 Nordhoff St.
Chatsworth, CA 91311
(818) 709-3300
(800) 395-3748
Fax: (818) 718-5312

Microsoft Corporation
One Microsoft Way
Redmond, WA 98052-6399
(206) 882-8080
(800) 227-4679
Fax: (206) 635-6100

Microsystems Software
600 Worcester Rd.
Framingham, MA 01701
(508) 879-9000
Fax: (508) 626-8515

Micro Technology
4905 E. La Palma Ave.
Anaheim, CA 92807
(714) 970-0300
(800) 999-9684
Fax: (714) 970-5413

Microtest, Inc.
4747 N. 22nd St.
Phoenix, AZ 85016
(602) 952-6400
(800) 526-9675
Fax: (602) 952-6401

Microtronix DataCom Ltd.
200 Aberdeen Dr.
London, ON N5V 4N2
Canada
(519) 659-9500
Fax: (519) 659-8500

Millemet
4039 Clipper Ct.
Fremont, CA 94538
(510) 770-9390
Fax: (510) 770-9123

Minuteman
P.O. Box 815888
Dallas, TX 75381
(214) 446-7363
(800) 238-7272
Fax: (214) 446-9011

Miramar Systems
121 Gray Ave., Suite 200 B
Santa Barbara, CA 93101
(805) 966-2432
(800) 862-2526
Fax: (805) 965-1824

Mitron Computer
2220 S. Bascom Ave.
Campbell, CA 95008
(408) 371-8166
(800) 713-6888
Fax: (408) 371-8167

Mitsubishi
201 Broadway
Cambridge, MA 02139
(617) 621-7500
Fax: (617) 621-7550

Modular Software Systems
25825 104th Ave. S.E.,
Suite 208
Kent, WA 98031
(206) 631-5781
(800) 438-3930
Fax: (206) 631-5779

Momentum Software Corp.
401 S. Van Brunt St.
Englewood, NJ 07631
(800) 767-1462
(201) 871-0077
Fax: (201) 871-0807

Morning Star Technologies
3518 RiverSide Dr., Suite
101
Columbus, OH 43221
(614) 451-1883
(800) 558-7827
Fax: (614) 459-5054

Moses Computer
15466 Los Gatos Blvd.
Suite 201
Los Gatos, CA 95032
(408) 358-1550
(800) 306-6737
Fax: (408) 356-9049

Most
11205 Knott Ave., Suite B
Cypress, CA 90630
(714) 898-9400
Fax: (714) 373-9960

Motorola Codex
20 Cabot Blvd.
Mansfield, MA 02048
(508) 261-4000
(800) 544-0062
Fax: (508) 261-7118

Motorola Computer Group
2900 S. Diablo Way
Tempe, AZ 85282
(800) 458-0300
Fax: (408) 438-7623

**Motorola Information
Systems Group**
5000 Bradford Dr.
Huntsville, AL 35805
(205) 430-8000
(800) 221-4380
Fax: (205) 830-5657

MountainGate Data Systems
9393 Gateway Dr.
Reno, NV 89511
(702) 851-9393
(800) 556-0222
Fax: (702) 851-5544

470

Multi-Tech Systems
2205 Woodale Dr.
Mounds View, MN 55112
(612) 785-3500
(800) 328-9717
Fax: (612) 785-9874

MultiAccess Computing
5350 Hollister, Suite C
Santa Barbara, CA 93111
(805) 964-2332
Fax: (805) 681-7469

Mustang Software
6200 Lake Ming Rd.
Bakersfield, CA 93306
(805) 873-2500
(800) 999-9619
Fax: (873-2599

Mux Lab
5450 Cote de Liesse
Mt.Royal, PQ H4P 1A5
Canada
(514) 735-2741
(800) 361-1965
Fax: (514) 735-8057

Mylex
34551 Ardenwood Blvd.
Fremont, CA 94555
(510) 796-6100
(800) 776-9539
Fax: (510) 745-8016

National Semiconductor
1111 W. Barton Ave.
Arlington, TX
(817) 468-6300
(800) 272-9959
Fax: (817) 468-6931

NBase Switch
   Communications
8943 Fullbright Ave.
Chatsworth, CA 91311
(818) 773-0900
(800) 858-7815
Fax: (818) 773-0906

NDC Communications
2180 Bering Dr.
San Jose, CA 95131
(408) 428-9108
Fax: (408) 428-9109

NEC America
1525 Walnut Hill Lane
Irving, TX 75038
(214) 518-5000
(800) 222-4632
Fax: (214) 518-5572

Neon Software, Inc.
3685 Mt. Diablo Blvd., #203
Lafayette, CA 94549
(510) 283-9771
(800) 283-6366
Fax: (510) 283-6507

NeoSoft
354 N.E. Greenwood Ave.
Suite 108
Bend, OR 97701
(503) 389-5489
(800) 545-1392
Fax: (503) 388-8221

Netcom Systems
21818 Lassen St., Unit G
Chatsworth, CA 91311
(818) 700-5100
Fax: (818) 709-7881

NetEdge Systems
P.O. Box 14993
Research Triangle Park, NC
   27709
(919) 361-9000
(800) 638-3343
Fax: (919) 361-9060

NetFrame Systems
1545 Barber Lane
Milpitas, CA 95035
(408) 944-0600
(800) 852-3726
Fax: (408) 434-4190

NetLabs Inc.
4920 El Camino Real
Los Altos, CA 94022
(415) 961-9500
(800) 447-9300
Fax: (415) 961-9300

Netlink
3214 Spring Forest Rd.
Raleigh, NC 27604
((919) 878-8612
(800) 638-5465
Fax: (919) 872-2132

NetManage, Inc.
10725 N. De Anza Blvd.
Cupertino, CA 95014
(408) 973-7171
Fax: (408) 257-6405

Netrix
6150 Lookout Rd.
Boulder, CO 80301
(303) 530-8600
(800) 621-0236
Fax: (303) 530-8625

NetSoft
31 Technology Dr., 2nd Fl.
Irvine, CA 92718
(714) 753-0800
(800) 352-3270
Fax: (714) 753-0810

NetSource
8470 Tyco Rd.
Vienna, VA 22182
(703) 827-8585
Fax: (703) 893-1911

Netwise
2477 55th St.
Boulder, CO 80301
(303) 442-8280
(800) 733-7722
Fax: (303) 442-3798

471

Network Application
    Technology Inc.
1686 Dell Ave.
Campbell, CA 95008
(408) 370-4300
(800) 474-7888
Fax: (408) 370-4222

Network Communications
5501 Green Valley Dr.
Bloomington, MN 55437
(612) 844-0584
(800) 333-1896
Fax: (612) 844-0487

Network Compatibility
    Group
130 E. Wilson Bridge Rd.,
    Suite 100
Columbus, OH 43085
(614) 436-2962
Fax: (614) 436-0116

Network Computing Inc.
100 N. Winchester Blvd.
Suite 262
Santa Clara, CA 95050
(408) 296-8080
(800) 736-3012
Fax: (408) 296-8329

The Network Connection
1324 Union Hill Rd.
Alpharetta, GA 30201
(404) 751-0889
(800) 327-4853
Fax: (404) 751-1884

Network Equipment
    Technologies Inc.
800 Saginaw Dr.
Redwood City, CA 94063
(415) 366-4400
(800) 234-4638
Fax: (415) 366-5675

Network General
4200 Bohannon Dr.
Menlo Park, CA 94025
(415) 688-2700
(800) 395-3151
Fax: (415) 321-0855

Network Instruments
P.O. Box 581156
Minneapolis, MN 55458
(612) 822-2025
Fax: (612) 825-5649

Network Integrators Assoc.
6007 Meridian Ave.
San Jose, CA 95120
(408) 927-0412
Fax: (408) 927-0412

Network Managers
73 Princeton St., Suite 305
N. Chelmsford, MA 01863
(508) 251-4111
(800) 821-5466
Fax: (508) 251-8562

Network Peripherals, Inc.
1371 McCarthy Blvd.
Milpitas, CA 95035
(408) 321-7300
Fax: (408) 321-9218

Network Products
1440 W. Colorado Blvd.
Pasadena, CA 91105
(818) 441-6504
(800) 638-7765
Fax: (818) 441-6894

Network Resources Corp.
    (NRC)
61 E. Daggett Dr.
San Jose, CA 95134
(408) 383-9300
Fax: (408) 383-0136

Network Systems Corp.
7600 Boone Ave. N.
Minneapolis, MN 55428
(612) 424-4888
(800) 248-8777
Fax: (612) 424-1661

Network Technologies
1275 Danner Dr.
Aurora, OH 44202
(216) 562-7070
(800) 742-8324
Fax: (216) 562-1999

Networks Northwest
3633 136th Place S.E.
Suite 100
Bellevue, WA 98006
(206) 641-8779
(800) 835-9462
Fax: (206) 641-8909

Networth, Inc.
8404 Esters Blvd.
Irving, TX 75063
(214) 929-1700
(800) 544-5255
Fax: (214) 929-1720

Newbridge Networks
593 Herndon Pkwy.
Herndon, VA 22070-5241
(703) 834-3600
Fax: (703) 471-7080

New Media
1 Technology, Bldg. A
Irvine, CA 92718
(714) 453-0100
(800) 227-3748
Fax: (714) 453-0114

Newport Systems Solutions
2569 McCabe Way
Irvine, CA 92714
(714) 752-1511
(800) 368-6533
Fax: (714) 752-8389

NHC Communications
5450 Cote de Liesse
Mount Royal, PQ H4P 1A5
Canada
(514) 735-2741
(800) 361-1965
Fax: (514) 735-8057

Niwot Networks
2200 Central Ave., Suite B
Boulder, CO 80301
(303) 444-7765
Fax: (303) 444-7767

Nonstop Networks
20 Waterside
New York, NY 10010
(212) 481-8488
Fax: (212) 779-2956

Norton-Lambert
P.O. Box 4085
Santa Barbara, CA 93140
(805) 964-6767
Fax: (805) 683-5679

Novell, Inc.
122 E. 1700 S.
Provo, UT 84606
(801) 429-7000
(800) 638-9273
Fax: (801) 429-5155

Novell, Inc.
2180 Fortune Dr.
San Jose, CA 95131
(408) 473-8333
(800) 243-8526
Fax: (408) 435-1706

**Novell Desktop Product
Group**
70 Garden Ct.
Monterey, CA 93940
(408) 649-3896
(800) 768-9771
Fax: (408) 646-6248

Noyes Fiber Systems
Eastgate Park/Belmont
P.O. Box 398
Laconia, N.H. 03247
(603) 528-7780
(800) 321-5298
Fax: (603) 528-2025

Nupon Computing
1391 Warner Ave., Suite A
Tustin, CA 92680
(714) 258-8622
Fax: (714) 258-0812

**Nynex Information Solu-
tions Group**
1113 Westchester
White Plains, NY 10604
(914) 644-6000
Fax: (914) 694-2609

OAZ Communications
44920 Osgood Rd.
Fremont, CA 94539
(510) 226-0171
(800) 638-3293
Fax: (510) 226-7079

Olicom USA
900 E. Park Blvd., Suite 180
Plano, TX 75074
(214) 423-7560
(800) 265-4266
Fax: (214) 881-2332

Olympus Image Systems
15271 Barranca Pkwy.
Irvine, CA 92718
(714) 753-5935
(800) 347-4027
Fax: (714) 453-4425

**OnDemand Software &
Services**
1100 Fifth Ave. S., Ste. 208
Naples, FL 33940
(813) 261-6678
(800) 672-6729
Fax: (813) 261-6549

Oneac
27944 N. Bradley Rd.
Libertyville, IL 60048
(708) 816-6000
(800) 327-8801
Fax: (708) 680-5124

Online Computer Systems
20251 Century Blvd.
Germantown, MD 20874
(301) 428-3700
(800) 922-9204
Fax: (301) 428-2903

Ontrack Computer Systems
6321 Bury Dr., Suites 15–19
Eden Prairie, MN 55346
(612) 937-1107
(800) 752-1333
Fax: (612) 937-5815

OpenConnect Systems Inc.
2711 LBJ Fwy., Suite 800
Dallas, TX 75234
(214) 484-5200
Fax: (214) 484-6100

Optical Cable
P.O. Box 11967
Roanoke, VA 24022
(703) 265-0690
(800) 622-7711
Fax: (703) 265-0724

Optical Data Systems (ODS)
1101 E. Arapahoe Rd.
Richardson, TX 75081
(214) 234-6400
Fax: (214) 234-4059

Optisys
9250 N. 43rd Ave., Suite 12
Glendale, AZ 85302
(602) 997-9699
(800) 327-1271
Fax: (602) 944-4051

Optus Software
100 Davidson Ave.
Somerset, NJ 08873
(908) 271-9568
Fax: (908) 271-9572

Oracle Corp.
500 Oracle Pkwy.
Redwood Shores, CA 94065
(415) 506-7000
(800) 392-2999
Fax: (415) 506-7255

Ositech Communications
679 Southgate Dr.
Guelph, ON N1G 4S2
Canada
(519) 836-8063
(800) 563-2386
Fax: (516) 836-6156

Overland Data
8975 Balboa Ave.
San Diego, CA 92123
(619) 571-5555
(800) 729-8725
Fax: (619) 571-0982

Pacer Software Inc.
7911 Herschel Ave.
Suite 402
La Jolla, CA 92037
(619) 454-0565
Fax: (619) 454-6267

Pacific Communication
  Sciences
9645 Scranton Rd.
San Diego, CA 92121
(619) 535-9500
(800) 933-7274
Fax: (619) 535-0106

Pacific Data Products
9855 Scranton Rd.
San Diego, CA 92121
(619) 552-0880
Fax: (619) 552-0889

Pacific Micro Data
3002 Dow Ave., Bldg 140
Tustin, CA 92680
(714) 838-8900
(800) 933-7575
Fax: (714) 838-9787

Pacific Softworks
4000 Via Pescador
Camarillo, CA 93012
(805) 484-2128
Fax: (805) 484-3929

Palindrome
600 E. Diehl Rd.
Naperville, IL 60563
(708) 505-3300
Fax: (708) 505-7917

PaperClip Imaging
401 Hackensack Ave.
Hackensack, NJ 07601
(201) 487-3503
(800) 929-3503
Fax: (201) 487-0613

Paralon Technologies
3650 131st Ave. S.E.
Suite 210
Bellevue, WA 98006
(206) 641-8338
Fax: (206) 641-1347

Paramax Defense Systems/
  Division of Unisys
5151 Camino Ruiz
Camarillo, CA 93011
(805) 987-6811
Fax: (805) 388-7790

Parsec Information
350 5th Ave., Suite 1905
New York, NY 10118
(212) 564-6922
Fax: (212) 564-7091

Passport Communications
1101 S. Capital of Texas Hwy.
Suite 250-F
Austin, TX 78746
(512) 328-9830
Fax: (512) 328-4773

PC Docs
124 Marriott Dr.
Tallahassee, FL 32301
(904) 942-3627
Fax: (904) 656-5559

PC Dynamics
31332 Via Colinas, Ste. 102
Westlake Village, CA 91362
(818) 889-1741
(800) 888-1741
Fax: (818) 889-1014

PDC
Continental Plaza
1002 W. Ninth Ave.
King of Prussia, PA 19406
(610) 265-3300
(800) 654-4732
Fax: (610) 265-2165

PEER Networks
1190 Saratoga Ave.
Suite 130
San Jose, CA 95129
(408) 556-0720
Fax: (408) 556-0735

Penril DataComm Networks
1300 Quince Orchard Blvd.
Gaithersburg, MD 20878
(301) 921-8600
(800) 473-6745
Fax: (301) 921-8376

Peregrine Systems
1959 Palomar Oaks Way
Carlsbad, CA 92009
(619) 431-2400
(800) 638-5231
Fax: (619) 431-0696

Performance Technology
7800 IH-10 W., Suite 800
San Antonio, TX 78230
(210) 979-2000
(800) 327-8526
Fax: (210) 979-2010

Perlan Networking
1181 N. 4th St.
San Jose, CA 95112
(510) 671-2800
Fax: (510) 798-6901

Persoft Inc.
465 Science Dr.
Madison, WI 53711
(608) 273-6000
(800) 368-5283
Fax: (608) 273-8227

Photonics
2940 N. First St.
San Jose, CA 95134
(408) 955-7930
(800) 628-3033
Fax: (408) 955-7950

Pinnacle Communications
Cross Westchester Executive
   Park
400 Executive Blvd.
Elmsford, NY 10523
(914) 345-8155
Fax: (914) 345-2807

Pinnacle Micro
19 Technology Dr.
Irvine, CA 92718
(714) 727-3300
(800) 553-7070
Fax: (714) 727-1913

Plaintree Systems
9 Hillside Ave.
Wellesley, MA 02154
(617) 290-5800
(800) 370-2724
Fax: (617) 290-0963

Plasmon Data Systems
1654 Centre Pointe Dr.
Milpitas, CA 95035
(408) 956-9400
(800) 445-9400
Fax: (408) 956-9444

Plexcom
2255 Agate Ct.
Simi Valley, CA 93065
(805) 522-3333
Fax: (805) 583-4764

Powersoft
70 Blanchard Rd.
Burlington, MA 01803
(617) 229-2200
(800) 937-7693
Fax: (617) 229-8104

Preferred Systems
250 Captain Thomas Blvd.
West Haven, CT 06516
(203) 937-3000
(800) 222-7638
Fax: (203) 937-3032

Premenos
1000 Burnett Ave., 2nd Fl.
Concord, CA 94520
(510) 602-2000
(800) 426-3836
Fax: (510) 602-2024

Presticom
3275 First St., Suite 1
St.Hubert, PQ J3Y 8Y6
Canada
(514) 443-2909
Fax: (514) 443-2878

Process Software Corp.
959 Concord St.
Framingham, MA 01701
(508) 879-6994
(800) 722-7770
Fax: (508) 879-0042

Progress Software
14 Oak Park
Bedford, MA 01730
(617) 280-4000
(800) 477-6473
Fax: (617) 280-4095

Protec Microsystems
297 Labrosse
Pointe-Claire, PQ H9R 1A3
Canada
(514) 630-5832
(800) 363-8156
Fax: (514) 694-6973

Proteon, Inc.
2 Technology Dr.
Westborough, MA 01581
(508) 898-2800
(800) 545-7464
Fax: (508) 366-8901

ProTools Inc.
14976 N.W. Greenbrier Pkwy.
Beaverton, OR 97006
(503) 645-5400
(800) 743-4335
Fax: (503) 645-3577

Proxim
295 N. Bernardo Ave.
Mountain View, CA 94043
(415) 960-1630
(800) 229-1630
Fax: (415) 964-5181

PSI
165 Jordan Rd.
Troy, NY 12180
(518) 283-8860
Fax: (518) 283-8904

PureData
180 W. Beaver Creek Rd.
Richmond Hill, ON L4B 1B4
Canada
(416) 731-6444
Fax: (416) 731-7017

Pyramid Technology Corp.
3860 N. 1st St.
San Jose, CA 95134
(408) 428-9000
(800) 333-5754
Fax: (408) 327-5691

QMS Corporation
1 Magnum Pass
Mobile, AL 36689
(205) 633-4300
(800) 523-2696
Fax: (205) 633-4866

Qstar Technologies
600 E. Jefferson St.
Rockville, MD 20852
(301) 762-9800
(800) 568-2578
Fax: (301) 762-9829

**Quality Decision
    Management**
200 Sutton St., Suite 225
N. Andover, MA 01845
(508) 688-8266
Fax: (508) 688-5181

Qualix Group
1900 S. Norfolk St., Ste. 224
San Mateo, CA 94403
(415) 572-0200
(800) 245-8649
Fax: (415) 572-1300

Quintessential Solutions Inc.
3570 Camino Del Rio N.
Suite 201
San Diego, CA 92108
(619) 280-7535
Fax: (619) 280-1628

Quintus
301 E. Evelyn Ave.
Mountain View, CA 94041
(415) 254-2800
Fax: (415) 428-0211

Racal-Datacom, Inc.
155 Swanson Rd.
Boxborough, MA 01719
(508) 263-9929
(800) 526-8255
Fax: (508) 263-8655

**Racal Data
    Communications**
1601 N. Harrison Pkwy.
Sunrise, FL 33323-2899
(305) 846-1601
(800) 722-2555
Fax: (305) 846-5510

Racal InterLan
155 Swanson Rd.
Boxboro, MA 01719
(508) 263-9929
(800) 526-8255
Fax: (508) 263-8655

Racore Computer Products
170 Knowles Dr., Suite 204
Los Gatos, CA 95030
(408) 374-8290
(800) 635-1274
Fax: (408) 374-6653

RAD Data Communications
900 Corporate Dr.
Mahwah, NJ 07430
(201) 529-1100
Fax: (201) 529-5777

RAD Network Devices Inc.
3505 Cadillac Ave.
Suite G5
Costa Mesa, CA 92626
(714) 436-9700
Fax: (714) 436-1941

Radio Mail Corp.
2600 Campus Dr.
San Mateo, CA 94403
(415) 286-7800
(800) 597-6245
Fax: (415) 286-7801

Raritan Computer
10-1 Ilene Ct.
Belle Mead, NJ 08502
(908) 874-4072
Fax: (908) 874-5274

Raylan
2525 E. Bayshore
Palo Alto, CA 94566
(415) 813-0400
(800) 472-9526
Fax: (415) 494-7844

Reach Software
827 Hermosa Dr.
Sunnyvale, CA 94086
(408) 733-8685
(800) 624-5356
Fax: (408) 733-9265

Relay Technology
1604 Spring Hill Rd.
Vienna, VA 22182
(703) 506-0500
(800) 795-8674
Fax: (703) 506-0510

Relia Technologies
761 University Ave., Suite B
Los Gatos, CA 95030
(408) 399-4350
Fax: (408) 354-2545

Remedy Corp.
1505 Solado Dr.
Mountain View, CA 94043
(415) 903-5200
Fax: (415) 903-9001

Rememory
3186 Airway Ave., Bldg. E
Costa Mesa, CA 92626
(714) 708-0990
(800) 644-2300
Fax: (714) 708-0993

Research Triangle Institute
3040 Cornwallis Rd.
Research Triangle Park, NC
27709
(919) 541-6000
Fax: (919) 541-5985

Retix
2401 Colorado Ave.
Suite 200
Santa Monica, CA 90404
(310) 828-3400
(800) 255-2333
Fax: (310) 828-2255

Revelation Technologies
181 Harbor Dr.
Stamford, CT 06902
(203) 973-1000
(800) 262-4747
Fax: (203) 975-8744

Rexon Software
2750 N. Clovis Ave.
Fresno, CA 93727
(209) 292-8888
(800) 228-9236
Fax: (209) 292-8908

RG Software Systems
6900 E. Camelback Rd.
Suite 630
Scottsdale, AZ 85251
(602) 423-8000
Fax: (602) 423-8389

Richard Hirschmann of
  America
Industrial Row
P.O. Box 229
Riverdale, NJ 07457
(201) 835-5002
(800) 225-0524
Fax: (201) 835-8354

RFI Communications &
  Security
360 Turtle Creek Ct.
San Jose, CA 95125-1389
(408) 298-5400
Fax: (408) 275-0156

RightFax
4400 E. Broadway
Suite 312
Tucson, AZ 85711
(602) 327-1357
Fax: (602) 321-7456

The Rip-Tie
458 Brannan St.
San Francisco, CA 94107
(415) 543-0170
Fax: (415) 777-9868

Riser Bond Instruments
5101 N. 57th St.
Lincoln, NE 68507
(402) 466-0933
(800) 688-8377
Fax: (402) 466-0967

Rivercomm Technology
2957 Glen Alden Ct.
San Jose, CA 95148
(408) 238-4764
Fax: (408) 238-8308

Rockwell Network Systems
7402 Hollister Ave.
Santa Barbara, CA 93117
(805) 968-4262
(800) 262-8023
Fax: (805) 968-6478

The Root Group
4700 Walnut St., Suite 110
Boulder, CO 80301
(303) 447-3938
Fax: (303) 447-0197

Rose Electronics
10850 Wilcrest, Suite 900
Houston, TX 77099
(713) 933-7673
(800) 333-9343
Fax: (713) 933-0044

RTMX-Uniflex
800 Eastowne Dr.
Suite 111
Chapel Hill, NC 27514
(919) 493-1451
Fax: (919) 490) 2903

RTZ Software
P.O. Box 567
Cupertino, CA 95015
(408) 252-2946
Fax: (408) 257-5274

Saber Software
5944 Luther Lane
Suite 1007
Dallas, TX 75225
(214) 361-8086
(800) 338-8754
Fax: (214) 361-1882

Sadelco R&D
452 Foxen Dr.
Santa Barbara, CA 93105
(805) 682-3341
Fax: (805) 682-3341

Saleskit Software
10845 Olive Blvd., Suite 190
St.Louis, MO 63141
(314) 567-0439
(800) 779-7205
Fax: (314) 432-7205

Salix Systems
9345 Byron St.
Schiller Park, IL 60176
(708) 678-5600
(800) 725-4948
Fax: (708) 678-7676

The Santa Cruz Operation
2100 Reston Pkwy.
Suite 102
Reston, VA 22091
(703) 715-8700
Fax: (703) 715-8750

Saros
10900 N.E. 8th St.
Suite 700
Bellevue, WA 98004
(206) 646-1066
(800) 827-2767
Fax: (206) 462-0879

Scope Communications
100 Otis St.
Northboro, MA 01532
(508) 393-1236
Fax: (508) 393-2213

Semaphore Communications
2040 Martin Ave.
Santa Clara, CA 95050
(408) 980-7750
Fax: (408) 980-7769

SBE, Inc.
4550 N. Canyon Rd.
San Ramon, CA 94583
(510) 355-2000
(800) 925—2666
Fax: (510) 355-2020

SCI Systems
1300 S. Memorial Pkwy.
Huntsville, AL 35803
(205) 882-4304
Fax: (205) 882-4305 or
    4871

SCOPE Inc.
1860 Michael Faraday Dr.
Reston, VA 22090
(703) 471-5600
Fax: (703) 471-1715

Server Technology
1288 Hammerwood Ave.
Sunnyvale, CA 94089
(408) 745-0300
(800) 835-1515
Fax: (408) 745-0392

Shany
101 San Antonio Rd.
Mountain View, CA 94043
(415) 694-7410
Fax: (415) 694-4728

Shaxon Industries
4950 E. Hunter Ave.
Anaheim, CA 92807
(714) 779-1140
(800) 345-1140
Fax: (714) 779-5091

Shiva Corporation
One Cambridge Center
Cambridge, MA 02142
(617) 252-6300
(800) 458-3550
Fax: (617) 252-6852

ShowCase
4909 Hwy. 52 N.
Rochester, MN 55901
(507) 288-5922
(800) 829-3555
Fax: (507) 287-2803

The Siemon Company
76 Westbury Park Rd.
Watertown, CT 06795
(203) 274-2523
Fax: (203) 345-4225

Siemens Stromberg-Carlson
900 Broken Sound Pkwy.
Boca Raton, FL 33487
(407) 955-6144
Fax: (407) 955-6538

Silcom Technology
4854 Old National Hwy.
Suite 110
Atlanta, GA 30337
(404) 767-3111
(800) 388-3807
Fax: (404) 767-0709

**Silicom Connectivity
   Solutions**
15311 N.E. 90th St.
Redmond, WA 98052
(206) 882-7995
(800) 474-5426
Fax: (206) 882-4775

Silicon Graphics Inc
2011 N. Shoreline Blvd.
Mountain View, CA 94043
(415) 960-1980
(800) 326-1020
Fax: (415) 961-0595

Simpact Associates, Inc.
9210 Sky Park Ct.
San Diego, CA 92123
(619) 565-1865
(800) 275-1860
Fax: (619) 292-8015

Simware Inc.
2 Gurdwara Rd.
Ottawa, ON K2E 1A2
Canada
(613) 727-1779
Fax: (613) 727-8797

Sirius Systems, Inc.
P.O. Box 2202
Petersburg, VA 23804
(804) 733-7944
Fax: (804) 861-0358

SMC Enterprise Networks
1 Riverside Dr.
Andover, MA 01810
(508) 691-1200
(800) 647-4462
Fax: (508) 691-2610

Smith Micro Software
51 Columbia
Eliso Viejo, CA 92656
(714) 362-5800
Fax: (714) 362-2300

SNMP Research
3001 Kimberlin Heights Rd.
Knoxville, TN 37920
(615) 573-1434
Fax: (615) 573-9197

Softronics
5085 List Dr.
Colorado Springs, CO 80919
(719) 593-9540
(800) 225-8590
Fax: (719) 548-1878

SoftSwitch Inc.
640 Lee Rd., Suite 200
Wayne, PA 19087
(215) 640-9600
Fax: (215) 640-7550

SoftArc
805 Middlefield Rd.
Suite 102
Scarborough, ON M1V 2T9
Canada
(416) 299-4723
Fax: (416) 754-1856

Software AG of North America, Inc.
11190 Sunrise Valley Dr.
Reston, VA 22091
(703) 860-5050
Fax: (703) 391-6975

Software Artistry
3500 DePauw Blvd.
Suite 1100
Indianapolis, IN 46268
(317) 876-3042
(800) 795-1993
Fax: (317) 876-3258

Software Engineering of America
1230 Hempstead Turnpike
Franklin Square, NY 11010
(516) 328-7000
(800) 272-7322
Fax: (516) 354-4015

Software Group
2 Director Ct., Suite 201
Woodbridge, ON L4L 3Z5
Canada
(905) 856-0238
Fax: (905) 856-0242

Software Kinetics Ltd.
65 Iber Road
Stittsville, ON K2S 1E7
Canada
(613) 831-0888
Fax: (613) 831-1836

Software Marketing Group
108 3rd St., Suite 202
Des Moines, IA 50309
(515) 284-0209
(800) 395-0209
Fax: (515) 284-5147

Sola Power Electronics
1717 Busse Rd.
Elk Grove, IL 60007
(708) 439-2800
(800) 289-7652
Fax: (708) 439-1190

Solectek
6370 Nancy Ridge Dr.
Suite 109
San Diego, CA 92121
(619) 450-1220
(800) 437-1518
Fax: (619) 457-2681

Solomon Software
1218 Commerce Pkwy.
P.O. Box 414
Findlay, OH 45840
(419) 424-0422
Fax: (419) 424-4300

Sonic Systems
1150 Kifer Rd., Suite 201
Sunnyvale, CA 94086
(408) 736-1900
(800) 535-0725
Fax: (408) 736-7228

SONY Corporation
677 River Oaks Pkwy.
San Jose, CA 95134
(408) 432-1600
Fax: (408) 432-1874

Sony Electronics
3300 Zanker Rd.
San Jose, CA 95134
(800) 352-7669
Fax: (408) 954-8339

SMC
35 Marcus Blvd.
Hauppauge, NY 11788
(516) 273-3100
(800) 992-4762
Fax: (516) 273-7935

Southern Computer Systems
2732 7th Ave. S.
Birmingham, AL 35233
(205) 251-2985
(800) 533-6879
Fax: (205) 322-4851

Spectra Logic
1700 N. 55th St.
Boulder, CO 80301
(303) 449-7759
(800) 833-1132
Fax: (303) 939-8844

Spider Communications
8255 Mountain Sights
Suite 305
Montreal, PQ J3V 2V8
Canada
(514) 653-7575
Fax: (514) 441-6224

Spider Software
33 Boston Post Rd. W.
Suite 270
Marlboro, MA 01752
(508) 460-0049
Fax: (508) 460-0107

Spry
316 Occidental Ave. S.
2nd Floor
Seattle, WA 98104
(206) 447-0300
(800) 777-9638
Fax: (206) 447-9008

SSDS
6595 S. Dayton St.
Englewood, CO 80111
(303) 790-0660
(800) 638-3375
Fax: (303) 790-1663

Stampede Technologies
78 Marco Lane
Dayton, OH 45448
(513) 291-5035
(800) 763-3423
Fax: (513) 291-5040

**Standard Microsystems
Corp.**
80 Arkay Dr.
Hauppauge, NY 11788
(516) 435-6255
(800) 762-4968
Fax: (516) 273-2136

Star Gate Technologies
29300 Aurora Rd.
Solon, OH 44139
(216) 349-1860
(800) 782-7428
Fax: (216) 349-2056

Starlight Networks
325 E. Middlefield Rd.
Mountain View, CA 94041
(415) 967-2774
Fax: (415) 967-0686

StarNine Technologies
2550 9th St., Suite 112
Berkeley, CA 94710
(510) 548-0391
Fax: (510) 548-0393

Star Tek Inc.
71 Lyman St.
Northborough, MA 01532
(508) 393-9393
(800) 225-8528
Fax: (508) 393-6934

Storage Dimensions
1656 McCarthy Blvd.
Milpitas, CA 95035
(408) 954-0710
Fax: (408) 944-1200

Sun Microsystems Inc.
2550 Garcia Ave.
Mountain View, CA 94043
(415) 960-1300
(800) 872-4786
Fax: (415) 856-2114

SunSelect
2060 Challenger Dr.
Alameda, CA 94501
(510) 769-9669
(800) 445-8677
Fax: (510) 769-8773

Superoffice
130 Great Rd.
Bedford, MA 01730
(617) 275-2140
(800) 328-6868
Fax: (617) 275-6921

Sureman Computer
15338 E. Valley Blvd.
City of Industry, CA 91746
(818) 333-7730
Fax: (818) 333-1803

SVEC Computer
2691 Richter Ave.
Suite 130
Irvine, CA 92714
(714) 756-2233
Fax: (714) 756-1340

Sybase Inc.
6475 Christie Ave.
Emeryville, CA 94608
(510) 596-3500
Fax: (510) 658-9441

Symantec
10201 Torre Ave.
Cupertino, CA 95014
(408) 253-9600
(800) 441-7234

Symplex Communications
5 Research Dr.
Ann Arbor, MI 48103
(313) 995-1555
Fax: (313) 995-1564

Sync Research
7 Studebaker Dr.
Irvine, CA 92718
(714) 588-2070
(800) 275-7965
Fax: (714) 588-2080

Synergy Software
2457 Perkiomen Ave.
Reading, PA 19606
(215) 779-0522
Fax: (215) 370-0548

Synergy Solutions
2150 S. Country Club Dr.
Suite 1
Mesa, AZ 85210
(602) 545-9797
Fax: (602) 545-9827

Synernetics Inc.
85 Rangeway Rd.
North Billerica, MA 01862
(508) 670-9009
(800) 992-2446
Fax: (508) 670-9015

SynOptics Communications
4401 Great America Pkwy.
P.O. Box 58185
Santa Clara, CA 95052
(408) 988-2400
Fax: (408) 988-5525

Syntax, Inc.
840 S. 333rd St.
Federal Way, WA 98003
(206) 833-2525
Fax: (206) 838-9836

Syskonnect Inc.
12930 Saratoga Ave.
Suite D-1
Saratoga, CA 95070
(408) 725-4650
(800) 752-3334
Fax: (408) 725-4654

Syspro
P.O. Box 243
Orinda, CA 94563
(510) 254-9755
Fax: (510) 254-4377

Systems Center Inc.
1800 Alexander Bell Dr.
Reston, VA 22091
(703) 264-8000
(800) 533-5128
Fax: (703) 264-1308

Systems Enhancements
11605 Lilburn Park Rd.
St. Louis, MO 63146
(314) 997-7717
Fax: (314) 997-1501

Sytron
134 Flanders Rd.
Westboro, MA 01581
(508) 898-0100
(800) 877-0016
Fax: (508) 898-2677

T3plus Networking Inc.
3393 Octavius Dr.
Santa Clara, CA 95054
(408) 727-4545
(800) 477-7585
Fax: (408) 727-5151

T4 Systems
3 Inwood Circle, Suite 16
Little Rock, AR 72211
(501) 227-6637
(800) 233-1526
Fax: (501) 227-6245

TAC Systems
1031 Putnam Dr.
Huntsville, AL 35816
(205) 721-1976
Fax: (205) 721-0242

Tally Systems
P.O. Box 70
Hanover, NH 03755
(603) 643-1300
(800) 262-3877
Fax: (603) 643-9366

Tandberg Data
2685 Park Center Dr.
Simi Valley, CA 93065
(805) 579-1000
(800) 258-8285
Fax: (805) 579-2555

Tandem Computers, Inc.
14231 Tandem Blvd.
Austin, TX 78728-6699
(512) 244-8359
Fax: (512) 244-8037

Tangent Computer Inc.
197 Airport Blvd.
Burlingame, CA 94010
(800) 800-6060
Fax: (415) 342-9388

Tangram Enterprise
   Solutions
7 Great Valley Pkwy. E.
Malvern, PA 19355
(610) 647-0440
(800) 722-2482
Fax: (610) 640-1379

Tangram Systems
5511 Capital Center Dr.
Suite 400
Raleigh, NC 27606
(919) 851-6000
Fax: (919) 851-6004

TCE Technology Group
1977 O'Toole Ave.
Suite B202
San Jose, CA 95131
(408) 321-7600
(800) 424-2388
Fax: (408) 321-7601

TCL
41829 Albrae St.
Fremont, CA 94538
(510) 657-3800
Fax: (510) 490-5814

481

Technically Elite Concepts
2615 Pacific Coast Hwy.
Suite 322
Hermosa Beach, CA 90254
(310) 379-2505
(800) 659-6975
Fax: (310) 379-5985

Technology Works
4030 W. Braker Lane
Suite 350
Austin, TX 78759
(512) 794-8533
Fax: (512) 794-8520

Tecmar
6225 Cochran Rd.
Solon, OH 44139-3377
(216) 349-0600
(800) 624-8560
Fax: (216) 349-0851

Technology Exchange Co.
One Jacob Way
Reading, MA 01867
(800) 333-5177
Fax: (617) 944-3700

Tekelec
26580 W. Agoura Rd.
Calabasas, CA 91302
(818) 880-5656
(800) 835-3532
Fax: (818) 880-6993

TEKnique
911 N. Plum Grove Rd.
Schaumburg, IL 60173
(708) 706-9700
Fax: (708) 706-9735

Tektronix, Inc.
625 S.E. Salmon
Redmond, OR 97756
(503) 923-0333
(800) 833-9200
Fax: (503) 923-4434

Telco Systems Inc./
Magnalink
Communications
63 Nahatan St.
Norwood, MA 02062
(617) 255-9400
Fax: (617) 255-5885

Telebit Corporation
1315 Chesapeake Terr.
Sunnyvale, CA 94089
(408) 734-4333
(800) 835-3248
Fax: (408) 734-4333

Telecommunications
Techniques Corp.
20400 Observation Dr.
Germantown, MD 20874
(301) 353-1550
(800) 638-2049
Fax: (301) 353-0731

Telematics International
1201 Cypress Creek Rd.
Ft. Lauderdale, FL 33309
(305) 772-3070
Fax: (305) 351-4405

Telenex
13000 Midlantic Dr.
Mount Laurel, NJ 08054
(609) 234-7900
Fax: (609) 273-7688

Tenon Intersystems
1123 Chapala St., Suite 202
Santa Barbara, CA 93101
(805) 963-6983
Fax: (805) 962-8202

Texas Microsystems
5959 Corporate Dr.
Houston, TX 77036
(713) 541-8200
(800) 627-8700
Fax: (713) 541-8226

TGI Technologies
107 E.3rd Ave.
Vancouver, BC V5T 1C7
Canada
(604) 872-6676
Fax: (604) 872-6601

TGV, Inc.
101 Cooper St.
Santa Cruz, CA 95060
(408) 457-5329
Fax: (408) 457-5243

Themis Computer
6681 Owens Dr.
Pleasanton, CA 94588
(510) 734-0870
Fax: (510) 734-0873

The Mitre Corporation
7525 Colshire Dr.
McLean, VA 22102
(703) 883-6728
Fax: (703) 883-3315

The Santa Cruz Operation
400 Encinal St.
P.O. Box 1900
Santa Cruz, CA 95061
(408) 425-7222
Fax: (408) 458-4227

Thomas-Conrad Corp.
1908-R Kramer Lane
Austin, TX 78758
(512) 836-1935
(800) 332-8683
Fax: (512) 836-2840

3Com Corporation
5400 Bayfront Plaza
Santa Clara, CA 95052
(408) 562-6400
(800) 638-3266
Fax: (408) 764-5001

Tiara Computer Systems
1091 Shoreline Blvd.
Mountain View, CA 94043
(415) 965-1700
(800) 638-4272
Fax: (415) 965-2677

Token Technology
1265 Montecito Ave.
Suite 101
Mountain View, CA 94043
(415) 965-8607
Fax: (415) 965-8658

Traffic Software
360 W. 31st St.
New York, NY 10001
(212) 714-1584
Fax: (212) 794-7168

Transarc Corp.
707 Grant St. Gulf Tower
20th Floor
Pitsburgh PA 15219
(412) 338-4400
Fax: (412)338-4404

Transfax
6133 Bristol Pkwy.
Suite 275
Culver City, CA 90230
(310) 641-0439
Fax: (310) 641-4076

Transition Engineering
7090 Shady Oak Rd.
Eden Prairie, MN 55344
(612) 941-7600
(800) 325-2725
Fax: (612) 941-2322

Transitional Technology
5401 E. La Palma Ave.
Anaheim, CA 92807
(714) 693-1133
Fax: (714) 693-0255

Transport
127 Jetplex Circle
Madison, AL 35758
(205) 772-3770
(800) 926-0085
Fax: (205) 772-3388

TRW Inc.
1760 Glenn Curtiss St.
Carson, CA 90746
(310) 764-9467
Fax: (213) 764-9491

Traveling Software
18702 N. Creek Pkwy
Bothell, WA 98011
(206) 483-8088
(800) 343-8080
Fax: (206) 487-1284

Trax Softworks
5840 Uplander Way
Culver City, CA 90230
(310) 649-5800
(800) 367-8729
Fax: (310) 649-6200

Trellis Network Services
225 Turnpike Rd.
Southboro, MA 01772
(508) 485-7200
(800) 793-3390
Fax: (508) 485-3044

Trend Micro Devices
2421 W. 205th St.
Suite D100
Torrance, CA 90501
(310) 782-8190
(800) 228-5651
Fax: (310) 328-5892

Tribe Computer Works
960 Atlantic Ave., Suite 101
Alameda, CA 94501
(510) 814-3900
Fax: (510) 814-3900

Tricord Systems
3750 Annapolis Lane
Plymouth, MN 55447
(612) 557-9005
(800) 874-2673
Fax: (612) 557-8403

Tri-Data Systems, Inc.
3270 Scott Blvd.
Santa Clara, CA 94054
(408) 727-3270
(800) 874-3282
Fax: (408) 980-6565

Trinzic
1 Harbour Pl., Suite 500
Portsmouth, NH 03801
(603) 427-0444
(800) 952-8779
Fax: (603) 427-0385

Trio Information Systems
88601 Six Forks Rd.
Suite 105
Raleigh, NC 27615
(919) 846-4990
(800) 880-4400
Fax: (919) 846-4997

Tripp Lite
500 N. Orleans
Chicago, IL 60610
(312) 329-1601
Fax: (312) 644-6505

Triticom
11800 Single Tree Lane
Suite 310
Eden Prairie, MN 55344
(612) 937-0772
Fax: (612) 937-1998

Triton Technologies Inc.
200 Middlesex Turnpike
Iselin, NJ 08830
(908) 855-9440
(800) 322-9440
Fax: (908) 855-9608

TTC/LP Com
270 Santa Ana Ct.
Sunnyvale, CA 94086
(408) 749-8008
Fax: (408) 736-1951

Tut Systems
2446 Estand Way
Pleasant Hill, CA 94523
(510) 682-6510
(800) 998-4888
Fax: (510) 682-4125

Tylink Corp.
10 Commerce Way
Norton, MA 02766
(508) 285-0033

UB Networks
3900 Freedom Circle
Santa Clara, CA 95052
(408) 496-0111
(800) 777-4526
Fax: (408) 970-7337

Uconix Corp.
4669 Murphy Canyon Rd.
San Diego, CA 92123
(619) 627-1700
Fax: (619) 627-1710

Ungermann-Bass, Inc.
3990 Freedom Circle
Santa Clara, CA 95052-
    8030
(408) 496-0111
(800) 873-6381
Fax: (408) 727-4456

Unicom Electric
11980 Telegraph Rd.
Suite 103
Santa Fe Springs, CA 90670
(310) 946-9650
(800) 346-6668
Fax: (310) 946-9473

UniPress Software
2025 Lincoln Hwy.
Edison, NJ 08817
(908) 287-2100
(800) 222-0550
Fax: (908) 287-4929

Unitrol Data Protection
    Systems
2108 1177 W. Hastings
Vancouver, BC V6E 2K3
Canada
(604) 681-3611
(800) 665-2212
Fax: (604) 681-3615

UniSoft Systems
1250 Bayhill Dr., Suite 200
San Bruno, CA 94066
(415) 794-2666
Fax: (415) 794-2668

Unisys
Township Line and Union
    Meeting Rd.
Blue Bell, PA 19422
(215) 986-4011
Fax: (215) 986-6850

UNIX Systems
    Laboratories, Inc.
190 River Rd.
Summit, NJ 07901
(908) 522-5006
Fax: (908) 522-5463

Upsonic
29 Journey
Aliso Viejo, CA 92656
(714) 448-9500
(800) 877-6642
Fax: (714) 448-9555

U.S. Robotics Software
8100 N. McCormick Blvd.
Skokie, IL 60076-2920
(504) 923-0888
(800) 292-2988

UUNET
    Technologies/AlterNet
3110 Fairview Park Dr.,
    Suite 570
Falls Church, VA 22042
(703) 204-8000
Fax: (703) 204-8001

Verilink Corp.
145 Baytech Dr.
San Jose, CA 95134
(408) 945-1199
(800) 543-1008
Fax: (408) 262-6260

Viacrypt
9033 N. 24th Ave., Suite 7
Phoenix, AZ 85021
(602) 944-0773
Fax: (602) 943-6201

ViewStar
1101 Marina Village Pkwy.
Alameda, CA 94501
(510) 337-2000
Fax: (510) 337-2222

Vinca
1815 S. State, Suite 4000
Orem, UT 84058
(801) 223-3100
(800) 934-9530
Fax: (801) 223-3107

Vinzant
600 E. 3rd St.
Hobart, IN 46342
(219) 942-9544
(800) 355-3443
Fax: (219) 942-1480

Visionware
4500 Bohannon Dr.
Suite 280
Menlo Park, CA 94026
(415) 325-2113
(800) 949-8474
Fax: (415) 325-8710

484

VisiSoft
2700 N.E. Expressway
Suite B-700
Atlanta, GA 30345
(404) 320 0077
Fax: (404) 320-0450

Vtel Corp.
108 Wild Basin Rd.
Austin, TX 78746
(512) 314-2700
Fax: (512) 314-2792

Vycor Corp.
5411 Berwyn Rd., M/S 304
College Park, MD 20740
(800) 888-9267
Fax: (301) 220-0727

**Walker Richer and
    Quinn, Inc.**
1500 Dexter Ave. N.
Seattle, WA 98109
(206) 324-0407
(800) 872-2829
Fax: (206) 322-8151

Wall Data, Inc.
17769 N.E. 78th Pl.
Redmond, WA 98052-4992
(206) 883-4777
(800) 487-8622
Fax: (206) 861-3175

Wandel and Goltermann
2200 Gateway Centre Blvd.
Morrisville, NC 27560
(919) 460-3300
(800) 346-6332
Fax: (919) 481-4372

Wang Laboratories
1 Industrial Ave.
Lowell, MA 01851
(508) 459-5000
(800) 225-0654
Fax: (508) 967-7020

Wavetek
9045 Balboa Ave.
San Diego, CA 92123
(619) 279-2200
(800) 854-2708
Fax: (619) 450-0325

Web Technologies Inc.
150 S. Front St.
Souderton, PA 18964
(215) 723-6400
(800) 724-9300
Fax: (215) 723-0333

Webster Computer Corp.
2109 O'Toole Ave., Suite J
San Jose, CA 95131
(408) 954-8054
(800) 457-0903
Fax: (408) 954-1832

Westbrook Technologies
22 Pequot Park Rd.
P.O.Box 910
Westbrook, CT 06498
(203) 399-7111
(800) 949-3453
Fax: (203) 399-7137

Western Digital Corp.
8105 Irvine Center Dr.
Irvine, CA 92718
(714) 932-5000
(800) 832-4778
Fax: (714) 932-6098

White Pine Software, Inc.
40 Simon St., Suite 201
Nashua, NH 03060
(603) 886-9050
Fax: (603) 886-9051

Winchester Systems
400 W. Cummings Park
Woburn, MA 01801
(617) 933-8500
(800) 325-3700
Fax: (617) 933-6174

Wi-LAN
308-809 Manning Rd. N.E.
Calgary, AB T2E 7M9
Canada
(403) 273-9133
(800) 658-6876
Fax: (403) 273-5100

Wilcom Products
Rt. 3, Daniel Webster Hwy.
Laconia, NH 03246
(603) 524-2622
(800) 222-1898
Fax: (603) 528-3804

Windata
543 Great Rd.
Littleton, MA 01460
(508) 952-0170
(800) 553-8008
Fax: (508) 952-0168

Wingra Software Inc.
450 Science Dr., Suite 1 W.
Madison, WI 53711
(608) 238-8637
Fax: (608) 238-8986

The Wollongong Group
1129 San Antonio Rd.
Palo Alto, CA 94303
(415) 962-7100
(800) 872-8649
Fax: (415) 962-0286

**WordPerfect,The Novell
    Applications Group**
1555 N.Technology Way
Orem, UT 84057
(801) 222-5000
(800) 451-5151
Fax: (801) 222-5077

World Software Corp.
124 Prospect St.
Ridgewood, NJ 07450
(201) 444-3228
Fax: (201) 444-9065

Worldtalk
475 Alberto Way
Los Gatos, CA 95032
(408) 399-4000
Fax: (408) 399-4013

WRQ Reflection
1500 Dexter Ave. N.
Seattle, WA 98109
(206) 217-7500
(800) 872-2829
Fax: (206) 217-0293

Xavier Technology
14904 N.E. 31st Circle
Redmond, WA 98052
(206) 869-5252
Fax: (206) 869-5252

XCd
3002 Dow Ave., Suite 110
Tustin, CA 92680
(714) 573-7055
Fax: (714) 573-7084

Xcellenet
5 Concourse Pkwy.
Suite 200
Atlanta, GA 30328
(404) 804-8100
Fax: (404) 804-8102

Xedia Corp.
301 Ballardvale St.
Wilmington, MA 01887
(508) 658-7200
Fax: (508) 658-7204

Xerox Corporation
100 Clinton Ave. S.
Rochester, NY 14644
(716) 423-5090
Fax: (716) 423-5733

Xinet
2560 9th St., Suite 312
Berkeley, CA 94710
(510) 644-0146
Fax: (510) 644-2680

Xinetron Inc.
2348 Walsh Ave.
Santa Clara, CA 95051
(408) 727-5509
(800) 345-4415
Fax: (408) 727-6499

Xircom
26025 Mureau Rd.
Calabasas, CA 91302
(800) 874-7875
(818) 878-7600
Fax: (818) 878-7630

XNet Technology
426 S. Hillview Dr.
Milpitas, CA 95035
(408) 263-6888
(800) 788-0148
Fax: (408) 263-8898

Xylan Corp.
26679 W. Agoura Rd.
Suite 100
Calabasas, CA 91302
(818) 880-3500
(800) 999-9526
Fax: (818) 880-3505

Xylogics
53 Third Ave.
Burlington, MA 01803
(617) 272-8142
(800) 225-3317
Fax: (617) 273-5392

Xyplex, Inc.
295 Foster St.
Littleton, MA 01460
(508) 952-4700
(800) 338-5316
Fax: (508) 952-4702

Z-Code Software
101 Rowland Way, Suite
300
Novato, CA 94945
(415) 898-8649
Fax: (415) 898-8299

Zenith Electronics Corp.
Communication Products
Division
1000 Milwaukee Ave.
Glenview, IL 60025
(708) 391-8000
(800) 788-7244
Fax: (708) 391-8919

Zero One
Networking/Zyxel
4920 E. La Palma Ave.
Anaheim, CA 92807
(714) 693-0804
Fax: (714) 693-0705

G Acronyms and Abbreviations

A	Ampere
AA	Administrative Authority
AAL	ATM Adaption Layer
AARP	AppleTalk Address Resolution Protocol
ABM	Asynchronous Balanced Mode (of HDLC)
ABP	Alternate Bipolar
ACF	Access Control Field
ACK	Acknowledgement
ACS	Asynchronous Communication Server
ACTLU	Activate Logical Unit
ACTPU	Activate Physical Unit
ADPCM	Adaptive Differential Pulse Code Modulation
ADSP	AppleTalk Data Stream Protocol
AEP	AppleTalk Echo Protocol
AFI	Authority and Format Identifier
AFP	AppleTalk Filing Protocol
AFRP	ARCNET Fragmentation Protocol

AGS	Asynchronous Gateway Server
AI	Artificial Intelligence
AIN	Advanced Intelligent Network
AIS	Alarm Indication Signal
AL	Alignment
AMI	Alternate Mark Inversion
AMT	Address Mapping Table
ANS.1	Abstract Syntax Notation One
ANSI	American National Standards Institute
API	Applications Program Interface
APPC	Advanced Program-to-Program Communication
ARE	All Routes Explorer
AREA	Area Identifier
ARI	Address Recognized Indicator Bit
ARM	Asynchronous Response Mode
ARP	Address Resolution Program
ARPA	Advanced Research Projects Agency
ARPANET	Advanced Research Projects Agency Network
ACCE	Association Control Service Element
ASCII	American Standard Code for Information Interchange
ASP	AppleTalk Session Protocol
ATIS	Alliance for Telecommunications Industry Solutions
ATM	Asynchronous Transfer Mode
ATM DXI	ATM Data Exchange Interface
ATM UNI	ATM User-Network Interface
ATP	AppleTalk Transaction Protocol
AU	Access Unit
B	B Channel
B	Broadband
B8ZS	Bipolar with 8 ZERO Substitution

BAsize	Buffer Allocation size
BC	Block Check
BC	Bearer Capability
Bc	Committed Burst
BCD	Binary Coded Decimal
BCN	Backward Congestion Notification
Be	Excess Burst
BECN	Backward Explicit Congestion Notification
BER	Basic Encoding Rules
BER	Bit Error Ratio
BEtag	Beginning-End tag
B-ICI	Broadband Inter Carrier Interface
BIF	Bus Indentification Field
BIOS	Basic Input/Output System
BIP	Bit Interleaved Parity
BIP-n	Bit Interleaved Parity-n
B-ISDN	Broadband Integrated Services Digital Network
B-ISSI	Broadband Inter-Switching System Interface
BITNET	Because It's Time NETwork
BIU	Basic Information Unit
B-NT1	Network Termination 1 for B-ISDN
B-NT2	Network Termination 2 for B-ISDN
BOC	Bell Operating Company
BOM	Beginning-of-message
BOOTP	Bootstrap Protocol
BPDU	Bridge Protocol Data Unit
bps	Bits Per Second
BPV	Bipolar Violations
BRI	Basic Rate Interface
BSC	Binary Synchronous Communication

BSD	Berkeley Software Distribution
BSS	Broadband Switching System
B-TA	Terminal Adapter for B-ISDN
B-TE	B-ISDN Terminal Equipment
B-TE1	Terminal Equipment 1 for B-ISDN
B-TE2	Terminal Equipment 2 for B-ISDN
BTag	Begin Tag
BTU	Basic Transmission Unit
BWBM	BandWidth Balancing Machine
BWB_CNTR	BandWidth Balancing CouNTeR
BWB_MOD	BandWidth Balancing MODulus
CAD/CAM	Computer-Aided Design and Manufacturing
CBR	Constant Bit Rate
CC	Configuration Control
CDV	Cell Delay Variance
CI	Congestion Indication
CIR	Committed Information Rate
CLP	Cell Loss Priority
CLS	Connectionless Service
COM	Continuation of Message
CP	Common Part
CPCS	Common Part Convergence Sublayer
CPE	Customer Premises Equipment
CPI	Common Part Indicator
CRC	Cyclic Redundancy Check
C/R	Command/Response bit
CRS	Cell Relay Service
CS	Convergence Sublayer
CSI	Convergence Sublayer Indicator
CSMA/CD	Carrier Sense Multiple Access with Collision Detection

CSNET	Computer+Science Network
CSPDN	Circuit Switched Public Data Network
CSU	Channel Service Unit
CTERM	Command Terminal Protocol
D	D Channel
DA	Destination Address
DAP	Data Access Protocol
DARPA	Defense Advanced Research Projects Agency
DAT	Duplicate Address Test
DCA	Defense Communications Agency
DCC	Data Country Code
DCE	Data Circuit-Terminating Equipment
DCN	Data Communications Network
DCS n/n	Digital Cross connect System at Level n
DDCMP	Digital Data Communications Message Protocol
DDI	Direct Dialing In
DDN	Defense Data Network
DDP	Datagram Delivery Protocol
DDS	Digital Data Service
DE	Discard Eligible
DECmcc	DEC Management Control Center
DEMPR	DEC Multiport Repeater
DFI	DSP Format Identifier
DH	DMPDU Header
DIX	DEC, Intel, and Xerox
DL	Data Link
DLC	Data Link Control
DLCI	Data Link Connection Identifier
DMA	Direct Memory Access
DMDD	Distributed Multiplexing Distributed Demultiplexing

DMPDU	Derived MAC Protocol Data Unit
DNIC	Data Network Identification Code
DNS	Domain Name System
DOD	Department of Defense
DPA	Demand Protocol Architecture
DQDB	Distributed Queue Dual Bus
DQSM	Distributed Queue State Machine
DRP	DECnet Routing Protocol
DSAP	Destination Service Access Point
DSG	Default Slot Generator
DSGS	Default Slot Generator Subfield
DS0	Digital Signal Level 0 (64 kbps)
DS1	Digital Signal Level 1 (1.544 Mbps)
DS3	Digital Signal Level 3 (44.736 Mbps)
DSP	Domain Specific Part
DSU	Data Service Unit
DSU/CSU	Data Service Unit/Channel Service Unit
DSX-n	Digital Signal Cross Connect Level n
DT	DMPDU Trailer
DTE	Data Terminal Equipment
DTR	Data Terminal Ready
DXC	Digital Cross-Connect
DXI	Data Exchange Interface
EA	Extended Address
EBCDIC	Extended Binary Coded Decimal Interchange Code
ECL	End Communication Layer
ECSA	Exchange Carriers Standards Association
ED	End Delimiter
EDI	Electronic Data Interchange
EFCN	Explicit Forward Congestion Notification

EGA	Enhanced Graphics Array
EGP	Exterior Gateway Protocol
EIA	Electronic Industries Association
ELAP	EtherTalk Link Access Protocol
EOM	End-of-Message
EOT	End of Transmission
ES	Errored Second
ESF	Extended Superframe Format
ESI	End System Identifier
ESIG	European SMDS Interest Group
ES-IS	End System to Intermediate System Protocol
ET	Exchange Termination
ETS	External Timing Source
ETag	End Tag
ETSS	External Timing Source Subfield
ETSI	European Telecommunications Standards Institute
Ext	Extension
FAL	File Access Listener
FAT	File Access Table
FCC	Federal Communications Commission
FCI	Frame Copied Indicator Bit
FCN	Forward Congestion Notification
FCS	Frame Check Sequence
FDDI	Fiber Data Distributed Interface
FDM	Frequency Division Multiplexing
FEBE	Far End Block Error
FEC	Forward Error Correction
FECN	Forward Error Congestion Notification
FERF	Far End Receive Failure
FFS	For Further Study

FH	Frame Handler
FID	Format Identifier
FIFO	First-in First-out
FIPS	Federal Information Processing Standard
FM	Function Management
FMD	Function Management Data
FMIF	Frame Mode Information Field
FOTS	Fiber Optic Transport System
FR	Frame Relay
FRS	Frame Relay Service
FR-UNI	Frame Relay User Network Interface
FRAD	Frame Relay Assembler/Disassembler
FRND	Frame Relay Network Device
FR-SSCS	Frame Relay Service Specific Convergence Sublayer
FT1	Fractional T1
FTAM	File Transfer Access and Management
FTP	File Transfer Protocol
G	Giga-
GB	Gigabyte
GFC	Generic Flow Control
GHz	Gigahertz
GOSIP	Government OSI Profile
GUI	Graphical User Interface
HA	Hardware Address
HCS	Header Check Sequence
HDLC	High Level Data Link Control
Hdr	Header
HEC	Header Error Control
HEL	Header Extension Length
HEMS	Higg-level Entity Management System

HLC	High Layer Compatability
HLLAPI	High Level Language API
HLPI	Higher Layer Protocol Identifier
HOB	Head-of-Bus
HOB_A	Head of Bus A
HOB_B	Head of Bus B
HOBS	Head of Bus Subfield
HSSI	High Speed Serial Interface
Hz	Hertz
I	Information
IA5	International Alphabet No. 5
IAB	Internet Architecture Board
IANA	Internet Assigned Numbers Authority
ICD	International Code Designator
ICF	Isochronous Convergence Function
ICI	Interexchange Carrier Interface
ICIP	Inter Carrier Interface Protocol
ICIP_CLS	ICIP Connectionless Service
ICMP	Internet Control Message Protocol
ICP	Internet Control Protocol
IDI	Initial Domain Identifier
IDP	Internetwork Datagram Protocol
IDU	Interface Data Unit
IE	Information Element
IEC	International Electrotechnical Commission
IEEE	Institute of Electrical and Electronics Engineers
IETF	Internet Engineering Task Force
I/G	Individual/Group
IGP	Interior Gateway Protocol
IGRP	Internet Gateway Routing Protocol

ILMI	Interim Local Management Interface
IMPDU	Initial MAC Protocol Data Unit
IMPS	Interface Message Processors
I/O	Input/Output
IOC	Inter-Office Channel
IP	Internet Protocol
IPC	Interprocess Communications Protocol
IPX	Internetwork Packet Exchange
IR	Internet Router
IRTF	Internet Research Task Force
ISA	Industry Standard Architecture
ISDN	Integrated Services Digital Network
ISDU	Isochronous Service Data Unit
IS-IS	Intermediate System to Intermediate System Protocol
ISO	International Organization for Standardization
ISODE	ISO Development Environment
ISSI	Inter-Switching System Interface
ISSIP_CLS	Inter-Switching System Interface Protocol Connectionless Service
ISU	Isochronous Service User
IT	Information Type
ITU	International Telecommunication Union
ITU-T	ITU Telecommunication Standardization Sector (formerly CCITT)
IVDLAN	Integrated Voice/Data Local Area Network
IWF	Interworking Function
IWU	Interworking Unit
IXC	Inter-Exchange Carrier
Kbps	Kilo Bits per Second
KHz	Kilohertz

LAA	Locally-Administered Address
LAN	Local Area Network
LAP	Link Access Procedure
LAPB	Link Access Procedure Balanced
LAPD	Link Access Procedure D Channel
LAPF	Link Access Procedures to Frame Mode Bearer Services
LAT	Local Area Transport
LATA	Local Access Transport Area
LAVC	Local Area VAX Cluster
LE	Local Exchange
LEC	Local Exchange Carrier
LEN	Length
LF	Largest Frame
LFC	Local Function Capabilities
LI	Link Identifier
LI	Length Indicator
LL	Logical Link
LLAP	LocalTalk Link Access Protocol
LLC	Logical Link Control
LLI	Logical Link Identifier
LME	Layer Management Entity
LMI	Local Management Interface
LMI	Layer Management Interface
LMM	LAN/WAN Management User
LMMP	LAN/MAN Management Protocol
LMMPE	LAN/MAN Management Protocol Entity
LMMS	LAN/MAN Management Service
LMMU	LAN/MAN Management User
LOC	Loss of Cell delineation
LOF	Loss of Frame

LOH	Line Overhead
LOP	Loss of Pointer
LOS	Loss of Signal
LPP	Lightweight Presentation Protocol
LSB	Least Significant Bit
LSL	Link Support Layer
LSS	Link Status Signal
LT	Line Termination
LTE	Line Terminating Equipment
MAC	Medium Access Control
MAN	Metropolitan Area Network
MAP	Management Application Protocol
Mbps	Mega Bits Per Second
MCF	MAC Convergence Function
MCP	MAC Convergence Protocol
MHS	Message Handling Service
MHz	Megahertz
MIB	Management Information Base
MID	Message IDentifier
MID	Multiplexing IDentifier
MILNET	MILitary NETwork
MIPS	Millions Instructions Per Second
MIS	Management Information Systems
MLID	Multiple Link Interface Driver
MMF	Multi Mode Fiber
MNP	Microcom Networking Protocol
M/O	Mandatory/Optional
MOP	Maintenance Operations Protocol
MPA	MID Page Allocation
MPAF	MID Page Allocation Field

ms	Milliseconds
MSAP	MAC Service Access Point
MSAU	Multistation Access Unit
MSB	Most Significant Bit
MSDU	MAC Service Data Unit
MSN	Monitoring Cell Sequence Number
MSS	MAN Switching System
MTA	Message Transfer Agent
MTBF	Mean Time Between Failure
MTTR	Mean Time To Repair
MTU	Maximum Transmission Unit
MUX	Multiplex, Multiplexor
NACS	NetWare Asynchronous Communications Server
NAK	Negative Acknowledgement
NASI	Netware Asynchronous Service Interface
NAU	Network Addressable Unit
NAUN	Nearest Active Upstream Neighbor
NBP	Name Binding Protocol
NCP	Network Control Program
NCP	NetWare Core Protocol
NCSI	Network Communications Services Interface
NDIS	Network Driver Interface Standard
NetBEUI	NetBIOS Extended User Interface
NetBIOS	Network Basic Input/Output System
NFS	Network File System
NIC	Network Information Center
NIC	Network Interface Card
NIC	Network Independent Clock
NICE	Network Information and Control Exchange
NIS	Names Information Socket

NIST	National Institute of Standards and Technology
NLM	NetWare Loadable Module
NMP	Network Management Process
NMS	Network Management Station
NNI	Network-Network Interface
NNI	Network-Node Interface
NOC	Network Operations Center
NOS	Network Operating System
NPC	Network Parameter Control
NRM	Normal Response Mode
NRZ	Non-Return to Zero
NSAP	Network Service Access Point
NSF	National Science Foundation
NSP	Network Services Protocol
NT	Network Termination
NT1	Network Termination of type 1
NT2	Network Termination of type 2
OAM	Operations and Maintenance
OC1	Optical Carrier, Level 1 (51.84 Mbps)
OC3	Optical Carrier, Level 3 (155.52 Mbps)
OCn	Optical Carrier, Level n
ODI	Open Data Link Interface
OID	Object Identifier
OIM	OSI Internet Management
OOF	Out of Frame
OS	Operating System
OSF	Open Software Foundation
OSI	Open Systems Interconnection
OSI-RM	Open Systems Interconnection Reference Model
OSPF	Open Shortest Path First

OUI	Organizationally Unique Identifier
PA	Pre-arbitrated Functions
PA	Protocol Address
PABX	Private Automatic Branch Exchange
PAD	Packet Assembler and Disassembler
PAD	Padding
PAP	Printer Access Protocol
PBX	Private Branch Exchange
PC	Personal Computer
PCI	Protocol Control Information
PCM	Pulse Code Modulation
PCSM	Page Counter State Machine
PDN	Public Data Network
PDU	Protocol Data Unit
PEP	Packet Exchange Protocol
PH	Packet Handler
Ph-SAP	Physical layer Service Access Point
PHY	Physical Layer Protocol
PI	Protocol Identification
PID	Protocol Identifier
PL	PAD Length
PL	Physical Layer
PLCP	Physical Layer Convergence Protocol
PLCSM	Physical Layer Connection State Machine
PLEN	Protocol Length
PLP	Packet Layer Protocol
PM	Physical Medium
POH	Path Overhead
POI	Path Overhead Identifier
POP	Point of Presence

POSIX	Portable Operating System Interface—UNIX
POTS	Plain Old Telephone Service
PPP	Point-to-Point Protocol
PRSIG	Pacific Rim SMDS Interest Group
PSN	Packet Switch Node
PSP	Presentation Services Process
PSPDN	Packet Switched Public Data Network
PSR	Previous Segment Received
PSTN	Public Switched Telephone Network
PT	Payload Type
PTN	Personal Telecommunications Number
PTP	Point-to-Point
PUC	Public Utility Commission
PVC	Permanent Virtual Circuit
PVC	Permanent Virtual Connection
QA	Queued Arbitrated
QOS	Quality of Service
RARP	Reverse Address Resolution Protocol
RBOC	Regional Bell Operating Company
RC	Routing Control
RD	Route Descriptor
RD	Routing Domain Identifier
RDT	Remote Digital Terminal
RDTD	Restricted Differential Time Delay
REQ	Request
RFC	Request for Comments
RFH	Remote Frame Handler
RFS	Remote File System
RH	Request/Response Header
RI	Routing Information

RII	Route Information Indicator
RIP	Routing Information Protocol
RJE	Remote Job Entry
RMON	Remote Monitoring
ROSE	Remote Operations Service Element
RPC	Remote Procedure Call
RPS	Ring Parameter Service
RQ	Request Counter
RQM	Request Queue Machine
RSM	Reassembly State Machine
RSX	Realtime resource-Sharing eXecutive
RT	Routing Type
RU	Request/Response Unit
RX	Receive
SA	Source Address
SABME	Set Asynchronous Balanced Mode Extended
SAP	Service Access Point
SAP	Service Advertising Protocol
SAPI	Service Access Point Identifier
SAR	Segmentation and Reassembly
SAT	Subscriber Access Termination
SCS	System Communication Services
SDH	Synchronous Digital Hierarchy
SDL	Functional Specification and Description Language
SDLC	Synchronous Data Link Control
SDN	Software Defined Network
SDSU	SMDS Data Service Unit
SDU	Service Data Unit
SEL	NSAP Selector
SEQ	Sequence

SET	Switching System (SS) Exchange Termination
SG_1	Slot Generator type 1 function
SG_2	Slot Generator type 2 function
SG_D	Default Slot Generator function
SGMP	Simple Gateway Management Protocol
SIG	SMDS Interest Group
SIP	SMDS Interface Protocol
SIP_CLS	SIP Connectionless Service
SIR	Sustained Information Rate
SIU	Subscriber Interface Unit
SLIP	Serial Line IP
SMAE	System Management Application Entity
SMB	Server Message Block
SMDS	Switched Multimegabit Data Service
SMF	Single Mode Fiber
SMI	Structure of Management Information
SMT	Station Management
SMTP	Simple Mail Transfer Protocol
SN	Sequence Number
SNA	System Network Architecture
SNADS	Systems Network Architecture Distribution Services
SNAP	Sub-Network Access Protocol
SNCF	SubNetwork Configuration Field
SNI	Subscriber-Network Interface
SNMP	Simple Network Management Protocol
SOH	Start of Header
SOH	Section Overhead
SONET	Synchronous Optical Network
SPE	Synchronous Payload Envelope
SPN	Subscriber Premises Network

SPP	Sequenced Packet Protocol
SPX	Sequenced Packet Exchange
SR	Source Routing
SRF	Specifically Routed Frame
SRI	Stanford Research Institute
SRI	SIP Relay Interface
SRT	Source Routing Transparent
SS	Switching System
SSAP	Source Service Access Point
SSCS	Service Specific Convergence Sublayer
SSCF	Service Specific Coordination Function
SSCOP	Service Specific Connection Oriented Protocol
SSM	Single Segment Message
SS7	Common Channel Signalling System No. 7
ST	Segment Type
STE	Spanning Tree Explorer
STE	Section Terminating Equipment
STM	Synchronous Transfer Mode
STS-N	Synchronous Transport Signal level-N
SUA	Stored Upstream Address
SVC	Switched Virtual Connection
SVC	Switched Virtual Circuit
TA	Technical Advisory
TA	Terminal Adapter
TAG	Technology Advisory Group
TB	Terabyte
TC	Transmission Convergence
TCP	Transmission Control Protocol
TCP/IP	Transmission Control Protocol/Internet Protocol
TDM	Time Division Multiplexing

TE	Terminal Equipment
TE1	Terminal Equipment of type 1
TE2	Terminal Equipment of type 2
TEI	Terminal Endpoint Identifier
TELNET	Telecommunications Network
TFTP	Trivial File Transfer Protocol
TH	Transmission Header
TID	Terminal Identifier
TLAP	TokenTalk Link Access Protocol
TLI	Transport Layer Interface
TLV	Type-Length-Value Encoding
TP	Transport Protocol
TR	Technical Reference
TS	Time Stamp
TSR	Terminate-and-Stay Resident
TUC	Total User Cell Number
TX	Transmit
UA	Unnumbered Acknowledgement
UA	User Agent
UAS	Unavailable Seconds
UDI	Unrestricted Digital Information
UDI-TA	Unrestricted Digital Information with Tones/Announcements
UDP	User Datagram Protocol
UI	Unnumbered Information Frame
U/L	Universal/Local
ULP	Upper Layer Protocols
UNI	User Network Interface
UNMA	Unified Network Management Architecture
UPC	Usage Parameter Control
USID	User Service Identificator

UT	Universal Time
UTP	Unshielded Twisted Pair
UU	User-to-User
UUCP	UNIX to UNIX Copy Program
V	Volt
VAN	Value Added Network
VAP	Value Added Process
VARP	VINES Address Resolution Protocol
VBR	Variable Bit Rate
VC	Virtual Channel
VCC	Virtual Channel Connection
VCI	Virtual Channel Identifier
VF	Voice Frequency Services
VFRP	VINES Fragmentation Protocol
VGA	Video Graphics Array
VICP	VINES Internet Control Protocol
VINES	Virtual Networking System
VIP	VINES Internet Protocol
VIPC	VINES Interprocess Communications
VLSI	Very Large Scale Integration
VMS	Virtual Memory System
VP	Virtual Path
VPC	Virtual Path Connection
VPI	Virtual Path Identifier
VRTP	VINES Routing Update Protocol
VSPP	VINES Sequenced Packet Protocol
VT	Virtual Terminal
VT	Virtual Tributary
WAN	Wide Area Network
WDM	Wavelength Division Multiplexing

WIN	Window
X	Unassigned Bit
XA-SMDS	Exchange Access SMDS
XDR	External Data Representation
XID	Exchange Identification
XMP	X/Open Management Protocol
XNS	Xerox Network System
ZIP	Zone Information Protocol
ZIS	Zone Information Socket
ZIT	Zone Information Table

Trademarks

ADC Kentrox is a registered trademark of ADC Telecommunications, Inc.

ACC, Express Queuing, Amazon, Nile and Danube are registered trademarks, and Bandwidth Optimization is a trademark of Advanced Computer Communication.

AppleTalk, LocalTalk, EtherTalk and TokenTalk are trademarks, and

Macintosh is a registered trademark of Apple Computer, Inc.

ACCUNET is a registered trademark; and GlobeView is a trademark of AT&T.

Banyan, the Banyan logo and VINES are registered trademarks of Banyan Systems, Inc.

Arpanet is a trademark of Bolt, Baranek and Newman, Inc.

MMAC-Plus is a registered trademark, and Spectrum 3.0 is a trademark of Cabletron Systems, Inc.

Cisco, Cisco Systems and the Cisco logo are registered trademarks of Cisco Systems, Inc.

CompuServe is a registered trademark, and FRAME-Net SDLC FRAD is a trademark of CompuServe Network Services.

PCTerm and OutsideView are trademarks of Crystal Point, Inc.

ARCNET is a trademark of Datapoint Corporation.

DCA is a registered trademark of Digital Communication Associates.

DEC, DECnet, VT100 and VT220 are trademarks, and Ethernet is a registered trademark of Digital Equipment Corporation.

EiconCard is a trademark of Eicon Technology Corporation.

FORE Systems is a registered trademark of FORE Systems, Inc.

ForeRunner, ForeThought, ForeView and SPANS are trademarks of FORE Systems, Inc.

HP is a trademark of Hewlett-Packard Company.

PDMF is a registered trademark of Innosoft International, Inc.

Ethernet is a registered trademark of Intel Corporation.

NetBIOS is a trademark; and IBM and OS/2 are registered trademarks of International Business Machines Corporation.

Leverage is a registed trademark of InterConnections, Inc.

Chameleon, ChameleonNFS, Chameleon32 and NEWT are trademarks of NetManage, Inc.

Network General and Sniffer Analyzer are trademarks of Network General Corporation.

LAN WorkPlace, NetWare and Novell are registered trademarks; and IPX, LAN WorkGroup, LAN WorkShop, NLM, ODI and SPX are trademarks of Novell, Inc.

Microsoft, MS and Windows are registered trademarks and LAN Manager is a trademark of Microsoft Corporation.

LAN2LAN, LAN2LAN/MPR Enterprise, LAN2LAN/MPR Remote Office and WNIC are trademarks of Newport Systems Solutions, Inc.

ChatterBox/NRS, Network Communication Server, Network Resource Server, NRS, and Processing Unit are trademarks of J&L Information Systems, a Division of Astro Sciences Corp.

Proteon is a trademark of Proteon, Inc.

Retix is a trademark of Retix.

AIRLAN and Solectek are trademarks of Solectek Corporation.

StrataCom is a trademark of StrataCom, Inc.

Sun is a registered trademark of Sun Microsystems, Inc.

pcAnywhere is a trademark of Symantec, Inc.

BONeS is a registered trademark, and PlanNet and NetDESIGNER are trademarks of Systems & Networks.

NFS is a trademark of Sun Microsystems, Inc.

3Com, LANPlex, LinkBuilder, NETBuilder, and NETBuilder II are registered trademarks of 3Com Corporation; and 3TECH, AccessBuilder, Boundary Routing, SuperStack and Transcend are trademarks of 3Com Corporation.

CO/Session is a trademark of Triton Technologies, Inc.

Ungermann-Bass is a registered trademark, and UB Networks is a trademark of Undermann-Bass Networks, Inc.

WINS, WIN/TCP and WIN/ROUTE are trademarks of The Wollongong Group, Inc.

UNIX is a registered trademark in the United States and other countries, licensed exclusively through X/Open Company, Ltd.

Burroughs and Unisys are trademarks of Unisys Corporation.

Xerox and XNS are trademarks; and Ethernet and Xerox are registered trademarks of Xerox Corporation.

All other trademarks are the property of their respective owners.

Index

A